CATERPILLAR

SEVENTY-FIVE YEARS
75 JAHRE

Verlag Podszun-Motorbücher
Elisabethstraße 23-25, D-59929 Brilon
Production/Herstellung: Druckhaus Cramer, Greven
Printed in Germany
Pictures/Abbildungen: Thomas Wilk
www.tom-the-cat.de
ISBN 3-86133-247-7
Cover illustration: Karl Ziegelmaier moves mountains with his Caterpillar D10 (84W) track type tractor
Umschlagfoto: Karl Ziegelmaier bewegt Berge mit seinem Caterpillar D10 (84W) Kettendozer

THOMAS WILK

CATERPILLAR®

SEVENTY-FIVE YEARS
75 JAHRE

PODSZUN

This is the Caterpillar 950 (43J10509) built in 1978, driven by my father. Everything began with this machine. When I was a little boy, I was allowed to drive the first few metres on a construction site by myself. My feet hardly reached the pedals, but I was fascinated, I heard the sound of the 4-cylinder turbo engine. I felt the movement of the machine, I raised the bucket and subsided it. I was the happiest little boy on earth.

Das ist die Caterpillar 950 (43J10509) Baujahr 1978, die mein Vater fuhr. Mit dieser Maschine begann alles. Als kleiner Junge durfte ich auf der Baustelle die ersten Meter selbst fahren. Meine Füße reichten kaum an die Pedale, doch ich war fasziniert. Ich hörte den Sound des 4-Zyl.-Cat-Turbomotors, spürte, wie sich die Maschine hin- und herbewegte, hob die Schaufel hoch und und senkte sie und war der glücklichste kleine Junge der Welt.

Here you are facing a proud Caterpillar operator, who is very content with his loader. The wheel loader is more than 15 years old. In the winter my father painted it and now it is looking brand-new. During all these years the Caterpillar didn't need anything else but some new tires, a new bucket floor, a few tubes of Caterpillar grease and a regular oil change. Father mainly worked on road construction, house foundation, earth fills and a few times at an asphalt plant with his 950. Once father had been ill. He wanted to make sure that no other operator worked with his machine. He was really worried about that. During the 35 years he was working for this company, he had only been ill three times. In the meantime the loader was at a standstill, as if it was on holiday.

Man schaut in das Gesicht eines stolzen Caterpillar-Fahrers, der mit seinem Lader mehr als zufrieden ist. Der Lader ist schon 15 Jahre alt. Über den Winter lackierte ihn mein Vater neu und er schaut so aus, als wäre er erst gestern vom Band gelaufen. Außer einigen neuen Reifen, einem neuen Schaufelboden und einigen Kartuschen Caterpillar-Fett sowie einem regelmäßigen Ölwechsel benötigte der Caterpillar 950 in all den Jahren nicht mehr. Eingesetzt war diese 950 hauptsächlich im Straßenbau, auf Erddeponien und vereinzelt an einem Asphaltmischwerk. Vaters größte Sorge war, dass er einmal krank werden könnte und ein anderer Fahrer mit seiner Maschine fahren würde. Doch das kam zum Glück in den 35 Jahren, die Vater für die Firma arbeitete, nur dreimal vor, und der Radlader stand während dieser Zeit genau so, als wenn er Urlaub hatte.

Forword

Vorwort

Hello, my name is Thomas Wilk. The start of all was the apprenticeship in my father's place of work. There I became a construction equipment mechanic. I soon appreciated the reliability of the Caterpillar machines 950, 955L, 977L and D4D. While I was with this contractor as a trainee for three years, these Caterpillar machines ran without any standstill. In the wintertime we made the service and changed the facing wear parts. I remember well that we only once had to go out with the service truck to the construction site to change a brittle O-ring from an hydraulic hose on the Cat 977L. After a short time as an operator of a wheel loader I left the company and began a ten-years evening study program at the DVS (German Association for Welding Technology). I finished with the certificate as a welding teacher for the metal-shield-gas process. After reaching the diploma as an EWS (European Welding Specialist) I am still working on this job today. After all these years my interests and my love for the big yellow earthmoving machines from Caterpillar remained unchanged. Now I am 32 years old and I am still busy with the documentation and the archives of Cat-machine pictures. In the meantime I've collected more than 15,000 slides and for about two years, now I've been fond of opening it to the public. I wanted to write a book to get some more people interested in the history of the Caterpillar company and its machines. I also want to make the readers to understand the drivers on the construction site. When we watch an operator at work, it seems to be very easy: he scrapes earth on the left and fills it on the right side and gets a smooth level. But you are wrong. One of my friends is the owner of an old Cat D4. Once or twice a year he allows me to test my skills as an operator. It is great fun to work with a Cat bulldozer, but it is hard work to make a nearly smooth level. It's a good piece of work and you have got to have the right feeling for it to work with an earthmoving machine efficiently.

All the declarations of contents as there are technical specifications, weight, engine power and dimensions, are inquired carefully. Nevertheless I can't make any guarantees, that everything is right. Names of models and designations are only used to recognize the different models. They all are Caterpillar Inc. ownerships. This book is no official publication of Caterpillar Inc.

Hallo, mein Name ist Thomas Wilk. Angefangen hat alles mit einer Lehre als Baumaschinenmechaniker bei der Firma, in der mein Vater arbeitete. Schnell lernte ich die Zuverlässigkeit der dort eingesetzten Caterpillar-Maschinen 950, 955L, 977L und D4D zu schätzen; arbeiteten sie doch die gesamten drei Jahre während meiner Ausbildung ohne Stillstandszeiten durch. Im Winter wurden der Service durchgeführt und anfallende Verschleißteile gewechselt. Ich kann mich noch gut daran erinnern: Wir mussten nur ein einziges Mal mit dem Werkstattwagen auf die Baustelle rausfahren, um einen O-Ring, der an einer Hydraulikleitung spröde geworden war, an der Cat 977L zu wechseln. Nach kurzer Zeit als Maschinist auf einem Radlader verließ ich die Firma und begann eine zehnjährige Ausbildung an der Abendschule des "Deutschen Verbandes für Schweißtechnik" mit dem Abschluss als Lehrer für das Metall-Schutzgas-Schweißverfahren. Danach folgte die Qualifikation zum European Welding Spezialist. Auf diesem Gebiet arbeite ich heute. Nach all diesen Jahren blieb mein Interesse, ja, meine Liebe, unverändert zu den großen gelben Baumaschinen des Hauses Caterpillar. Inzwischen bin ich 32 Jahre alt und

beschäftige mich intensiv mit der Dokumentation und Archivierung von Cat-Baumaschinen. Mit einem Archiv von mehr als 15.000 Dias war es nur naheliegend, mehr daraus zu machen, als nur zu archivieren. Seit ungefähr zwei Jahren reifte in mir der Wunsch, ein eigenes Caterpillar-Buch zu schreiben, um somit einem größeren Publikum die Entstehungsgeschichte der Firma Caterpillar und deren Baumaschinen nahe zu bringen. Auch das Interesse und Verständnis für die Leute vom Bau möchte ich mit diesem Buch wecken. Wenn man einem Baumaschinenführer bei der Arbeit zuschaut, sieht alles so einfach aus. Er nimmt hier Erde weg, füllt sie dort wieder auf und fertig ist das Planum. Ein Freund von mir besitzt eine alte Cat D4, auf ihr kann ich mich ein bis zwei Tage im Jahr als Fahrer versuchen. Es macht riesigen Spaß, damit zu arbeiten, doch es kostet mich viel Mühe, um ein halbwegs ebenes Planum zu erstellen. Es gehört doch eine ordentliche Portion Erfahrung und auch Fingerspitzengefühl dazu, eine Baumaschine wirtschaftlich zu bedienen.

Alle Angaben wie technische Daten, Gewicht, Motorleistung und Abmessungen sind nach bestem Wissen wiedergegeben, eine Garantie kann gleichwohl nicht übernommen werden. Modellnamen und Bezeichnungen werden nur für das Wiedererkennen der einzelnen Maschinentypen verwendet, sie sind Warenzeichen und Eigentum der Firma Caterpillar Inc. Das Buch ist keine offizielle Publikation des Hauses Caterpillar Inc.

Acknowledgements

I want to say thanks to all the people and Caterpillar dealers, I visited the last 15 years, who gave me some information and helped me to organize meetings with the customers and their machines. Thanks to all the operators who were so kind to restart their machines so that I could take a really good picture for my Caterpillar-archive. Thanks to the Caterpillar plants in Gosselies /Belgium, Grenoble/France and EDC-Wackersdorf/Germany to show me their latest products. Especially thanks to the Caterpillar Overseas S. A., located in Geneva/Switzerland, for the longstanding friendship. Last but not least I want to say thanks to all my friends. Thank you for the marvelous support from my parents, who accept my crazy passion, and who shut their eyes to the many photostops on the road for taking photos of the big yellow Cat-machines.

Danksagung

Ich möchte mich bei allen Leuten und Caterpillar-Händlern bedanken, die ich in den letzten 15 Jahren besucht habe, und die mir mit Informationen oder bei der Organisation eines Fototermins mit den jeweiligen Firmen und ihrer Maschinen halfen. Danke an alle Fahrer, die ihre Maschinen nochmals starteten oder besser plazierten für ein gutes Bild für mein Caterpillar-Archiv. Danke an die Caterpillar-Werke in Gosselies/Belgien, Grenoble/Frankreich und EDC-Wackersdorf/Deutschland, die mir ihre neuesten Produkte während einer Führung durch das Werk zeigten. Ein spezieller Dank geht an die Caterpillar S. A.R.L., mit Sitz in Genf/Schweiz, für die langjährige Freundschaft und die Unterstützung in Form von Informationen. Last but not least bedanke ich mich bei allen Freunden und bei meinen Eltern für die sehr gute Unterstützung und Akzeptanz meiner außergewöhnlichen Sammelleidenschaft, insbesondere für die Geduld bei den unzähligen Fotostops für die großen gelben Cat-Maschinen auf der Straße.

Introduction

Caterpillar Inc., located in Peoria, Illinois, is the world's largest manufacturer of construction and mining equipment, diesel and natural gas engines and industrial gas turbines. Caterpillar is a 'Fortune Hundered Company' with more than US $ 25 billion in assets. Caterpillar's broad product line ranges from the company`s new line of compact construction equipment to hydraulic excavators, bakkhoe loaders, loaders, track type tractors, forest products, off-highway trucks, ag-tractors, diesel and natural gas engines and industrial gas turbines. Cat-products are used in construction, road building, mining, forestry, energy, transportation and material-handling industries. Over the years Caterpillar made a name for machines that typically set industrial standard for performance, durability, quality and value. Only in 1998 the company introduced 44 new or improved products. Caterpillar products are sold in nearly two hundred countries all over the world. An extensive worldwide network of 195 dealers serves the customers. There are about 64 dealers in the USA and another 131 of them spread over the other countries. Caterpillar's commitment to customer service is demonstrated by the fastest replacement part delivery system in the industry. Caterpillar ships them anywhere in the world within twelve hours, often much faster. Today Caterpillar products and components are manufactured at 41 plants in the USA and 43 plants elsewhere. In the USA Caterpillar employs 33,222 workers, outside the USA 48,601 employees work for Caterpillar. That means a worldwide employment of 81,823 persons. Caterpillar`s total estimated net worth goes to US $ 6.04 billion.

Einführung

Caterpillar Inc. mit Hauptfirmensitz in Peoria Illinois ist der weltgrößte Hersteller von Bau- und Tagebaumaschinen, Diesel- und Gasmotoren und Industriegasturbinen. Die Firma Caterpillar besteht aus 100 Firmen mit einem Vermögenswert von 25 Milliarden US $. Caterpillars Produktpalette reicht von der neuen Kompaktbaumaschinenserie über Hydraulikbagger, Baggerlader, Radlader, Kettendozer, Forstprodukte, Muldenkipper, Landwirtschaftstraktoren bis hin zu Diesel- und Gasmotoren und Industriegasturbinen. Caterpillar-Produkte werden auf Baustellen, im Straßenbau, im Tagebau, in der Forstwirtschaft, bei der Energieerzeugung, sowie in der Transport- und der Materialumschlagindustrie benötigt. Caterpillar erlangte über Jahre hinweg bei der Industrie den Ruf, daß seine unterschiedlichen Produkte Maßstäbe in Sachen Leistung und Stabilität, Langlebigkeit, Qualität und Wert setzen. Allein 1998 führte die Firma 44 neue oder verbesserte Produkte ein. Caterpillar-Produkte werden in rund 200 Ländern verkauft. Caterpillar bietet einen hervorragenden Händlerservice durch ein weltweites Händlernetz von 195 Händlern, davon 64 in den Vereinigten Staaten von Amerika und 131 außerhalb des Landes. Caterpillars Engagement bei den Händlern bietet für den Kunden den schnellsten Ersatzteilservice in dieser Branche. Caterpillar sendet jedes Teil, egal an welchen Ort in der Welt, innerhalb von 12 Stunden oder schneller. Caterpillar-Produkte und -Komponenten werden heute in 41 Fabriken in den Vereinigten Staaten von Amerika und in 43 Fabriken außerhalb der Staaten hergestellt. Caterpillar beschäftigt derzeit in den USA 33.222 Mitarbeiter, außerhalb der USA 48.601. Insgesamt arbeiten 81.823 Personen für Caterpillar. Der geschätzte Netto-Wert beläuft sich weltweit auf 6,04 Milliarden US $.

Crawlers

Traktoren

At the end of the 18th century it was realized that the outgrowing combined harvesters, ploughs and other agricultural machinery could never be pulled efficiently by oxen and horses. New technology was needed to cultivate the acres and acres of America. At the same time two men were successful in developing the first steam traction engines. Daniel Best built combines. In 1886 he expanded and moved from Oakland to San Leandro, California. There he presented the first steam traction engine in 1889. The other person was Benjamin Holt. He produced wagon wheels and threshing-machines in Stockton, California. His first steam traction engine was presented in 1890. These heavy steam tractors often subsided in the soft soils. Big wheels were used to prevent these problems. But that was no longterm solution. They couldn`t go on like that forever. So they tried to find another solution. Holt developed the world`s first crawler tractor in 1904. It crawls like a Caterpillar. So the name for a crawler tractor was born – Caterpillar. In 1910 Holt applied for a patent and the name Caterpillar became a trademark. Because the steam engines weren`t to use efficiently, Daniel Best developed his first gasoline engine in 1895. In 1908 Benjamin Holt presented a production model of a gasoline crawler tractor to the market. In the same year Daniel Best sold his company to Benjamin Holt. Five years later Best's son C.L. Best introduced his own crawler tractor and registered the name 'Tracklayer' as a trademark. In 1925 both companies, C.L. Best and Holt merged to the Caterpillar Tractor and Co. They built up a worldwide operating dealer's network to sell their products. After the merger they built together five tractor models, three of them were from Holt – the "2-ton", the "5-ton" and the "10-ton" – and two were taken over from Best – the "Thirty" and the "Sixty". The first new models after the merger in 1925 were the "Twenty" in 1927, the "Ten" in 1928 and the "Fifteen" in 1929. Caterpillar tractors were used in agriculture as a pull tractor, also in forestry and by the road builders. One could attach these tractors with different bulldozer blades, winches and cranes. These tractors could be turned into track loaders or graders. In those days the tractor was the universal implement.

Ende des 18. Jahrhunderts war es klar, daß man die immer größer werdenden Dreschmaschinen, Pflüge und andere für die Landwirtschaft benötigten Maschinen nicht mehr mit Ochsen und Pferden ziehen kann. Eine neue Technologie musste her, um die großen Anbauflächen Amerikas schneller und besser zu bearbeiten und zu nutzen. Zwei Männer entwickelten fast zeitgleich die ersten Dampftraktoren. Daniel Best baute Dreschmaschinen. Im Jahr 1886 vergrößerte er seine Firma und zog von Oakland nach San Leandro/ Kalifornien. Dort stellte er 1889 seinen ersten Dampftraktor vor. Der andere Mann hieß Benjamin Holt. Er baute Wagenräder und Dreschmaschinen in Stockton/Kalifornien. Er präsentierte 1890 seinen ersten Dampftraktor. Die immer größer werdenden Dampfzugmaschinen wurden gleichzeitig immer schwerer und sanken oftmals in den weichen Boden ein. Riesige Räder sollten das Einsinken verhindern, doch waren auch hier Grenzen gesetzt und man suchte nach einer anderen Lösung. Holt entwickelte 1904 den ersten Kettentraktor der Welt. Da sich die Maschine wie eine Raupe fortbewegte, war der Name Caterpillar (Raupe) geboren. 1910 ließ Holt den Namen Caterpillar als Warenzeichen eintragen. Da auch die Dampfmotoren nicht sehr wirtschaftlich zu betreiben waren, entwickelte Best 1895 seinen ersten Benzinmotor. Holt zog 1908 mit einem serienreifen Benzin-Kettentraktor nach. 1908 verkaufte Daniel Best seine Firma an Benjamin Holt, und fünf Jahre später stellte Bests Sohn C.L. Best seinen eigenen Kettentraktor vor, den er auf den Namen Tracklayer als Warenzeichen eintragen ließ. 1925 war es soweit: Die beiden Firmen C.L. Best und Holt schlossen sich zur Caterpillar Tractor & Co. zusammen und bauten ein weltweites Händlernetz auf. Zunächst wurden gemeinsam fünf Traktor-Modelle gebaut, drei kamen von Holt: der "2-Ton", der "5-Ton", und der "10-Ton". Zwei Modelle wurden von Best übernommen: die "Thirty" und die "Sixty". Die ersten neuen Modelle, die nach dem Zusammenschluß 1925 entwickelt wurden, waren die Cat Twenty 1927, die Ten 1928 und die Fifteen 1929. Caterpillar-Traktoren wurden in der Landwirtschaft, in der Forstwirtschaft und im Straßenbau als Zugmaschinen eingesetzt. Man konnte Traktoren mit verschiedenen Planiereinrichtungen, Seilwinden und Anbaukranen ausrüsten oder zu einem Grader oder einer Laderaupe umbauen. Der Traktor war zu dieser Zeit das Universalgerät.

This is a Holt 45 of 1917. The allied troops in France used it as a military tractor at the end of World War I to haul artillery, remarkable the cushioned tractor undercarriage.

Ein Holt 45 von 1917 kam als Militärzugmaschine Ende des Ersten Weltkrieges zu den Alliierten Truppen nach Frankreich. Bemerkenswert das schon damals gefederte Laufwerk.

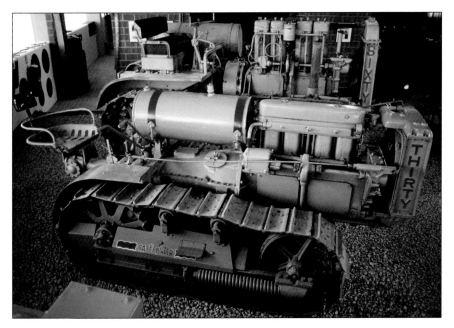

This is a Thirty of 1930 and it weighs 9,040 lb and is power-driven by a 4-cylinder gasoline engine rated at 30 hp. This Caterpillar Thirty is US $ 3,400 in 1926. The picture shows an orchard version with a rear-mounted seat.

Dieser 4.100 kg schwere Kettentraktor Thirty von 1930 wird von einem 4-Zyl.-Benzinmotor mit 30 PS ange-trieben. 1926 kostete dieser Caterpillar Thirty 3.400 US $. Das Bild zeigt eine Obstplantagenversion mit einem nach hinten verlegten Fahrersitz.

The Caterpillar Thirty was built from 1921 to 1932, this Thirty is equipped with a hydraulic bulldozer blade from La Plant Choate.

Die Caterpillar Thirty wurde von 1921 bis 1932 gebaut. Diese Thirty ist mit einem hydraulisch betätigten La Plant Choate Bulldozerschild ausgerüstet.

This Thirty from 1921 is standing in front of an office of a Caterpillar dealer. The Best Company developed this very popular model. It was used as a tractor in agriculture, forestry and road building.

Eine Thirty von 1921 steht vor dem Bürogebäude eines Cat-Händlers. Die Firma Best entwickelte diesen Ketten-traktor. Das beliebte Modell wurde in der Land- und Forstwirtschaft und im Straßenbau als Zugtraktor eingesetzt.

The next size up tractor is the Best Sixty, built from 1919 to 1931. The picture shows a Cat Sixty from 1929 with an operating weight of 19,845 lb. In 1931, Caterpillar built its first D9900 diesel engine rated at 70 hp, the first crawler, equipped with this modern engine, was the Sixty, called the "Diesel Sixty".

Der nächstgrößere Traktor ist die Best Sixty. Er wurde von 1919 bis 1931 gebaut. Im Bild eine Caterpillar Sixty von 1929 mit einem Einsatzgewicht von 9.000 kg. 1931 wird in die Caterpillar Sixty der erste Caterpillar Dieselmotor, der D9900, mit 70 PS eingebaut.

Many Caterpillar Sixty models were used for road construction. With the 4-cylinder gasoline engine, rated at 60 hp, the crawler was strong enough to pull scrapers, graders and wagons. Very often there was a blade fixed.

Viele Caterpillar Sixtys wurden für den Straßenbau eingesetzt. Mit dem 4-Zyl.-Benzinmotor, der 60 PS leistet, sind sie stark genug, um Anhänge-Scraper, Grader und Hänger zu ziehen. Oft wurde auch ein Bulldozerschild angebaut.

This is a Caterpillar Fifteen (PV) tractor. It was built from 1929 to 1932 with 22 d.h.p (drawbar horsepower). It is very similar to the Caterpillar Ten (PT) with 15 d.h.p, but it's a little bigger. On the right: Built from 1934 to 1937, the Caterpillar Twenty-Two (2F-1J) crawler with a traction of 25 d.h.p.

Ein Caterpillar Fifteen (PV) Traktor. Er wurde von 1929 bis 1932 mit einer Zugleistung von 22 PS gebaut. Er ist fast identisch mit dem Caterpillar Ten (PT) mit einer Zugleistung von 15 PS, nur etwas größer. Rechts: Von 1934 bis 1937 wird der Caterpillar Twenty-Two (2F-1J) Traktor mit einer Zugleistung von 25 PS gebaut.

A Caterpillar Twenty-Two tractor from 1934 is equipped with wooden boards on the tracks. So, a better flotation on very soft soils is ensured and, on the other hand, the tractor can run well on paved roads without damaging them.

Ein Caterpillar Twenty-Two Traktor von 1934 ist mit angeschraubten Holzbalken auf den Ketten ausgerüstet. Dies verhindert ein Einsinken auf sehr weichen Böden und ermöglicht die Fahrt auf geteerten Wegen, ohne selbige zu beschädigen.

The successive model of the Twenty-Two was the Caterpillar R2, first built in 1938. The picture shows the Caterpillar R2 (6J121) gasoline model with 25 d.h.p, built in 1939. The R2 remained in the dealers' sales lists until 1942.

Der Caterpillar R2 wird 1938 Nachfolger der Twenty-Two. Das Bild zeigt einen Caterpillar R2 (6J121) Benzinmodell mit einer Zugleistung von 25 PS aus dem Jahr 1939. Er blieb bis 1942 im Verkaufsprogramm der Händler.

Successor of the Caterpillar R2 was the Caterpillar D2 (3J/5J) diesel tractor, built from 1938 to 1947, with a traction of 25.8 hp. This picture shows a Cat D2 (3J) with a gauge of 40".

Dem Caterpillar R2 folgt der von 1938 bis 1947 gebaute Caterpillar D2 (3J/5J) Dieseltraktor mit einer Zugleistung von 25,8 PS. Das Bild zeigt eine Cat D2 (3J) mit einer Spurweite von 1.312 mm.

All the early vintage caterpillar models with their diesel engine couldn't be started directly. A starting engine was needed, a 2-cylinder four-stroke gasoline engine. This picture shows the starting procedure from a Caterpillar D2 (3J) on a very cold day in winter. The operator wrapped a cable around the crankshaft pulley from the 2-cylinder ‚pony' engine. With a supreme effort the driver pulled the cable fast enough, so that the engine began to run.

Wie alle frühen Caterpillar-Modelle konnte man den Diesel-Motor nicht direkt starten, sondern er wurde von einem 2-Zyl.-Viertakt-Benzinmotor gestartet. Das Bild zeigt den Startvorgang einer Caterpillar D2 (3J) im Winter. Der Fahrer wickelt ein Seil um die Schwungscheibe des 2-Zylinder "pony" Motors. Beim Anziehen des Seils wird der Benzinmotor angedreht.

After the gas engine runs well, the operator used the clutch to move the diesel engine.

Nach Anspringen des Benzinmotors wird mittels einer handbetätigten Kupplung der Dieselmotor durchgedreht.

This is the moment the 4-cylinder Cat diesel began to run and the Caterpillar D2 is ready to work. With this kind of starting system there were no battery-problems. Even after a very long stand-still or really bad weather the operator could start his Caterpillar well without having any problems.

Der 4-Zyl. Cat-Dieselmotor springt an. Jetzt ist der Caterpillar D2 fahrbereit. Mit diesem batteriefreien Anlaßsystem gab es nie Probleme, auch nicht nach monatelangem Stillstand. Der Caterpillar konnte immer, egal bei welchem Wetter, gestartet werden.

This is Hans Hählen with his own "Räupder D2" from the Balstaler Oberberg. After I had sent him some photos showing his Cat, his wife wrote the following text: "This is the old man and the flowersea" (lean on Ernest Hemingway). It was a great event for me meeting Hans Hählen and his wife in 1993. He drives a rare Caterpillar D2 (4U) with a rear mounted fuel tank. This early version has the straight levers, and the drawbar pull is 32 hp, it was introduced in 1947. The successor is the stronger D2 with 35 d.h.p in 1954, the model was phased out of the sales lists in 1957.

Dieses Bild zeigt Hans Hählen mit seinem "Räupder D2" vom Balstaler Oberberg. Als ich ihm das Bild zusendete, schrieb seine Frau zurück und sagte zu dem Bild: "Der alte Mann und das Blumenmeer" (nach Ernest Hemingway). Es war für mich ein großes Erlebnis, Hans Hählen und seine Frau 1993 kennengelernt zu haben. Er fährt einen Caterpillar D2 (4U) mit einem selten zu findenden heck-montierten Tank. Diese frühe Ausführung hat noch die gerade Form der Bedienhebel, die Zugleistung beträgt 32 PS. Dieses Modell wurde 1947 vorgestellt. Nachfolger wird die etwas stärkere D2 mit einer Zugleistung von 35 PS im Jahr 1954. Das Produktionsende dieses beliebten Caterpillar-Typs kam 1957.

The previous models of the Caterpillar D4 tractor were the Thirty and afterwards the Cat RD4. From 1936 on Cat built the RD4 tractor. In 1938 the ,R' was left out and since then all Caterpillar tractors used the ,D-designation' up to now. The picture shows a Caterpillar D4 from 1939. It is equipped with an R.G. Le Tourneau angle blade.

Vorgänger des Caterpillar D4 Traktors waren der Cat RD4 und davor die Thirty. Von 1936 an wird der Cat RD4 Traktor gebaut. Im Jahr 1938 fällt das "R" weg und alle Caterpillar Dozer tragen bis heute die "D-Bezeichnung". Das Bild zeigt eine Caterpillar D4 Baujahr 1939, die mit einem R.G. Le Tourneau Schwenk-schild ausgerüstet ist.

This vintage Caterpillar D4 with an R.G. Le Tourneau straight blade helped to build the legendary Alaska Highway in 1942.

Diese Caterpillar D4, mit einem R.G. Le Tourneau Schild ausgerüstet, half 1942 bei dem Bau des legendären Alaska-Highways.

Two old Caterpillar tractors waiting for the next job, on the right a Cat D2 and on the left a Cat D4 with 35 d.h.p.

Zwei alte Caterpillar Traktoren warten auf den nächsten Einsatz. Rechts eine Cat D2 und links eine Cat D4 mit einer Zugleistung von 35 PS.

The operator Bert Vogels works with his Caterpillar D4 (2T) from 1943. Equipped is this tractor with an hydraulic angle blade and a rear mounted Hyster D4 cable winch.

Bert Vogels arbeitet mit seinem Caterpillar D4 (2T) von 1943, ausgerüstet ist dieser Traktor mit einem hydraulisch betätigten Schwenkschild und einer heckmontierten Hyster D4 Seilwinde.

The Trackson Company of Milwaukee, Wisconsin produced the first loader attachements for the Cat tractors D2, D4, D6, and D7. The picture shows a Caterpillar T2 from 1951 with an operating weight of 12,348 lb and a bucket capacity of 3/4 yd³, powered by a 32 hp diesel engine. All Trackson "Traxcavators" are fitted with longer track frame for a better stability when loading trucks.

Die Firma Trackson aus Milwaukee, Wisconsin, baute für Caterpillar die ersten Ladeeinrichtungen für die Cat Traktoren D2, D4, D6, D7. Im Bild ein Caterpillar T2, Baujahr 1951, mit einem Einsatzgewicht von 5.600 kg, einem Schaufelinhalt von 0,57 m³ und einem 32 PS-starken Dieselmotor. Für bessere Standsicherheit beim Beladen von Lastkraftwagen werden die T-Kettenlader mit einem längeren Laufwerk ausgestattet.

The next size up track loader is the Traxcavator model HT4. This Caterpillar D4 (6U1295), built in 1950, had an hydraulic loader equipment HT4 from Trackson. The powerfull 60 hp Traxcavator weighed 18,081 lb and carried a bucket 1 yd³.

Der nächstgrößere Kettenlader ist das Traxcavator Modell HT4. Dieser Caterpillar D4 (6U1295), Baujahr 1950, wurde mit der hydraulischen Ladeeinrichtung HT4 von Trackson ausgerüstet. Der 60 PS-starke Kettenlader wiegt nun 8.200 kg und hat einen Schaufelinhalt von 0,76 m³.

For the 125th anniversary celebration of the Swiss Caterpillar dealer Ammann this No. 6 track loader was restored. This was the first developed and produced track loader: the Cat No. 6 (10A) from 1953. It was the forerunner of all the following Caterpillar track loaders. The 29,165 lb heavy track loader is powered by a Cat D318 engine with 90 hp and had a bucket capacity of 2.0 yd³.

Für die 125-Jahrfeier des Schweizer Caterpillar Händlers Ammann wurde dieser No. 6 Kettenlader restauriert. Das Bild zeigt den ersten Kettenlader von Cat, den No. 6 (10A), Baujahr 1953, der als komplett neue Maschine entwickelt und gebaut wurde und Vorläufer aller modernen Kettenlader wurde. Angetrieben wird der 13.229 kg schwere Kettenlader von einem Cat D318 Motor mit 90 PS, der Schaufelinhalt beträgt 1,5 m³.

This early Caterpillar D6, with 55 d.h.p is standing in a barn. It was built from 1941 to 1947. Its forerunner was the last big gasoline tractor, the Cat R6 with 55 d.h.p, it was only built in 1941.

Eine frühe Caterpillar D6 mit einer Zugleistung von 55 PS steht in einer Scheune. Dieser Typ wurde von 1941 bis 1947 gebaut. Sein Vorgänger war der letzte große Benzinmotor-Traktor, der Cat R6, mit einer Zugleistung von 55 PS. Er wurde nur 1941 gebaut.

This picture dates from the time when self propelled motor graders weren`t available. Koos Bakker's D6 (8U/9U), built in 1947 with 65 d.h.p, pulls a rubber tyred Adams Grader.

Das Bild stammt aus einer Zeit, in der es noch keine Motorgrader gab. Koos Bakkers D6 (8U/9U), Baujahr 1947, mit einer Zugleistung von 65 PS, zieht einen luftbereiften Adams Grader.

A Caterpillar D6 (9U3394), built in 1949, upgraded with a dozer blade and a rear power control unit. This 22,050 lb dozer with 65 d.h.p was in use until 1991 on different construction projects. Now, 42 years later, it is retired.

Ein Caterpillar D6 (9U3394), Baujahr 1949, ausgestattet mit einem Planierschild und einer heck-montierten Seilwinde. Dieser 10.000 kg schwere Kettendozer mit einer Zugleistung von 65 PS wurde bis 1991 noch auf verschiedenen Baustellen eingesetzt. Nach 42 Jahren hat dieses Arbeitspferd den wohlverdienten Ruhestand erreicht.

STRAIGHT BLADE BULLDOZER
FOR RUBBER-TIRED D6 TRACTOR
NOW AVAILABLE

BALDERSON INC.   Wamego, Kansas

MODEL BDW6X INSIDE DOZER for rubber-tired CAT D6 TRACTOR

Salesgram BALDERSON

A Balderson sales brochure from 1955 shows the re-equipped rubber tired Caterpillar D6 wheel dozer with inside dozer blade.

Ein Verkaufsprospekt der Firma Balderson von 1955 zeigt den umgerüsteten Caterpillar D6 Raddozer mit einem innenliegenden Planierschild.

A Caterpillar D7 (7M/3T) is equipped with a R.G. Le Tourneau dozer blade.

Ein Caterpillar D7 (7M/3T), ausgerüstet mit einem R.G. Le Tourneau Planierschild.

This Caterpillar D7 (4T) from 1944 pulls an Adams (104S) pull type grader built in 1944. With a drawbar pull of 80 hp the Cat is strong enough to pull this large grader. The (4T) model was not built in the Cat plant. Another manufacturer was supplied with the original Cat parts to build this D7 (4T) model for Caterpillar.

Diese Caterpillar D7 (4T) von 1944 zieht einen Adams (104S) Grader von 1944. Mit einer Zugleistung von 80 PS ist die Cat D7 stark genug, um diesen großen Grader zu ziehen. Die 4T wurde nicht bei Caterpillar produziert, sondern von einer anderen Firma für Caterpillar mit deren Originalteilen als Kettendozer zusammengebaut.

A friend of mine, Ad Gevers, operates this almost new Cat D7 (4T). When I asked the boy on the tractor, if he needed any toys, he quickly answered, "I don`t need any toy, I have the best I could get, I have a Caterpillar with a fantastic sound".

Ein Freund von mir, Ad Gevers, fährt diese fast neue Cat D7 (4T). Als ich den Jungen, der mitfuhr, fragte, ob er sich etwas schöneres zum Spielen wünsche, antwortete er: "Nein, ich brauche kein Spielzeug, ich habe ein richtiges Original. Einen Caterpillar mit einem tollen Sound".

It looks like a Caterpillar D7, but you are wrong. It's a D7 built in Russia under licence from Caterpillar.

Sie sieht zwar aus wie eine Caterpillar D7, ist aber keine Cat D7. Es ist eine in Russland unter Lizenz von Caterpillar gebaute D7.

Joop Vellinga is a really true Caterpillar operator from the fifties. He started on a Cat D2, then he had a D4, D6, D7, D8, D9, even a DD9G. He operated almost every machine with tracks. He had neither any trouble with the Caterpillar scrapers nor with the tractors. He started with the DW20, followed by a DW21, a 631 and a 657, the list seems to be endless. The picture shows himself and his Cat D7 (3T), built in 1951. After 24 years as an operator Joop changed the job and moved to a school called Soma in the Netherlands as a teacher to train operators on different earthmoving machines.

Joop Vellinga ist noch ein echter Caterpillar-Fahrer aus den Fünfzigern. Angefangen hat er auf einer Cat D2 und über die D4, D6, D7, D8, D9 bis hin zur DD9G hat er schon alles gefahren, was Ketten hat. Aber auch mit Caterpillar Scrapern hat er große Erfahrung, angefangen mit DW20, DW21, 631 und 657, die Aufzählung könnte noch endlos weitergehen. Das Bild zeigt ihn mit seiner eigenen Cat D7 (3T) von 1951. Nach 24 Jahren als Fahrer wechselte Joop seinen Job und wurde Lehrer an der Schule für Maschinisten (Soma) in den Niederlanden.

Joop wrote the following two pages from his point of view of an experienced tractor operator. It was the time, you had to move a blade by the cable.

Joop schrieb für mich die nächsten beiden Seiten aus der Sicht eines erfahrenen Kettendozer-Fahrers aus einer Zeit, als man das Schild noch mit dem Seil bediente.

De Kabeldozer

Het kabelbediende dozerblad, in het kort kabeldozer genoemd, is vele jaren een veel toegepast grondverzetwerktuig geweest. Dit eenvoudig geconstrueerde, mechanische hef-systeem werd in het beginstadium van de dozer ontwikkeld en de productie eindigde in de zeventiger jaren toen hydraulische syste-men steeds beter werden en de voordelen van kabelbediening bijna waren verdwenen. De kabeldozer wordt bediend door een sneldraai-ende lier, ook wel bedieningsinstallatie ge-noemd. Deze lier kan zowel voor- als achterop een rupstractor worden geplaatst. Een voorop geplaatste bladlier wordt direct door de motor aangedreven en de machinist kan het blad hef-fen, ongeacht de stand van de hoofdkoppeling, die de aandrijving van een achterop gemonte-erde lier kan uitschakelen. Een achterlier kan zijn uitgerust met een of met twee trommels. Als het blad door een achterlier wordt bediend, kan de kabel zowel over de machine, langs de machine als door het chassis gevoerd worden. Het toepassen van de kabel over de machine werd al gauw lastig vanwege de doorrijdhoog-te op een dieplader. Achterop gemonteerde bedieningslieren werden veel gebruikt voor getrokken scrapers, maar ook voor rippers, bomenslepers en kranen.

De Bediening

De bediening van een kabeldozer vereist enige ervaring. Het systeem had bepaalde voordelen ten opzicht van een hydraulisch systeem. Ervaren machinisten hielden van het snellere kabelsysteem. Het laten zakken van het blad kon worden gedaan in vrije val, alleen maar door de rem van de kabeltrommel te lossen. De eerste hydraulische systemen waren traag en de werksnelheid werd beïnvloed door hitte en kou. Bij egaliseerwerk en dergelijke kon je met een kabeldozer vaak in een hogere versnelling werken. Het systeem was betrouwbaar, een-voudig en iedereen begreep de werking en was in staat om een kabel te vervangen en de rem en koppeling bij te stellen. Het grote nadeel was dat het blad niet omlaag gedrukt kon wor-den. Bij het werken in stenen konden grote keien het blad wel omhoog tillen en eronder door gaan, wat ten koste ging van de produc-tie. In taaie grondsoorten was het lastig om het blad goed te vullen. Goede machinisten had-den echter voor de meeste problemen wel een oplossing. Beginnende machinisten konden wel eens iets onverwachts meemaken. Ik beschrijf een situatie die echt is voorgevallen: het werk bestond uit het afschuiven van een talud in een taaie grondsoort. Als een talud wordt aangezet vanuit een vlakke opstelling

laat men het blad langs het te maken talud zakken terwijl de machine vooruit gaat. Een voordeel van de kabeldozer was, dat het blad onbegrensd beneden het maaiveld kon zak-ken! De machinist, die de mogelijke gevolgen niet kende, begon te rijden en liet het blad zover zakken dat de kabel uit de trommel los-schoot! Het blad ging steeds dieper en de machine tuimelde over het blad heen in een korte vlucht. Gelukkig liep alles goed af, maar het blad lag op de kop achter de machine. Ka belbediende installaties waren iets gevaarlijker dan hydraulische. Met onervaren personeel gingen de kabels ook niet lang mee omdat de hefhoogte geen veiligheidsafslag had. Ervaren mensen werkten echter een lange tijd met een en dezelfde kabel en ze wisten precies wan-neer een nieuw stukje kabel op de trommel moest worden gedaan en een versleten stuk moest worden afgehakt. Dit alles behoorde tot het normale onderhoud. Ten slotte: het groot-ste bezwaar van de kabeldozer gold als de machine verzakt was; hij was niet in staat om zich op te drukken en zo proberen eruit te ko-men. Als meerdere dozers samen aan het werk waren, kreeg de kabeldozer meestal de stevig-ste grond om te verwerken.
Mijn dank gaat naar alle nederlandje Vrienden.

Cable-Dozers

The cable-controlled dozer-blade, or cable-dozer for short, was a very popular earthmoving implement for many years. This simple, mechanical lifting-system was introduced in the very beginning of the tractor-dozer combination, and production of these systems ended in the seventies, when hydraulic systems became superior and the advantages of cable-dozers became of minor importance. Cable-dozers are controlled by a high-speed winch, called power-control-unit or p.c.u. This control-unit can be mounted either on the rear of the track-type tractor or on the front of it. Front mounted units are driven directly by the engine, so the operator can lift the blade, regardless of the position of the flywheel-clutch, which disengages the drive-shaft to the rear p.c.u. This unit can be single or double drum equipped. When the blade is controlled by a rear p.c.u., the cable moves to the front either over the machine, alongside through a pipe or even through the main-frame. Overhead systems rapidly lost popularity because of the height of the machine on a low-loader. Rear mounted control-units were used very much for pull-type scrapers, but also for rippers, logging equipment and cranes.

The Operation

The operation of a cable-dozer requires some experience. The system had advantages over the hydraulic lifting system. Experienced operators loved its lifting and dropping speeds.

Dropping could be done by "gravity", just by releasing the brake which holds the cable-drum. In those years hydraulic systems were slow, and working speed was very much affected by heat and cold. In levelling and spreading operations, cable-dozers were able to produce more because of a higher tractor-speed. The system was reliable, simple, so easy to understand and everybody was able to change a cable and to adjust the brake and clutch of the control- unit. The great disadvantage was the absence of positive down-pressure on the blade. Working in rocky conditions, boulders could lift the blade and pass under it, reducing production. In hard soils there was no penetration to get a full blade. However, good operators found some solution for most of these problems. In the hands of a novice operator the cable-dozer could give many surprises. I'll describe one, which has really happened: the job was pushing down a slope in sticky material. When starting a down-slope from a level position, the blade is normally lowered along the desired slope while the machine moves forward. An advantage of the cable-dozer was the unlimited drop below ground level: The operator, who was not aware of the possible results, moved on and lowered the blade so deep that the cable got free from the drum: The blade lowered and lowered and the machine moved over the blade, making a short fly-over. Fortunately everything ended well, but the blade was at the rear of the machine in upside-down position. Cable-equipped machinery could be somewhat more dangerous than hydraulic systems. In the hands of unexperienced people cables had short lives because lif-

ting-heights normally had no safety-limits. Experienced operators, however, worked many hours with cables, knowing when to put a newer piece of cable on the drum and removing worn cable. This all was a matter of routine work. Finally, in soft conditions the greatest disadvantage appeared: when the machine was bogged down, it was unable to lift itself to put soil under the tracks in order to try to get out. When working together with more dozers, the cable-machine was given the best and driest soil to handle.

This picture shows two bogged down Cat dozers. Right in front you see a D8H (52A), a rare Birtley D8 built in the United Kingdom. A Cat D6 (5R) with a Le Tourneau cable blade wanted to move the big Cat D8 out, but got bogged, too. This was the greatest disadvantage of a cable dozer, it couldn't push itself out of the mud. The picture was taken near Harlem, Amsterdam/ Netherlands in 1961.

Das Bild zeigt zwei eingesunkene Cat Kettendozer, im Vordergrund steht eine D8H (52A). Es handelt sich hierbei um eine seltene Birtley D8, die in Großbritannien gebaut wurde. Die D6 (5R) mit einem Le Tourneau Seilschild sollte die D8 herausschieben und sank selbst ein. Es war der größte Nachteil eines Kettendozers mit Seilschild, dass man sich nicht selbst herausdrücken konnte. Das Bild entstand 1961 in der Nähe von Harlem, Amsterdam/Niederlande.

From 1933 until 1935 Caterpillar built the Diesel Seventy-five with 82 d.h.p. The Diesel Seventy-five was the forerunner of all the RD8 and D8.

Von 1933 bis 1935 wird der Caterpillar Diesel Seventy-five mit einer Zugleistung von 82 PS gebaut. Der Diesel Seventy-five war der Vorläufer aller RD8 und D8.

This Caterpillar "team" of the Diesel Seventy-five and a No.48 elevating grader was used in Grande Prairie Alberta/Canada from 1950 until 1966.

Dieser Caterpillar-Zug aus einer Diesel Seventy-five und einem No. 48 Elevator Grader wird von 1950 bis 1966 in Grande Prairie Alberta/Kanada eingesetzt.

This is a big Caterpillar D8 (1H) from 1936 with 95 d.h.p, equipped with an R.G. Le Tourneau angle cable blade. Without blade, the 15'22" long and 6'49" wide Caterpillar tractor weighs 32,611 lb.

Dieser D8 (1H) von 1936 mit 95 PS ist ausgerüstet mit einem R.G. Le Tourneau A-Seilschild. Der 4.640 mm lange und 1.980 mm breite Caterpillar Traktor wiegt ohne Planierschild 14.790 kg.

The Cat D8 (1H) was built from 1935 to 1936 and was replaced by the Caterpillar D8 (8R) with now 113 d.h.p.

Nachfolger des Cat D8 (1H), der von 1935 bis 1936 gebaut wurde, wird der Caterpillar D8 (8R) mit einer Zugleistung von nun 113 PS.

A younger Caterpillar D8E/F (14A) is attached with an 8A blade. It was built with 155 d.h.p and was in the sales lists of the Cat dealers from 1955 to 1957.

Ein neuerer Caterpillar D8E/F (14A) ist mit einem 8A-Planierschild ausgerüstet. Mit einer Zugleistung von 155 PS blieb er von 1955 bis 1957 im Verkaufsprogramm der Händler.

In 1955 Caterpillar introduced the world`s largest and most powerful track type tractor, the D9D (18A/19A) with 230 d.h.p. The picture shows a Cat D9E (49A) with 268 d.h.p, it is equipped with a No.9U blade and a No.29 rear power control unit. It was built from 1959 to 1960.

1955 stellte Caterpillar den weltgrößten Kettendozer, die D9D (18A/19A) mit einer Zugleistung von 230 PS vor. Im Bild ein D9E (49A) mit einer Zugleistung von 268 PS, ausgerüstet mit einem No. 9U-Planierschild und einer No. 29-Seilwinde. Er wurde von 1959 bis 1960 gebaut.

The Race

It was Sunday, August 29th, 1999 near Osnabrück, "High noon"! Four determined men made up their mind to the first tractor race in Germany. All tractors were standing in a row neatly, all eyes were watching the man with the yellow flag far left. The flag dropped. Who will win the race? Directly after having started the little Caterpillar D4 with its operator left the others behind. Were they able to catch up? We can see the enormous lead of the Caterpillar D4 with his "Top Gun" operator Ad Gevers.

A memorable day this August, 29th 1999. This is the winner, Ad Gevers, the operator of his Caterpillar D4 (2T), built in 1943. Congratulations on AD/$_4$!

Das Rennen

Es ist Sonntag, der 29. August 1999 in der Nähe von Osnabrück, "High noon". Vier entschlossene Männer machen sich auf den Weg zum ersten Traktorrennen Deutschlands. Alles steht in einer Reihe, alle Augen sind auf den Mann mit der gelben Fahne gerichtet. Die Fahne fällt. Wer wird das Rennen gewinnen? Sofort setzt sich der kleine Caterpillar D4 mit seinem Fahrer ab. Können die anderen Traktoren aufholen? Man kann nun deutlich den Vorsprung erkennen, den der Caterpillar D4 mit seinem "Top Gun"-Fahrer Ad Gevers vorlegt.

Ein denkwürdiger Tag, der 29. August 1999. Gratulation an den Sieger Ad Gevers mit seinem Caterpillar D4 (2T) von 1943!

Wheel Loaders

Radlader

With the appeareance of the paved roadnet many contractors asked for a different loading machine. It should be easy and quick to transport and it should be able to move from job site to job site on its own axles. Caterpillar introduced his first wheel loader, the 944, in 1959. Followed by the Cat 966A and the smallest of the series, the Cat 922A. All three wheel loaders were rigid frame models and were steered by the rear wheels. They were strong and powerfull and they reached a travelspeed up to 26.7 mph. This allowed a quick changing of the job site with less costs and time than a flatbed transport. Many of those old Caterpillar loaders are still running today as if they came out of the plant yesterday. Very important in the development of the Caterpillar wheel loaders was the Cat 988 with articulation, introduced in 1963. Only five years later Caterpillar presented his biggest loader in the seventies to the market, the 992. With an operating weight up to 105,100 lb and a bucket capacity of 10 yd³ this heavyweight is powered by a Cat V12 engine rated at 550 hp. In 1990 Caterpillar introduced the powerful 1250 hp 'super' loader, the 994, with an operating weight up to 390,285 lb. with a bucket of 18.3 to 40.5 yd³. This wheel loader is the greatest mechanical driven loader of the world. A further milestone in the development of Caterpillar loaders is the 992D with STIC Control Steering, introduced in 1992. This means with a STIC Control lever you can steer the machine as well as shift and change the directions. The continued cranking of the steering wheel was removed and the operator could concentrate upon the loadwork. In 1998, with the introduction of the new Cat G-series, a new command control steering was presented: a half moon steering wheel, including transmission controls to change the directions and up and down shift. Turning the command control steering plus or minus 70 degrees left or right from the center point, the loader achieves a full articulation. Today Caterpillar wheel loaders are often used on construction sites, in quarries and for material handling. Thanks to a quick coupler system we can use a variety of different work tools like forks, brooms, log forks and different buckets for all jobs. This system allows to change the tools in a few seconds.

Mit dem Aufkommen unseres geteerten Straßennetzes fragten viele Bauunternehmer nach einem anderen Ladegerät. Es sollte einfach und schnell zu transportieren sein und auf eigener Achse zur nächsten Baustelle fahren können. 1959 war es dann soweit: Caterpillar stellte seinen ersten Radlader, den 944, vor. Ihm folgte der Cat 966A und der kleinste aus dieser Serie, der Cat 922A. Alle drei Radladermodelle waren Starr-Rahmen-Radlader, es wurde mit den Hinterrädern gelenkt. Sie waren robust, leistungsstark und erreichten eine Transportgeschwindigkeit von 43 km/h, dies ermöglichte ein schnelles Umsetzen des Radladers von einer Baustelle zur anderen, ohne einen kosten- und zeitaufwendigen Tiefladertransport in Anspruch zu nehmen. Viele der ersten Caterpillar Radlader arbeiten noch heute, als wären sie erst gestern vom Band gelaufen. Der nächste Meilenstein Caterpillars in der Radladerentwicklung war der 1963 vorgestellte Cat 988 mit Rahmen-Knicklenkung,

nur fünf Jahre später kam Caterpillar mit seinem größten Radlader auf den Markt, dem 992. Mit dem Einsatzgewicht von 47.670 kg und einem Schaufelinhalt von 7,65 m³. Angetrieben wird dieser Gigant von einem V12 Caterpillar-Motor mit 550 PS. 1990 stellt Caterpillar den 1.250 PS-starken Super-Radlader 994, mit einem Einsatzgewicht von 177.000 kg und einem Schaufelinhalt von 14 m³ bis 31 m³ vor. Dieser Radlader ist der größte mechanisch angetriebene Radlader der Welt. Ein weiterer Meilenstein in der Entwicklung der Caterpillar-Radlader wird die 1992 vorgestellte STIC-Control-Lenkung in der 992D: mit einem Kombihebel wird gelenkt, geschaltet und die Fahrtrichtung geändert. Das mühsame Kurbeln am Lenkrad entfällt und der Fahrer kann sich voll auf den Ladevorgang konzentrieren. 1998 wird eine neuartige Direktlenkung in der neuen G-Radladerserie vorgestellt: ein Halblenkrad mit integrierter Getriebeschaltung für das Hoch- und Herunterschalten und das Umschalten der Fahrtrichtung. Von der Mittelstellung werden jeweils nur 70° am Lenkrad benötigt, um ganz einzuknicken. Caterpillar Radlader sind heute auf vielen Baustellen in der Gewinnungsindustrie und im Materialumschlag eingesetzt, dank eines Schaufelschnellwechselsystems können verschiedenste Anbauwerkzeuge wie Gabeln, Kehrbesen, Baumstammgreifer und unterschiedlichste Schaufeln für jeden Einsatzzweck sekundenschnell angebaut werden.

On an earthmoving equipment exhibition in Munich in 1998 Caterpillar introduced its smallest line of wheel loaders. The smallest is the 902 with 45 hp and a weight of 9,437 lb. The Cat 906 shown in the picture is powered by a 4-cylinder diesel engine 3034NA with 62 hp. It weighs 10,936 lb, the bucket capacity rated 1.04 yd³.

Auf der Baumaschinenmesse 1998 in München wurde Caterpillars kleinste Radladerserie vorgestellt. Der kleinste, der 902, wiegt 4.280 kg und sein Cat-Motor leistet 45 PS. Der Cat 906 auf dem Bild wird von einem 4-Zyl.-Dieselmotor 3034 NA mit 62 PS angetrieben und wiegt 4.960 kg. Die Schaufelkapazität beträgt 0,8 m³.

A Caterpillar sales manager presents the new loader. Because of the round engine hood the operator has a very high visibility round the back. The biggest loader of this series is the Cat 908 attached with a 1.30 yd³ bucket, an operating weight up to 13,230 lb and an engine output of 80 hp. This model separated 1295 hp from Caterpillar's largest wheel loader, the 994D.

Ein Caterpillar-Verkaufsleiter präsentiert den neuen Radlader, der mit seiner abgerundeten Motorhaube für den Fahrer eine sehr gute Sicht nach hinten ermöglicht. Der größte Lader in der Serie ist der Cat 908 mit einer 1,0 m³ Schaufel, einem Einsatzgewicht von 6.000 kg und einer Leistung von 80 PS, ihn trennen noch 1.295 PS von Caterpillars größtem Radlader, dem 994D.

STANDARD BUCKET:

Capacity, SAE rating ....1¼ cu. yd.
Width ....83½"
Tilt-back:
   At ground level ....41°
   At carry position (18" off ground) ....45°
   At maximum lift ....50°
Maximum dumping angle at maximum lift ....50°
Grading angle ....60°
Maximum lift height (center hinge
   pin to ground) ....11' 2"
Dumping clearance, 45° discharge angle —
   max. height ....8' 7"
Dumping reach, 45° discharge angle —
   7' clearance ....40¾"
Dumping reach, 45° discharge angle —
   max. height ....25¾"
Digging depth (below ground at 10°
   digging angle) ....8⅜"
Break-out Force ....13,700 lb.

HYDRAULIC SYSTEM (Reservoir encloses valves):

Full flow filter protects pump and cylinders from
   abrasive particles in oil.
Pump (vane type) driven from transmission.
   Output .... 34.4 GPM @ 1800 RPM @ 1000 PSI
               SAE No. 10 oil @ 150° F.
Relief valve opening pressure ....1500 PSI

CONTROL POSITIONS:

Lift circuit ....Raise, hold, lower, float
   (Automatic kickout at full height)

Tilt circuit ....Tilt back, hold, dump
   (Automatic bucket positioner adjustable to desired loading angle)

CYLINDERS (double action):

Lift cylinders, bore and stroke ......4½" x 32½"

Tilt cylinders, bore and stroke ......4½" x 15½"

POWER TRAIN:

Torque Converter: Single stage, single phase with
   2.75:1 stall ratio.

Transmission: Power shift forward and reverse in
   all speeds with power shift between 1st and 2nd
   in work range or travel range — shift to travel
   range automatically disconnects rear wheel drive.

Axles: All wheel drive with planetary reduction in
   wheels, conventional differentials, front axle
   fixed, rear axle oscillation 18° (±9°).

Speeds, MPH	Work Range		Travel Range	
	1st	2nd	1st	2nd
Forward	0 - 3.8	0 - 6.8	0 - 11.8	0 - 18.9
Reverse	0 - 5.0	0 - 8.7	0 - 14.9	0 - 20.4

This is a sales brochure from 1960. Ein Verkaufsprospekt aus dem Jahr 1960.

From 1960 to 1962 the Caterpillar 922 (59A) was built. You could choose between a 4-cylinder diesel or a 6-cylinder gasoline engine, both power ratings are 80 hp.

Von 1960 bis 1962 wurde die Caterpillar 922 (59A) gebaut und war wahlweise mit einem 4-Zyl.-Diesel- oder einem 6-Zyl.-Benzinmotor erhältlich. Beide Motoren leisten 80 PS.

The Caterpillar 922B (88J) was built from 1962 to 1968. Optional you could order a 4-cylinder turbo engine with 105 hp instead of the standard engine with 80 hp. The bucket capacity grew from 1.25yd³ to 1.50yd³. The operating weight stayed nearly constant, for the A-series 16,200 lb and 16,900 lb for the B-series.

Die Caterpillar 922B (88J) wurde von 1962 bis 1968 gebaut. Als Option konnte man einen 4-Zyl.-Turbo-Motor ordern, der dann 105 PS leistet, anstatt der 80 PS des Serienmotors. Die Schaufelkapazität wuchs von 0,93 m³ auf 1,15 m³ bei der 922B. Das Einsatzgewicht blieb nahezu konstant. 7.350 kg bei der A-Serie und 7.670 kg bei der B-Serie.

The first rigid frame wheel loader introduced by Caterpillar in 1959 was the 944 (87J) model, steered by the rear axle. The first modern steering came with the Cat 988 articulated wheel loader in 1963. As an option you could order the Cat 944 with a 6-cylinder turbo engine rated at 140 hp. The end of the production came in 1968. The picture was taken in 1991. More than 23 years later the loader runs well each day on a concrete plant.

Der erste Starr-Rahmen-Radlader, den Caterpillar 1959 baute, war die 944 (87J). Gelenkt wurde mit der Hinterachse. Die Knicklenkung, so wie wir sie heute kennen, wurde erst 1963 mit der Cat 988 eingeführt. Als Option war die 944 mit einem 6-Zyl.-Turbo-Motor mit 140 PS erhältlich. Produktionsende war 1968. Die Aufnahme entstand 1991. Seit mehr als 23 Jahren ist dieser Radlader noch täglich in einem Betonwerk im Einsatz.

LOADER ATTACHMENTS —
Matched to job conditions and production requirements.
- 2 to 4 cu. yd. (1,53 to 3,10 m³) General Purpose Buckets.
- 2 cu. yd. (1,53 m³) Side Dump Bucket.
- 2¼ cu. yd. (1,72 m³) Multi-Purpose Bucket.
- 2 cu. yd. (1,53 m³) Quarry Bucket.
- Log & Lumber Fork information is on separate specification sheet.

STATIC TIPPING LOAD RATING —
- 14,000 lb. (6350 kg).

MAX. HINGE PIN HEIGHT —
- 12′ ⅜″ (3667 mm).

REACH —
- 4′ 2⅝″ (1290 mm) @ 7′ (2134 mm) clearance, 45° discharge angle.

STABILITY —
- Long 96″ (2438 mm) wheelbase.
- Wide 77″ (1956 mm) tread.
- Approx. weight of 21,850 lb. (9910 kg).

MANEUVERABILITY with 17.5-25 tires —
- Turning radius (outside rear tires) is 21′ 11″ (6687 mm).

DIESEL POWER —
- 105 flywheel (135 max.) horsepower engine with excellent lugging ability.

POWER SHIFT TRANSMISSION —
- Caterpillar-built, planetary-type provides easy full-power shifting on-the-go for fast cycles.
- Speeds from zero to 29.3 MPH (47,2 km/h).

AE4034811 (5-66)

This is a sales brochure from 1966. Ein Verkaufsprospekt aus dem Jahr 1966.

With 140 hp and a weight of 28,800 lb the Cat 966A (33A) was Caterpillar's biggest loader model of that time. The bukket was carrying 2.75 yd³. Because of the high speed of 26.7 mph the loader could change the job sites without wasting time or needing an expensive flatbed transport. It was built from 1960 to 1963.

Mit 140 PS und einem Einsatzgewicht von 13.060 kg war die 966A (33A) der größte Radlader seiner Serie. Mit seiner 2,10 m³-Schaufel war er auf vielen Baustellen anzutreffen. Dank der hohen Transportgeschwindigkeit von 43 km/h war er schnell von einer zur anderen Baustelle umgesetzt. Gebaut von 1960 bis 1963.

A Caterpillar 910 (41Y) with 65 hp built in 1980. It is an ideal machine for garden and landscape contractors. The first 910 was put on the market in 1973. It was improved up to the 910F in 1995.

Eine Cat 910 (41Y) Baujahr 1980 mit 65 PS ist eine ideale Maschine für den Garten- und Landschaftsbau. Die erste 910 kam 1973 und wurde kontinuierlich verbessert bis zur 910F im Jahr 1995.

This Caterpillar IT12 (2YC) with 65 hp works on a waste site. It is attached with a bucket with top clamp. The wheel loader was built from 1984 to 1989, and it is similar to the Cat 910.

Auf einer Mülldeponie wird dieser IT12 (2YC) mit 65 PS eingesetzt, ausgerüstet mit einer Schaufel mit Klammer. Der Radla-der wurde von 1984 bis 1989 gebaut und ist als Grundgerät identisch mit der 910.

Caterpillar introduced the new G-series wheel loader at the Bauma exhibit in Munich in 1995. With a weight up to 15,970 lb and a power rating of 98 hp the new 914G wheel loader replaced the old 910F. Buckets are available from 1.56 to 1.83 yd³.

Auf der Bauma 1995 in München wird Caterpillars G-Serie Radlader vorgestellt. Mit einem Einsatzgewicht von 7.243 kg und einer Leistung von 98 PS löst der Cat 914G Radlader die 910F ab. Schaufeln sind in der Größe von 1,2 bis 1,4 m³ erhältlich.

The Caterpillar IT14G integrated tool-carrier is the matching piece to the Cat 914G, the only difference is the front end with the different loader frame and a parallel linkage design. More than 200 different work tools are available for the Cat integrated toolcarriers.

Der Caterpillar IT14G Industrielader ist das passende Gegenstück zur Cat 914G, der einzige Unterschied ist der Lade-rahmen mit Parallelkinematik. Über 200 verschiedene Anbaugeräte sind für die Cat-Industrielader erhältlich.

A Caterpillar 920 (62K) wheel loader with 80 hp and a 1.5 yd³ bucket is loading rocks directly into a crusher at a gravel plant in Switzerland. This 18,600 lb heavy loader was built from 1969 to1984.

Ein Caterpillar 920 (62K) Radlader mit 80 PS und einer 1,2 m³-Schaufel beschickt einen Brecher in einem Kieswerk in der Schweiz. Von 1969 bis 1984 wurde dieser 8.440 kg schwere Radlader gebaut.

The former model of the Caterpillar 918/IT18 generation was the Cat 916 (2XB) wheel loader built from 1986 to 1992. The Cat 916 replaced the old 920 loader. The picture shows an IT18B integrated toolcarrier equipped with an hydraulic drilling unit. The Cat IT18B (4ZD) is powered by a Cat 3204 diesel engine with 4-cylinders and a rated output up to 95 hp. The operating weight amounts 21,540 lb.

Der Vorgänger der Caterpillar 918/IT18-Generation war der Cat Radlader 916 (2XB), gebaut von 1986 bis 1992. Der Cat 916 wiederum löste die alte 920 ab. Das Bild zeigt einen IT18B, ausgerüstet mit einem hydraulischen Bohrwerk. Der Cat IT18B (4ZD) wird von einem 4-Zyl.-Diesel-motor des Typs 3204 mit 95 PS ange-trieben. Einsatzgewicht 9.770 kg.

This Caterpillar IT18B (4ZD) works on a road project in the Netherlands.
In 1992 came the model change to the new F-series and stopped in 1994.

Dieser Caterpillar IT18B (4ZD) wird ein-gesetzt bei Straßenbauarbeiten in den Niederlanden. 1992 kam der Modell-wechsel zur F-Serie, der 1994 endete.

A Caterpillar 930 (41K) with Zeppelin cab is back filling. The bucket range reaches from 2.00 to 2.25 yd³ capacity.

Ein Caterpillar 930 (41K) mit Zeppelin-Fahrerhaus verfüllt den Arbeitsraum. Die Palette der Schaufeln reicht von 1,53 m³ bis zu 1,72 m³.

The Kanderkies company in Thun, Switzerland, used a Cat 930 (41K) for gravel loading. The 930 was built from 1968 to 1985. The Cat diesel engine 3304 with a displacement of 427 in³ rated at 100 hp.

Die Firma Kanderkies in Thun, Schweiz, setzt einen Caterpillar 930 (41K) für die Verladung von Kies ein. Die 930 wurde von 1968 bis 1985 gebaut. Der Cat-Dieselmotor 3304 mit 7,0 l Hubraum leistet 100 PS.

This Caterpillar 926E (94Z) works on a waste site in the Netherlands. The first unit from the 926 loader came in 1984, successor is the E-series with 110 hp and an operating weight up to 20,794 lb, introduced in 1987. The production stopped in 1992.

Auf einer Mülldeponie in den Niederlanden arbeitet dieser Caterpillar 926E (94Z). Der erste 926 Radlader wurde 1984 vorgestellt. Nachfolger wurde 1987 die E-Serie mit 110 PS und einem Einsatzgewicht von 9.432 kg. Produktionsende des Laders: 1992.

The Caterpillar 926E (94Z) replaced the old 930. Both wheel loaders were attached with 2.25 yd³ buckets. By changing of the old lift arms to the new Z-bar linkage design the breakout force of the Cat 926E rose from 17,410 lb up to 22,143 lb by the Cat 926E

Der Caterpillar 926E (94Z) löst die alte 930 ab. Beide Radlader wurden mit 1,7 m³-Schaufeln ausgerüstet. Durch das Ändern des Hubrahmens auf die neue Z-Kinematik konnte die Ausbrechkraft von 7.900 kg auf 10.044 kg bei der Cat 926E gesteigert werden.

The follow up model of the Caterpillar 926E was the 928/IT28 (2KC). Introduced in 1984, the IT28B (1HF) was built from 1986 to 1993 and then replaced by the F-series. The picture shows a Cat IT28F (3CL). It handles material in the Netherlands. The operating weight is about 25,200 lb. The power comes from a Cat 3116T 6-cylinder turbo engine with an output of 133 hp.

Das Nachfolgemodell des Caterpillar 926E ist der 928/IT28 (2KC), vorgestellt 1984. Der IT28B (1HF) wurde von 1986 bis 1993 gebaut und durch die F-Serie abgelöst. Das Bild zeigt einen Cat IT28F (3CL) beim Materialumschlag in den Niederlanden. Das Einsatzgewicht liegt bei 11.430 kg. Angetrieben wird der IT28F von einem Cat 3116T 6-Zyl.-Turbo-Motor mit einer Leistung von 133 PS.

This is the latest IT-generation from Caterpillar, the IT28G with 137 hp and a weight of 27,509 lb. Some advantages of the new G-series: lower noise levels, both interior and exterior, new G-series cab, more rim pull, bigger tilt cylinder.

Dies ist die neueste IT-Generation von Caterpillar: der IT28G mit 137 PS und einem Einsatzgewicht von 12.476 kg. Weitere Vorteile der G-Serie: niedrigere Geräuschpegel innen und außen, neues Fahrerhaus, bessere Felgenzugkraft und größere Kippzylinder, um nur einige der vielen Verbesserungen aufzuzählen.

Now I am happy having reached the Cat 936, because I think there had been such a variety of the previous different model designations. The Cat 936 is to assign between the old Cat 930 and the old 950. The picture shows a Cat 936 (33Z) that is used for maintenance work on the legendary Dempster highway in the Yukon in Canada. It had only 5 hp less than the old Cat 950 had with 130 hp. Built from 1983 to 1987.

Nun bin ich glücklich, bei der Cat 936 angelangt zu sein, diese Typenvielfalt ist doch verwirrend. Die 936 ist zwischen der alten 930 und der alten 950 einzuordnen. Das Bild zeigt eine 936 (33Z) die für Unterhaltsarbeiten in Kanada eingesetzt wird. Mit 125 PS hatte sie nur 5 PS weniger als die alte 950. Sie wurde von 1983 bis 1987 gebaut.

From 1987 to 1992 this type 936E (33Z) was built. The bucket ranges up to 3.0 yd^3. Pay attention to the little white polar bear at the top of the radiator. This is the licenseplate from Canada's North-West-Territories. This machine is working in Tuktoyaktuk, a place you can only reach on a frozen road in winter. In the summertime the soil is so soft that all tired vehicles bog down into the mud.

Eine Caterpillar 936E (33Z), gebaut von 1987 bis 1992. Die Größe der Schaufel reicht bis zu 2,3 m^3. Der Eisbär am Kühlergrill ist das Kennzeichen für Kanadas North-West-territories. Die Maschine arbeitet in Tuktoyaktuk. Diesen Ort kann man nur im Winter auf einer Eisstraße erreichen. Im Sommer ist der Boden zu sumpfig für ein Radfahrzeug. Es würde einsinken und stecken bleiben.

On this picture you can see a Caterpillar 936F (4TKO1175) in front of the Scheib-administration office. My father worked for Scheib as an operator of on-highway trucks and wheel loaders for more than 35 years. The F-series was built between 1992 and 1994. When my father tested this Cat 936F for the first time in 1994 he was surprised by the operator`s comfort, the fast cycle times and the higher break-out force.

Vaters Caterpillar 936F (4TK01175) steht vor dem Bürogebäude der Baufirma, bei der er mehr als 35 Jahre als Fahrer von Lkws und Radladern gearbeitet hat. Die F-Serie wurde von 1992 bis 1994 gebaut. Als mein Vater 1994 die Cat 936F testete, war er begeistert vom Komfort und von der hohen Ausbrechkraft.

The Caterpillar 938F replaced the 936F. With 149 hp the new model had 9 hp more than father`s 936F. The weight increased from 27,060 lb of the 936F up to 28,730 lb of the 938F. There are different buckets available, from 2.75 up to 3.27 yd³. The picture shows a bucket with top clamp to load brush wood and compost material. The 938F was replaced in 1998 by the new Caterpillar 938G.

Der Caterpillar 938F löste den 936F ab. Mit 149 PS leistet der Neue 9 PS mehr als die 936F meines Vaters. Das Gewicht stieg von 12.300 kg bei der 936F auf 13.030 kg bei der 938F an. Von 2,1 bis 2,5 m³ stehen verschiedene Schaufeln zur Auswahl. Das Bild zeigt eine Schaufel mit Klammer, speziell angefertigt für das Laden von Reisig u. a. kompostierbarem Material. Der 938F wurde 1998 durch den neuen Caterpillar 938G abgelöst.

This was father's first Caterpillar wheel loader 950 (43J10509). It was delivered on October 2nd 1978. The power of this Cat D330 4-cylinder turbo engine was increased to 140 hp at 2150 r.p.m. Father loaded 3-axle on-highway-trucks with a loading capacity of 10 tons in 2-3 passes with a 3 yd³ bucket.

Das war Vaters erster Caterpillar- Radlader 950 (43J10509), der am 2. Oktober 1978 ausgeliefert wurde. Die Leistung des 4-Zyl.-Cat. D330-Turbo-Motors wurde an diesem Lader um 10 PS erhöht, so daß 140 PS bei 2.150 U/min zur Verfügung stehen. Vater belud 3-Achs-Lkws mit 10 t Nutzlast in 2-3 Ladespielen mit einer 2,3 m³ fassenden Schaufel.

A Caterpillar 950 (81J), modified as a forklift, stands at a gas station in Whitehorse in the Yukon territory/Canada. The first Cat 950 was delivered on January 27th, 1965.

Ein Caterpillar 950 (81J), der als Stapler umgebaut wurde, stand an einer Tankstelle in Whitehorse im Yukon Territory, Kanada. Der erste Cat 950 wurde am 27.Januar 1965 ausgeliefert.

This a little bit newer Caterpillar 950 (81J) is equipped with Caterpillar's own ROPS (Roll over Protective Structure) cab. It works at a Swiss gravel plant with an operating weight of 28,500 lb. The Cat 950 was replaced by the 950B in 1981.

Ein etwas neuerer 950 (81J) mit Caterpillars eigenem ROPS (Roll over Protective Structure)-Fahrerhaus arbeitet in einem Schweizer Kieswerk mit einem Einsatzgewicht von 13.000 kg. Der Cat 950 wurde bis 1981 gebaut und durch den 950B abgelöst.

Nearly brand-new is this Caterpillar 950F (7ZF) with an output of 170 hp. It loads sand in the Netherlands. It was built from 1990 until 1992. The former model, the Cat 950B (22Z) with 155 hp, was built from 1981 to 1987, and was replaced by the 950E (22Z) which was 5 hp stronger than the other one.

Fast neu ist dieser Caterpillar 950F (7ZF) mit einer Leistung von 170 PS, der von 1990 bis 1992 gebaut wurde. Er lädt Sand in den Niederlanden. Vorgänger war der Cat 950B (22Z). Er wurde von 1981 bis 1987 mit 155 PS hergestellt, abgelöst wurde er durch den 5 PS stärkeren 950E (22Z).

A Cat 950F II (5SK) works on a concrete plant in the Netherlands to load on-highway trucks. Remarkable is the complete redesigned cab with integrated roll over bar. The 6-cylinder Cat 3116 turbo engine rated at 175 hp into the 950F II. Buckets are available from 3.27 up to 4.32 yd³. To supply the wheel loaders individually, you have got a variety of different, specially produced buckets.

Ein Caterpillar 950F II (5SK) wird in einem Betonwerk in den Niederlanden für das Beladen von Lkws eingesetzt. Man beachte das komplett überarbeitete Fahrerhaus mit integriertem Überrollschutz. Der 6-Zyl.-Cat 3116-Turbo-Motor leistet in der 950F II 175 PS. Schaufeln sind in der Größe von 2,5 bis 3,3 m³ erhältlich. Auf Wunsch sind auch viele Sonderschaufeln lieferbar, so daß der Kunde seinen Lader individuell ausrüsten kann.

In 1999 I visited a demonstration show of the latest wheel loader generation, the G-series from Caterpillar. The Swiss Cat-dealer Ammann invited for a test ride in a gravel pit. The most fascinating change was the new command control steering; a half-moon steering wheel, including transmission controls for changing the direction up and down shifting. Turning the command control steering plus or minus 70° left or right from the centerpoint, the loader achives full articulation.

1999 besuchte ich eine Vorführung der neuesten Radladergeneration der G-Serie von Caterpillar. Der Schweizer Cat-Händler Ammann lud ein zu einer Probefahrt in eine Kiesgrube. Faszinierend war die neue Direktlenkung. Ein Halblenkrad mit integrierter Getriebeschaltung für das Hoch- und Herunterschalten und das Umschalten von vorwärts auf rückwärts. Von der Mittelstellung werden jeweils nur 70° am Lenkrad benötigt, um ganz einzuknicken.

Zeppelin invited to come to a quarry. There the line of the new G-series loaders from Caterpillar was presented. The Cat 962G weighs 41,237 lb and is powered by a Cat engine with 203 hp. It is especially built as a mass loading loader with bigger buckets and faster cycle times to load trucks. The buckets range from 3.79 up to 5.62 yd³. The Cat 950G is only a little less powerful and the buckets are similar: 3.53 up to 5.23 yd³. The Caterpillar models 950G, 962G, 966G and 972G were all introduced in 1998 and they are today's most advanced wheel loaders at the market.

Auch Zeppelin lud zu den Feldtagen in einen Steinbruch ein. Die Cat 962G mit 18.702 kg und 203 PS ist speziell für den Güterumschlag und das schnelle Beladen von Lkws konzipiert. Der Schaufeninhalt reicht von 2,9 bis 4,3 m³. Die Cat 950G ist nur geringfügig schwächer. Auch bei den Schaufeln ist man nahezu gleich: 2,7 bis 4,0 m³. Die Caterpillar-Modelle 950G, 962G, 966G und 972G wurden 1998 vorgestellt und sind heute die modernsten Radlader auf dem Markt.

On October 22nd, 1963 the first Caterpillar 966B (75A) with articulated frame was delivered. Near Dawson City, the legendary goldrush town in Canada, people are still looking for the shiny metal, but the equipment they use is much more modern than in 1896. The picture was taken in 1992. Each day this old Cat 966B (75A) works in a gold mine operation without having any major technical problems.

Am 22.10.1963 wurde der erste Caterpillar 966B (75A) mit Rahmen-Knicklenkung ausgeliefert. In der Nähe von Dawson City, der legendären Goldgräberstadt in Kanada, wird auch heute noch nach Gold gesucht, nur mit weitaus moderneren Hilfsmitteln als während des Goldrausches 1896. Das Bild entstand 1992. Dieser alte Cat 966B (75A) arbeitet noch jeden Tag ohne größere technische Probleme in einer Goldmine.

In 1968 the Caterpillar 966C (76J) with 170 hp was released. Those were 20 hp more than the 966B had. The bucket capacity increased by 1.05 yd³ to 4.05 yd³. The operation weight is now 36,890 lb. A Caterpillar 966C (76J) loads 4-axle on-highway trucks on the Furkapass in the Swiss Alps. Notice the top mounted Swiss flag on the radiator.

1968 wurde der Caterpillar 966C (76J) mit 170 PS vorgestellt. Das sind 20 PS mehr als in der 966B. Auch das Schaufelvolumen stieg um 0,81 m³ auf nun 3,1 m³. Das Einsatzgewicht beträgt 16.730 kg. Ein Caterpillar 966C (76J) belädt 4-Achs-Kipper auf dem Furkapass in den Schweizer Alpen. Man beachte die Schweizer Flagge über dem Kühlergrill.

After a rock blasting this Caterpillar 966C (76J) is clearing the pit floor in a limestone quarry in Germany. It is equipped with a Caterpillar ROPS cab. The Cat 966C (76J) was listed until 1981.

Nach Sprengarbeiten räumt diese Caterpillar 966C (76J), ausgerüstet mit Caterpillars ROPS-Fahrerhaus, die Ladesohle eines Kalksteinbruchs in Deutschland, . Die Cat 966C (76J) blieb bis 1981 im Programm.

A Caterpillar 966D (99Y) is loading massive stone blocks onto an on-highway dump truck. It is powered by a Cat 3306DIT engine with 640 in³ displacement, rated 200 hp of 2200 r.p.m. It was built from 1980 to 1987.

Ein Caterpillar 966D (99Y) lädt große Felsblöcke auf Straßenmuldenkipper. Er wurde von 1980 bis 1987 gebaut. Angetrieben durch den Cat 3306DIT-Motor mit 10,5 l Hubraum beträgt die Leistung 200 PS bei 2.200 U/min.

The Cat 972G replaces the old 970F (7SK) with 266 hp in 1998. It is equipped with buckets from 4.97 up to 7.19 yd³. A 972G is loading a Cat D300E truck with 30 tons capacity in 4-passes.

Der 972G löst 1998 die 970F (7SK) mit 266 PS ab. Eine 972G, ausgerüstet mit Schaufeln von 3,8 bis 5,5 m³, lädt einen Cat D300E Dumper mit 27 t Nutzlast in vier Arbeitstakten.

This Caterpillar 966E (99Y) works in a gravel pit in Switzerland. It is attached with tire chains to reduce damage. The operating weight is now 44,767 lb and the engine power increased by 16 hp compared to the old D-series.

In einem Schweizer Kieswerk arbeitet dieser Caterpillar 966E (99Y) mit Reifenschutz-ketten. Das Einsatzgewicht beträgt nun 20.324 kg, die Motorleistung stieg um 16 PS gegenüber der alten D-Serie.

On the 1992 Bauma exhibit in Munich Cater-pillar showed the new 966F (4YG) with a power rating of 220 hp, a weight of 45,119 lb and a bucket ranged up to 5.0 yd³. In 1993 the new Cat 966F II (1SL) with increased horsepower and a new cab was offered. The current model is the Cat 966G with a top horse power of 257 hp and a bucket capacity up to 7.19 yd³.

Auf der Bauma 1992 in München wird der Caterpillar 966F (4YG) mit 220 PS bei 20.466 kg Einsatzgewicht und einer Schaufelkapazität bis zu 3,8 m³ vorge-stellt. 1993 wird die Cat 966F II (1SL) mit neuem Fahrerhaus und mehr Leistung präsentiert. Das aktuelle Modell ist der Cat 966G mit 257 PS und Schaufelinhalt von bis zu 5,5 m³.

After many years I finally found an old Caterpillar 980B (89P) while working. It was built from 1970 to 1978. The forerunner was the Cat 980 (42H) with 235 hp. On June 6th, 1966 the first machine was delivered. The B-series weight increased by 6,615 lb to 51,508 lb operating weight and the power grew up to 260 hp.

Nach vielen Jahren ist es mir doch noch gelungen einen alten Caterpillar 980B (89P) bei der Arbeit zu fotografieren. Gebaut wurde er von 1970 bis 1978. Sein Vorgänger wurde am 06.06.1966 ausgeliefert: der Cat 980 (42H) mit 235 PS. Die B-Serie wiegt über 3.000 kg mehr, insgesamt 23.360 kg, und hat zudem 25 PS mehr unter der Motorhaube.

The Caterpillar 980C (63X) replaced the 980B in 1979 and was in the sales list until 1991.

Der Caterpillar 980C (63X) löst den 980B im Jahr 1979 ab und bleibt bis 1991 im Verkaufsprogramm.

Equipped with a rock bucket this Caterpillar 980C (63X) and tire chains is loading limestone from the bank into 20 tons dump trucks.

Ausgerüstet mit Felsschaufel und Reifenschutzketten lädt dieser Cat 980C (63X) Kalkstein direkt vom Haufwerk auf 20 t Muldenkipper.

This Caterpillar 980C (63X) is a very special model. The Swiss Cat-dealer Ammann adapted the diesel engine to a natural gas model. Please pay attention to the two big separately mounted gas tanks on the fenders.

Speziell angefertigt ist dieser Caterpillar 980C (63X). Der Schweizer Cat-Händler Ammann rüstet den Motor von Diesel auf Gas um. Man beachte die zwei großen zusätzlich montierten Tanks auf den Kotflügeln.

The Caterpillar 980F (8CJ) was built from 1991 to 1992 with 275 hp. A Caterpillar 980F HL loads a Cat truck 769C in 5-passes. So about 500-600 tons can be reached within 50 minutes by 15 cycles. The Cat 980F II (8CJ) was built from 1992 to 1995.

Der Caterpillar 980F (8CJ) wurde von 1991 bis 1992 mit 275 PS gebaut. Ein Caterpillar 980F HL lädt einen Cat 769C in fünf Arbeitstakten. Bei 15 Ladespielen in einer 50 Min.-Stunde können so 500 bis 600 t/h geladen werden. Der Cat 980F II (8CJ) wurde von 1992 bis 1995 gebaut.

A Caterpillar 980G is loading limestone at a quarry in Southern-Germany. In a competition between the old Cat 980F II (8CJ) and the new 980G, they found out that the G-series reached 21% better results. The loaders loaded well shot limestone in 4 cycles in a Cat 773B truck with 59 tons capacity. The 980G was faster in speed, loading time and dumping time. A better and greater fill factor led to the better results of the Cat 980G.

In einem Steinbruch in Süddeutschland lädt dieser Caterpillar 980G Kalkstein. Bei einem Versuch zwischen der alten Cat 980F II (8CJ) und der 980G fand man heraus, daß die neue 980G 21% mehr Leistung erzielte. Man lud gesprengtes Material in vier Arbeitstakten auf den Cat 773B Muldenkipper mit 53 t Nutzlast. Durch schnellere Fahrzeiten, Ladezeiten und auch Entleerzeiten der Schaufel sowie durch einen besseren Füllungsgrad konnte man diesen Leistungsvorsprung der neuen 980G erzielen.

The new Caterpillar 980G wheel loader was introduced in 1996. In the Nether-lands this 980G works for the protection of the dikes in a block handling arrange-ment. The Cat 3406C TA diesel engine with 300 hp gives the loader the right power to move the heavy stone blocks.

Der neue Caterpillar 980G wurde 1996 der Öffentlichkeit vorgestellt. Eine 980G wird in den Niederlanden für die Erhöhung der Deiche eingesetzt. Der Cat 3406C TA-Diesel-Motor mit 300 PS gibt dem Lader die nötige Kraft, um die schweren Steinblöcke zu transportieren.

Brand-new is this 1998 Caterpillar 980G with an operating weight of 65,047lb. It is attached with a large coal bucket and it works near Rotterdam/the Netherlands.

Brandneu ist dieser 1998 gebaute Caterpillar 980G mit einem Einsatzgewicht von 29.500 kg. Er ist ausgerüstet mit einer großen Leichtgutschaufel und wird für den Kohleumschlag in der Nähe von Rotterdam eingesetzt.

CATERPILLAR 988
Carry Loader

Shown with Rock Buckets

Loading and hauling from a face or stockpile by one machine.

Rear bucket doubles the hauling capacity of a 988.

Hydraulic accummulator absorbs haul road shocks ... reduces loping and bouncing.

Proven reliability of 988 engine and power train ... 325 flywheel horsepower and full power shift transmission.

Rock or General Purpose buckets ... 6½ cu. yd. (4,95 m³) General Purpose, 6 cu. yd. (4,60 m³) Rock.

A sales brochure from 1970 shows the Caterpillar 988 (87A) carry loader with an operating weight of 79,821 lb.

Ein Verkaufsprospekt von 1970 zeigt den Caterpillar 988 (87A) carry loader mit einem Einsatzgewicht von 36.200 kg.

In a Swiss quarry a Cat 988 (87A) is loading a Cat 769B (99F) truck. The 988 was built between 1963 and 1976. In those times everybody was surprised by the high engine technology of Caterpillar. The Cat D343 with 890.6 in³ displacement had two intake and two exhaust valves per cylinder, the valves are directly actuated by two overhead camshafts. The 6-cylinder turbo rated at 325 hp.

In einem Schweizer Steinbruch lädt ein Caterpillar 988 (87A) einen Cat 769B (99F) Muldenkipper. Der 988 wurde von 1963 bis 1976 gebaut. Was erstaunlich für diese Zeit war, ist Caterpillars fortschrittliche Motorentechnik: Der D343 mit 14,6 l Hubraum hat zwei obenliegende Nockenwellen, die je zwei Einlass- und Auslassventile pro Zylinder steuern. Der 6-Zyl.-Turbo-Motor leistet 325 PS.

Block handling is the toughest application for loader and tires. Back in 1994 this Caterpillar 988 (87A) is still daily used.

»Block handling« ist Schwerstarbeit für Lader und Reifen. Dieser Caterpillar 988 (87A) ist 1994 noch täglich im Einsatz.

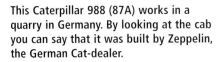

This Caterpillar 988 (87A) works in a quarry in Germany. By looking at the cab you can say that it was built by Zeppelin, the German Cat-dealer.

Eingesetzt wird der Caterpillar 988 (87A) in einem Steinbruch in Deutschland. Man kann es an dem Fahrerhaus erkennen, das Zeppelin aufgebaut hat.

I was fascinated by this old Caterpillar 988 when I took the pictures. It was the biggest Cat wheel loader between 1963 and 1968.

Ich war fasziniert, als ich diesen alten Caterpillar 988 fotografierte. War doch der 988 Caterpillars größter Radlader von 1963 bis 1968.

The model change for the old Caterpillar 988 came in 1976, when the new 988B (50W) was introduced. The biggest visual difference is the double Z-bar linkage. This Cat 988B (50W) waits in front of the crusher, it runs in a load and carry application in a quarry.

Der Modellwechsel für den alten Caterpillar 988 kam im Jahr 1976, als die neue 988B (50W) vorgestellt wurde. Auffälligstes Merkmal ist die Doppel-Z-Kinematik. Dieser Cat 988B (50W) wird im load-and-carry-Einsatz betrieben und wartet vor dem Brecher in einem Steinbruch.

In this picture we can obviously seethe Z-bar linkage.The Caterpillar 988B (50W) is now powered by a Cat V8 turbo engine rated at 375 hp, the operating weight goes up to 95,600 lb.

Man kann auf diesem Bild gut die Z-Kinematik erkennen. Der Caterpillar 988B (50W) wird von einem Cat V8-Turbo-Motor mit 375 PS angetrieben. Das Einsatzgewicht beträgt 43.365 kg.

In a cement plant this Caterpillar 988B (50W) high lift is loading a Cat 773B truck. With 5 cycles the 60 tons Cat hauler 773B is loaded. The 988B reaches an hourly production of 700-800 tons/h.

In einem Zementwerk lädt ein Caterpillar 988B (50W) high lift (verlängerter Hubrahmen) einen Cat 773B Muldenkipper. Mit fünf Ladespielen ist der 60-Tonner Cat 773B beladen. Man kommt auf eine rechnerische Stundenleistung von 700 bis 800 t/h.

The model change in 1993 brought the Caterpillar 988F (8YG) even more horsepower, 405 hp are available now at an operating weight of 95,900 lb. In the docks of Rotterdam these two Cat 988F are attached with large coal buckets.

Der Modellwechsel im Jahr 1993 brachte dem Caterpillar 988F (8YG) nochmals mehr Leistung. Es stehen jetzt 405 PS zur Verfügung bei einem Einsatzgewicht von 43.540 kg. Im Rotterdamer Hafen stehen zwei Cat 988F, ausgerüstet mit einer Spezialkohleschaufel.

This is another Caterpillar 988F (8YG), equipped with a large coal bucket, and a special protection frame for the radiator. These modifications were built by the Cat-dealer Geveke from the Netherlands.

Ein anderer Caterpillar 988F (8YG) mit Kohleschaufel. Der Kühler wurde zusätzlich durch einen speziellen Rahmen geschützt. Diese Umbauarbeiten führte der Cat-Händler Geveke mit Hauptsitz in Amsterdam/Niederlande aus.

A beautiful blue painted Caterpillar 988F (8YG) is also attached with a large special coal bucket.

Ein wunderschön blau lackierter Caterpillar 988F (8YG) ist ebenfalls mit einer Spezialkohleschaufel ausgerüstet.

The derivative of the Caterpillar 988F was the introduction of the series-II in1996. The top model now weighs 99,879 lb and the bucket capacity goes from 7.97 to 9.02 yd³, the power rates 430 hp. Attached with a big coal bucket this Cat 988F II is working near Rotterdam/Netherlands.

Die nächste Weiterentwicklung des Caterpillar 988F war 1996 die Einführung der Serie II, äußerlich gut zu erkennen durch das untere Fenster in den Türen. Das Top-Modell wiegt 45.297 kg, die Schaufeln werden von 6,1 bis 6,9 m³ angeboten, die Leistung beträgt hierbei 430 PS. Ausgerüstet ist dieser Caterpillar 988F II mit einer großen Kohleschaufel. Er wird eingesetzt in der Nähe von Rotterdam/Niederlande.

This is an ideal team: a Caterpillar 988F II wheel loader and a Cat 773B truck.

Ein ideales Paar: ein Caterpillar 988F II Radlader und ein Caterpillar 773B Muldenkipper.

The Caterpillar 990 (7HK) was presented at the Steinexpo in Germany in 1993. It loads a Cat 775B in 4 passes. It is rated at 610 hp and weighs 162,023 lb. The loader was replaced by the Cat 990 II in 1995.

Auf der Steinexpo 1993 in Deutschland wird der Caterpillar 990 (7HK) vorgestellt. Er lädt einen Cat 775B in vier Arbeitstakten. Das Einsatzgewicht beträgt 73.480 kg mit einer Leistung von 610 PS. Abgelöst wird der Lader 1995 durch den Cat 990 II.

In 6-7 passes a Caterpillar 990 HL loader charges a Cat 777D truck with a capacity of 90 tons. With the introduction of the Cat 990 came the new STIC Control steering. With the STIC stick you can steer, shift up and down and change all directions. The continuous cranking of the steering wheel was dropped, and the operator can concentrate on loading the truck.

In sechs bis sieben Arbeitstakten lädt ein Caterpillar 990 HL Radlader einen Cat 777D Muldenkipper mit 90 t Nutzlast. Mit dem Cat 990 wurde Caterpillars STIC-Control-Lenkung eingeführt. Mit dem linken Bedienhebel wird gelenkt, geschaltet und die Fahrtrichtung gewechselt. Das mühsame Kurbeln am Lenkrad entfällt, und der Fahrer kann sich voll auf seine Ladearbeit konzentrieren.

There`s a job disscusion. In front you see the new Caterpillar 990 II loader and in the back the older Cat 990. The power rose up to 625 hp and the bucket capacities held between 9.94 to 12.94 yd³. The only conspicuous difference you can make out: there is no hole in the lift arms and so you can distinguish between both machines.

Einsatzbesprechung: Im Vordergrund der neue Caterpillar 990 II Lader, im Hintergrund der alte Cat 990. Die Leistung wurde bei der neuen Serie II erhöht auf nun 625 PS. Der Schaufelinhalt stieg auf 7,6 bis 9,9 m³. Auffallendstes Merkmal der neuen Serie-II: er hat keine Bohrung mehr im Hubrahmen. So kann man die beiden Typen schon von weitem unterscheiden.

This Caterpillar 990 II, attached with a 14 yd³ coal bucket, works in the docks of Rotterdam. Every year the company moves approximately 13 million tons iron ore and 18 million tons coal.

Im Rotterdamer Hafen wird dieser Caterpillar 990 II mit 11 m³ Kohleschaufel eingesetzt. Seit ihrer Gründung im Jahr 1973 schlägt die Firma jährlich ungefähr 13 Mio t Eisenerz und 18 Mio t Kohle um.

Two are better than one, in front a Caterpillar 990 (7HK) is loading a Cat 777C truck. In the background a Caterpillar 990 II is loading a Cat 777D truck with 90 tons capacity. This picture was taken in a big quarry for the cement industry in Southern Germany.

Zwei sind besser als einer. Im Vordergrund ein Caterpillar 990 (7HK), der auf einen Cat 777C Muldenkipper lädt. Im Hintergrund ein Caterpillar 990 II. Er lädt auf einen Cat 777D mit 90 t Nutzlast. Aufgenommen ist dieses Foto in einem großen Steinbruch für die Zementindustrie in Süddeutschland.

The biggest Caterpillar wheel loader from the seventies is the Cat 992 (25K). It was built between 1968 and 1973. It is powered by a Caterpillar 12-cylinder four-stroke diesel engine, model D348 V 60° type, bore 5'44", stroke 6'5" and a displacement of 1786 in³. Twin turbochargers, parallel manifold porting with two intake and two exhaust valves per cylinder, and a power rating of 550 hp.

Der größte Radlader von Caterpillar aus den 70ern ist der 992 (25K). Er wurde gebaut von 1968 bis 1973 mit einem Caterpillar 12-Zyl.-Viertakt-Diesel-Motor Typ D348, 60°-V-Anordnung, Bohrung 137 mm, Hub 165 mm, Hubraum 29,3 l, Doppel-Turbolader, parallel geführte Krümmer mit zwei Einlass- und zwei Auslassventilen pro Zylinder und einer Leistung von 550 PS.

This is another Caterpillar 992 (25K): and it is no museum piece. It ran well during the last 29 years and is still used daily with great availability. It is attached by a 10 yd³ rock bucket.

Ein anderer Caterpillar 992 (25K): auch er ist noch kein Museumsstück. Trotz seines hohen Alters von ungefähr 29 Jahren ist er noch täglich im Einsatz, zur vollsten Zufriedenheit seines Betreibers. Ausgerüstet ist er mit einer 7,65 m³ Felsschaufel.

This is the Caterpillar 992B (25K) wheel loader. Weighing 36,713 lb more than the old 992, the 992B hits the scale at 141,800 lb. Further advantages: a new ROPS cab, the air cleaners are moved back to the engine hood and the travel speed increased from 22.1 mph to 25.0 mph.

Das ist der neue Caterpillar 992B (25K) Radlader. Der Hauptunterschied zur alten 992 besteht aus einem um 16.650 kg höheren Einsatzgewicht, das nun bei 64.230 kg liegt, einem neuen ROPS-Fahrerhaus und nach hinten auf die Motorhaube verlegte Luftfilter. Die Fahrtgeschwindigkeit wurde von 35,6 km/h auf 40,2 km/h erhöht.

In 1977 the Caterpillar 992C (97X) replaced the Cat 992B (25K). It is attached with a 12.5 yd³ rock bucket and a new Cat 3412 V12 turbo engine, rated at 140 hp more than the former model. The operating weight increased up to 188,800 lb.

Der Caterpillar 992C (97X) löste den Cat 992B (25K) im Jahr 1977 ab. Ausgerüstet mit einer 9,6 m³ Felsschaufel und einem neuen Cat 3412 V12-Turbo-Motor leistet er 140 PS mehr als sein Vorgänger. Das Einsatzgewicht beträgt nun 85.640 kg.

Not far from my hometown, in a big quarry, works this Caterpillar 992C (49Z01396) built in 1989. The Cat (49Z) was built between 1981 and 1992. It loads a Cat 773B truck in 3 cycles, so you can reach a capacity of 1100-1300 tons/h

Nicht weit weg von meinem Haus arbeitet dieser Caterpillar 992C (49Z01396), Baujahr 1989, in einem großen Steinbruch. Der (49Z) wurde von 1981 bis 1992 gebaut. Er lädt einen Cat 773B Muldenkipper in drei Arbeitstakten, man kommt dann auf eine rechnerische Leistung von 1.100 bis 1.300 t/h.

In Switzerland this Caterpillar 992C (49Z) is loading a Weserhütte mobil crusher, built in 1969, with a operating weigth of 793,800 lb and a maximum capacity of 500 tons/h. The Cat 992C (49Z) weighs 194,950 lb and carries a rock bucket of 13.5 yd³.

In der Schweiz lädt dieser Caterpillar 992C (49Z) einen Weserhütte Mobilbrecher, Baujahr 1969, mit 360 t Dienstgewicht und einer max. Leistung von 500 t/h. Der Cat 992C (49Z) wiegt 88.430 kg und hat eine 10,4 m³ fassende Felsschaufel.

A Caterpillar 992C (49Z) wheel loader and a Ford Fiesta (GFJ), built in 1992. Here the dimensions become obvious. If a 992C HL rises the V-rock bucket up to the top, it is nearly as high as the roof of a three floor building.

Ein Caterpillar 992C (49Z) Radlader und ein Ford Fiesta (GFJ), Baujahr 1992. Hier hat man den direkten Größenvergleich. Wenn man die V-Felsschaufel eines 992C HL ganz nach oben hebt, kommt dieser auf fast die Höhe eines 10 m hohen Sprungturms im Freibad.

In 1993 one of the first Caterpillar 992D (7MJ00102) was delivered to Germany. The final assembly begins with mounting the cab and the 7,188 lb heavy roll over bar. Each machine of these D-serie loaders weighs about 196,593 lb.

1993 wird einer der ersten Caterpillar 992D (7MJ00102) nach Deutschland ausgeliefert. Die Endmontage beginnt. Das Fahrerhaus wird aufgesetzt, danach wird der Überrollschutz, der allein schon 3.260 kg wiegt, montiert. Jede Maschine aus der D-Serie wiegt komplett 89.158 kg.

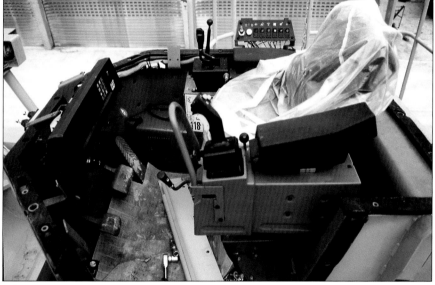

Here we have a good overview of the implement controls of the Caterpillar 992D wheel loader. On the left the STIC Control lever for shifting and steering, on the right the bucket levers to rise and lower the lift arms and the bucket tilt. In front of the operator is the computer aided monitoring system (CMS). It shows all the important informations.

Überblick über die Bedienungseinrichtung des Caterpillar 992D Radladers. Zur Linken der STIC-Kombihebel, mit ihm wird gelenkt und geschaltet. Zur Rechten die Schaufelbedienungshebel für das Heben und Senken und das Ein- und Auskippen der Schaufel. Vor dem Fahrer befindet sich das computergestützte Überwachungssystem CMS, das jederzeit gut ablesbar ist.

The following day the Caterpillar 992D was finally put together and ready to work. Attached is a 14.0 yd³ V-rock bucket. The Cat 12-cylinder V-type engine 3412C TA boosts now 710 hp into the loader.

An dem darauf folgenden Tag war der Caterpillar 992D komplett zusammengebaut und betriebsbereit. Ausgerüstet mit einer 10,7 m³ fassenden V-Felsschaufel. Der Cat 12-Zyl.-V-Motor 3412C TA leistet 710 PS.

This Caterpillar 992D (7MJ) runs in a load and carry application. "Load and carry" means direct loading from the bank into the crusher. With this system you can reach efficient production between 1100-1625 tons/h on a one way travel distance up to 100 yd.

Dieser Cat 992D (7MJ) wird im load-and-carry-Verfahren eingesetzt. Load-and-carry, d.h. laden von der Wand und mit dem Radlader den Brecher beschicken. Mit diesem System kann man auf kurzen Entfernungen (wirtschaftlich bis max. 100 m) Leistungen von 1.100 bis 1.625 t/h erzielen.

This picture gives a fascinating, even a tremendous atmosphere. It looks nearly artistic. A Caterpillar 992D (7MJ) works in a uranium mine in East Germany. The next step comes with the introduction of the 992G in 1996.

Von diesem Bild geht eine faszinierende Stimmung aus. Es wirkt schon fast künstlerisch: Ein Caterpillar 992D (7MJ) in einer Uranmine im Osten Deutschlands. Die Weiterentwicklung kommt 1996 mit der 992G.

Both loaders got names: in front "Pollux" behind it "Castor". The Caterpillar 992G is now powered by a new Cat 3508B EUI V8 twin turbo engine with 829 hp, has an operating weight of 202,441 lb, and buckets up to 16.08 yd³ capacity. The most conspicuous change is the revolutionary front linkage design, a one-piece box section. This steel casting replaces the steel plate lift arms. The design provides a better torsional loading strength, for the operator a better view to the bucket and a better horsepower to weight rate.

Beide Lader bekamen Namen: Im Vordergrund "Pollux", dahinter "Castor". Der neue 992G wird durch einen neu konzipierten Cat 3508B EUI-V8-Bi-Turbo-Motor mit 829 PS angetrieben, hat ein Einsatzgewicht von 91.810 kg und Schaufeln von 11,5 bis 12,3 m³. Die auffälligste Neuerung ist der mono boom Stahlguss-Laderahmen. Verbessert sind der Kräfteverlauf, das Leistungsgewicht und die Sicht des Fahrers auf die Schaufel.

The 994 (9YF) is Caterpillar's biggest wheel loader. The first units went into service in 1990. The first Cat 994 in Europe, came into a Belgium quarry in January 1994. The fuel consumption of this 1250 hp and 390,300 lb "super" loader is 37 US gal/h. The loader is attached with a 23.54 yd³ rock bucket and the production is 3.000 t/h.

Der 994 (9YF) ist Caterpillars größter Radlader, die ersten Maschinen wurden 1990 ausgeliefert. Der erste 994, der nach Europa geliefert wurde, kam 1994 in einen belgischen Steinbruch. Der Verbrauch dieses 1.250 PS starken und 177.000 kg schweren "Super" Laders liegt bei nur 140 l/h.

A Caterpillar 994 (9YF) requires only 12.5 sec. to rise a fully loaded rock bucket with approx. 30 tons up to 32'8" height. The fuel tank houses 800 US gallons. This unit runs in an iron ore and copper mine in Spain. Powered by a Cat 351b turbo engine with four turbo chargers and a displacement of 4209 in³.

Für das Heben der mit ca. 30 t voll beladenen Felsschaufel auf 10 m Höhe benötigt dieser Caterpillar 994 (9YF) gerade mal 12,5 Sekunden. Der Kraftstofftank fasst 3.030 l. Eingesetzt wird dieser 994 in einer Eisenerz- und Kupfermine in Spanien; angetrieben durch einen Cat3516 V16-Turbo-Motor mit vier Turbo-Ladern und einem Hubraum von 69l.

The Caterpillar 994 (9YF) wheel loader loads a Caterpillar 789B truck in 5-6 cycles. With a capacity up to 200 tons the truck runs to the crusher. Every five minutes a Cat 789B truck reaches the crusher, the production is nearly 2400 tons/h. The production of this loader came to an end in 1998.

Der Caterpillar 994 (9YF) Radlader lädt in fünf bis sechs Arbeitstakten einen Cat 789B Muldenkipper. Mit 177 t beladen macht er sich auf den Weg zum Brecher, wo alle fünf Minuten ein 789B Muldenkipper entlädt. Man kommt dann rechnerisch auf max. 2.124 t/h. Das Produktionsende für diesen Radlader kam 1998.

This picture from a sales brochure shows the current Caterpillar 994D wheel loader. It is now attached with STIC Control steering.

Dieses Bild aus einem Prospekt zeigt den aktuellen Caterpillar Radlader 994D, der nun mit STIC-Lenkung ausgestattet ist.

Track Loaders

Kettenlader

The Trackson Company from Milwaukee /Wisconsin built cable operated loader attachments for crawlers. In 1936 Trackson began building loader attachments for these Caterpillar D2, D4, D6 and D7 tractors. The smallest Traxcavator, the T2, had a bucket capacity of 3/4 yd³, the T4 had 1 yd³, the T6 1 3/4 yd³, and the biggest 'Trax' had a bucket capacity of 4 yd³. The vehicle length of the biggest Traxca-vator, the T7, amounts 19'6", the lift height 11'7" and the dumping height, noticeable, 8'. Already in the beginning there were a variety of buckets and bulldozer blades available for the Traxcavators. In 1950 Trackson built the first hydraulic loader attachement for a Caterpillar D4 with the designation HT4. The advantage of this new system is a better overview for the operator, easy control, the latest hydraulic system and, very important, the down pressure of the bucket for better digging. This was not possible with the former cable operated T-loader attachement models. In the same year Caterpillar purchased the Trackson Company and built its own hydraulic loader attachement for his Cat D4. The 60 hp strong Caterpillar HT4, with an operation weight of 18,000 lb carried a 1 yd³ bucket and was built until 1955. The first independent developed and built track loader was the Caterpillar No.6, with a weight of 29,324 lb and a bucket capacity of 2 yd³. It was powered by a 90 hp Cat engine. This model smoothed the way for a whole generation of new Caterpillar track loaders: The first new models, introduced in 1955 were the 933C, 955C and the 977D. The biggest track loader in the seventies was the Cat 983, rated at 275 hp and an operation weight of 75,980 lb. A further milestone in the development of Cat track loaders was the introduction of the rear engine track loader with hydrostatic drive. The first model, the Cat 943, was introduced in 1980. Now the operator has an excellent view over the bucket, and the engine is a natural counterweight to the full loaded bucket. The drive train allows a counter rotation of the tracks. This gives the loader a high manoeuvrability. Today Caterpillar's track loader line consists at five models from 70 hp to 210 hp. Caterpillar is today the biggest manufacturer of track loaders. Beneath the standard track loaders they sell a variety of special track loaders for demolition, for waste handling and steel mills.

Die Firma Trackson aus Milwaukee/Wisconsin begann mit dem Bau von seilbetätigten Ladeeinrichtungen, die man an einem Standardkettentraktor montierte. Im Jahr 1936 begann Trackson für Caterpillar Ladeeinrichtungen für die D2, D4, D6 und D7 zu bauen. Der kleinste Traxcavator T2 hat einen Schaufelinhalt von 0,57 m³, der T4 0,76 m³, der T6 1,33 m³ und der größte Trax hat max. 3 m³ Schaufelinhalt. Die Fahrzeuglänge des größten Traxcavator T7 beträgt 6.430 mm, die Hubhöhe 3.838 mm und die Auskipphöhe beachtliche 2.624 mm. Es standen schon damals eine Vielzahl von Schaufeln und sogar Planierschilde für die einzelnen Traxcavators zur Auswahl. 1950 wurde die erste hydraulische Ladeeinrichtung von Trackson für einen Caterpillar D4 gebaut mit der Bezeichnung HT4. Die Vorteile dieses neuen Systems: Bessere Übersicht für den Fahrer, einfachere Bedienung, das neueste Hydrauliksystem und, was sehr wichtig ist, man konnte nun auf die Schaufel erstmals Druck geben für besseres Graben. Dies war mit den früheren seilbetätigten T-Ladeeinrichtungen nicht möglich. Noch im gleichen Jahr übernahm Caterpillar die Firma Trackson und baute die hydraulisch betätigte Ladeeinrichtung für seine Cat D4 selbst. Der 60 PS starke Caterpillar HT4 mit einem Einsatzgewicht von 8.200 kg und einer

0,76 m³-Schaufel wurde bis 1955 gebaut. Der erste eigenständig entwickelte Kettenlader ist der Caterpillar No.6 mit 13.229 kg und 90 PS. Das Fassungsvermögen der Schaufel beträgt 1,5 m³. Dieses Modell ebnet den Weg für eine ganze Generation neuer Caterpillar Kettenlader. Die ersten neuen Modelle wurden 1955 vorgestellt: 933C, 955C und 977D. Der größte Kettenlader der 70er ist der Cat 983 mit 275 PS und einem Dienstgewicht von 34.460 kg. Ein weiterer Meilenstein in der Entwicklung der Cat-Kettenlader war die Einführung des Heckmotor-Kettenladers mit hydrostatischem Fahrantrieb. Das erste Modell, die Cat 943, wird 1980 präsentiert. Der Fahrer hat nun eine ausgezeichnete Sicht auf die Schaufel und der Motor ist ein natürliches Gegengewicht zur voll beladenen Schaufel. Der Fahrantrieb ermöglicht ein gegenläufiges Antreiben der Ketten. So kann auf engstem Raum gewendet werden. Heute bietet Caterpillar eine Reihe von fünf Kettenlader mit 70 PS bis 210 PS an und ist der größte Hersteller von Kettenladern. Neben den Standardgeräten werden Spezialkettenlader für Abbruch, Müllumschlag und Einsätze in Stahlwerken angeboten.

CATERPILLAR No. 933

1 CU. YD. BUCKET CAPACITY

STANDARD BUCKET

    CAPACITY.............................. 1 cu. yd.

    WIDTH .... 70"

MAXIMUM DUMPING ANGLE (At maximum lift).... 50°

DUMPING REACH (45° discharge angle)........ $29\frac{9}{16}$"

◆ **DUMPING CLEARANCE** (45° discharge angle).... $95\frac{5}{16}$"

TIP BACK:

    AT GROUND LINE........................... 40°

    AT CARRY POSITION (18" off ground)........ $51\frac{1}{2}$°

    AT MAXIMUM LIFT.......................... 48°

◆   MAXIMUM ($59\frac{13}{16}$" off ground).............. $58\frac{1}{2}$°

    GRADING ANGLE .... 75°

◆ **DUMPING HEIGHT** (Center of hinge pin
    to ground) .... $119\frac{1}{16}$"

◆ **DIGGING DEPTH** (Below ground line—with 5° initial
    digging angle) .... $9\frac{3}{4}$"

LIFTING ARMS—2" steel plate. Cross braced for rigidity.

CONTROLS, (Double spool-type valve, spring centered):
    Positions:
        Lifting Circuit.........Raise, lower, hold, float
        (Automatic kickout at full lift height)
        Tilting Circuit..........Tilt back, hold, dump
        (Automatic bucket positioner — adjustable to
        desired digging angle)

CYLINDERS (double action):

    Lift cylinders, bore and stroke......... 5" x 25"
    Tilting cylinders, bore and stroke..... $4\frac{1}{2}$" x 14"

FENDER MOUNTED HYDRAULIC CONTROL. Sealed reservoir
encloses control valves.

FULL FLOW FILTER. Protects pump and cylinders from
abrasive particles in oil.

PUMP (Vane-type, front-mounted. Driven from front
of engine.)
    Output..... 31 GPM @ 1800 RPM @ 1000 PSI —
                     SAE No. 10 oil at 150° F
    Relief valve opening pressure.......... 1450 PSI
    Lines (Pump to reservoir to cylinder hose). Steel
    tubing and high pressure hose.

HOSE AND FITTINGS (Cylinder to lines). High pressure
hose with flange fittings.

Sales brochure from 1957   Verkaufsprospekt von 1957

Praktische Winke für den Fahrer

CATERPILLAR
Traxcavatoren

Nr. 977, Nr. 955 & Nr. 933

Brochure from 1963   Broschüre von 1963

This Caterpillar 933F (11A) is grading soil. It was built between 1958 and 1965 with 50 hp and a weight of 16,850 lb.

Ein Caterpillar 933F (11A) bei Planierarbeiten. Er wurde gebaut von 1958 bis 1965 mit 50 PS und einem Gewicht von 7.640 kg.

A happy operator and his old Caterpillar 933F. It still runs as well as on the first day.

Ein glücklicher Fahrer. Seine alte Caterpillar 933F läuft noch genauso rund wie am ersten Tag.

CATERPILLAR 955

1¾ CU. YD. BUCKET CAPACITY

Series H

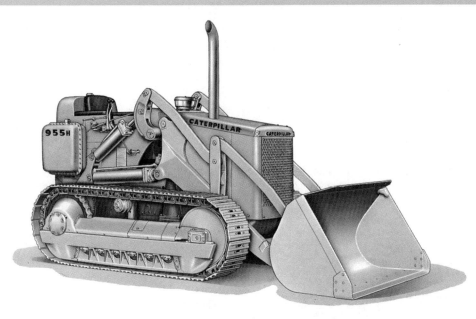

Track roller guards illustrated are available as attachment.

STANDARD BUCKET

Capacity .... 1¾ cu. yd.

Width .... 80″

Maximum dumping angle (at maximum lift).. 50°

♦ Dumping reach (45° discharge angle) .... 41″

♦ Dumping clearance (45° discharge angle)... 8′ 4″

♦ Maximum dumping height (center of hinge pin
    to ground) .... 10′ 10⅜″

Tilt-back:
    At ground line .... 40°
♦   At carry position (18″ off ground)........ 50°
    At maximum lift....................... 47½°
♦   Maximum (50½″ off ground)............ 58°

♦ Grading angle .... 74½°

♦ Digging depth (below ground line — with
    7½° initial digging angle at ground line)...9¾″

Lifting arms —
        Box section. Cross braced for rigidity.

♦ Breakout force .... 21,100 lb.

CONTROLS. (Double spool-type valve, spring centered)

Positions:
    Lift Circuit ....Raise, lower, hold, float
    (Automatic kickout at full lift height)
    Bucket tilt circuit ....Tilt back, hold, dump
    (Automatic bucket positioner — adjustable to
    desired digging angle)

CYLINDERS (double acting):

Lift cylinders, bore and stroke.......5½″ x 29¼″

Bucket tilt cylinders,
    bore and stroke ....5″ x 17⅛″

FENDER MOUNTED HYDRAULIC CONTROL. Sealed reservoir encloses control valves.

FULL FLOW FILTER. Protects pump and cylinders from abrasive particles in oil.

PUMP (Vane-type, transmission mounted and engine driven.)

Output....44½ GPM @ 1800 RPM @ 1000 PSI —
              SAE No. 10 oil @ 150° F.
♦ Relief valve opening pressure......... 1900 PSI

Lines (Pump to reservoir to cylinder). Steel tubing
              and high pressure hose.

HOSE AND FITTINGS (Cylinder to hydraulic lines: high pressure hose with flange fittings.)

Sales brochure from 1961   Verkaufsprospekt von 1961

This Caterpillar 955H (60A751) works in the high mountains of Switzerland. It was built between 1960 and 1966. The picture shows an early version with a straight engine hood.

Im Schweizer Hochgebirge arbeitet dieser Caterpillar 955H (60A751), gebaut von 1960 bis 1966. Das Bild zeigt eine frühe Ausführung mit gerader Motorhaube.

The Caterpillar 955H (60A751) is powered by a 4-cylinder turbo engine rated at 100 hp. The diesel starts with a 2-cylinder four-stroke gasoline engine. This was standard by Caterpillar in the sixties. As an option you could order an electric 12-volt starter for the 2-cylinder gasoline engine.

Angetrieben wird der Caterpillar 955H (60A751) durch einen 4-Zyl.-Turbo-Motor mit 100 PS. Den Diesel-Motor startet man mit einem 2-Zyl.-Viertakt-Benzin-Motor, wie das bei Caterpillar in den 60ern so üblich war. Als Option konnte man für den 2-Zyl.-Benzin-Motor einen elektrischen 12 Volt-Anlasser bestellen.

There isn`t anything you can`t get from Caterpillar. A Caterpillar 955H in Switzerland was transformed by an artist from a track loader into a work of art.

Es gibt nichts bei Caterpillar, was es nicht gibt. Ein Caterpillar 955H wurde in der Schweiz durch einen Künstler in ein Kunstwerk namens X-Art umgewandelt.

TRAXCAVATOR

CATERPILLAR No. 977

2½ CU. YD. BUCKET CAPACITY

Series H

STANDARD BUCKET

Capacity .... 2½ cu. yd.

Width .... 96″

Maximum dumping angle (at maximum lift) . 50°

Dumping reach (45° discharge angle) ..... 39½″

Dumping clearance (45° discharge angle) ... 112″

Tilt-back:

At ground line .... 40°

At carry position (24″ off ground) .... 50°

At maximum lift .... 46°

Maximum (66″ off ground) .... 55°

Grading angle .... 75°

Dumping height (center of hinge pin
to ground) .... 144″

Digging depth (below ground line — with
5° initial digging angle at ground line) .. 11¾″

Lifting arms —
Box section. Cross braced for rigidity.

Breakout force .... 25,500 lbs.

CONTROLS, (Double spool-type valve, spring centered)

Positions:

Lift Circuit .... Raise, lower, hold, float
(Automatic kickout at full lift height)

Bucket tilt circuit .... Tilt back, hold, dump
(Automatic bucket positioner—adjustable to
desired digging angle)

CYLINDERS (double acting):
Lift cylinders, bore and stroke .... 6½″ x 32″
Bucket tilt cylinders,
bore and stroke .... 5½″ x 21⅜″

FENDER MOUNTED HYDRAULIC CONTROL. Sealed reservoir encloses control valves.

FULL FLOW FILTER. Protects pump and cylinders from abrasive particles in oil.

PUMP (Vane-type, front-mounted. Driven from front of engine.)

Output..... 63 GPM @ 1800 RPM @ 1000 PSI —
SAE No. 10 oil @ 150° F.

Relief valve opening pressure .... 1900 PSI
Lines (Pump to reservoir to cylinder hose). Steel tubing and high pressure hose.

HOSE AND FITTINGS (Cylinder to lines. High pressure hose with flange fittings.)

Sales brochure from 1960   Verkaufsprospekt von 1960

A new overhauled Caterpillar 977H (53A) works at a Swiss contractor in 1994. With 150 hp and a weight of 37,500 lb this track loader has enough power to handle all coming up work.

Frisch überholt im Jahr 1994 tut diese Caterpillar 977H (53A) ihren Dienst bei einem Schweizer Bauunternehmer. Mit 150 PS und einem Einsatzgewicht von 17.000 kg hat der Kettenlader genug Kraft für alle anfallenden Arbeiten.

The first Caterpillar 977D (20A) was introduced in 1955. It was competed by the Cat 977E (20A), both models were in the sales lists until 1960. The power rated 100 hp, 50 hp less than the 977H (53A), shown in this picture. It was in the sales lists until 1966.

Der erste Caterpillar 977D (20A) wurde 1955 vorgestellt. Er wurde durch den Cat 977E (20A) ergänzt, beide Modelle blieben bis 1960 im Programm. Die Leistung beträgt 100 PS, 50 PS weniger als die 977H (53A), die das Bild zeigt. Die 977H blieb bis 1966 im Verkaufsprogramm.

The smallest track loader of the new generation was the Caterpillar 931(78U) with 62 hp and a weight of 15,300 lb. It was built between 1972 and 1979.

Der kleinste Kettenlader der neuen Generation war der Caterpillar 931 (78U) mit 62 PS und 6.940 kg. Gebaut wurde er von 1972 bis 1979.

From 1979 up to 1988 the successor, the Caterpillar 931B (29Y) was sold. A good small machine for small job sites, but also attached with the same advantages as the bigger Cat-track loaders.

Von 1979 bis 1988 wurde der Nachfolger, der Caterpillar 931B (29Y), verkauft. Eine gute, kleine Maschine für kleine Bauprojekte, aber dennoch mit den Vorteilen der großen Cat-Kettenlader ausgerüstet.

The new Caterpillar 933/933 LGP replaces the 931C II (9AG)/(6AJ) in 1994. A totally new developed cab with a good all around view and an ergonomical restyled operator station with all implement controls helps the operator to do the work faster and more efficiently. The next size is the 935C (8CF) built in 1991 with 18,089 lb and an output of 78 hp. Replaced in 1994 by the Cat 939C with 90hp.

Der neue Caterpillar 933/933 LGP löst die zuletzt gebaute 931C II (9AG)/(6AJ) im Jahr 1994 ab. Ein völlig neu entwickeltes Fahrerhaus steht jetzt zur Verfügung mit hervorragender Rundumsicht und ergonomisch platzierten Bedienelementen. Der nächstgrößere Kettenlader ist der 935C (8CF) von 1991 mit 8.205 kg und 78 PS, abgelöst durch den Cat 939C mit 90 PS.

From 1968 up to 1972 this Caterpillar 941 (80H) was built. In an old sales brochure you can read about the Cat 941: "a good operator station with a high operator comfort…, planetary-powershift transmission…, automatic bucket kick-out…, pedal steering and a walk thru cab." These are only a few aspects why the 941 is easier controlled than other track loaders of the same class.

Von 1968 bis 1972 wurde diese Cat 941 (80H) gebaut. In einer Werbebroschüre über die 941 heißt es: "Fahrerstand mit hohem Bedienungskomfort, Planeten-Last-Schaltgetriebe…, automatischer Schaufelendausschalter…, Pedallen-kung…, unverbauter Fahrerstand." Das sind nur einige Gründe, warum die Cat 941 leichter zu bedienen ist als andere Lader seiner Klasse.

The Cat 3304 engine with 427 in³ displacement rated now at 80 hp, 10 hp more than in the Cat 941.
This Caterpillar 941B (80H) with Zeppelin cab removes top soil.

Der Cat 3304 Motor mit 7 l Hubraum leistet nun 80 PS, das sind 10 PS mehr als in der Cat 941.
Ein Caterpillar 941B (80H) mit Zeppelin-Fahrerhaus trägt Humus ab.

The last models in 1981of the Caterpillar 941B (80H) having ROPS cabs.

Die letzten Ausführungen der Caterpillar 941B (80H) im Jahre 1981 hatten ein Überrollschutz-Fahrerhaus.

The first rear engine track loader from Caterpillar with hydrostatic drive was the model 943. It was introduced in 1980. A few advantages of this new concept: Higher visibility over the bucket, engine in the back as a natural counter weight to the full loaded bucket, Z-bar linkage. And counter-rotation of the tracks allow a full turn within the machine length.

Der erste Heckmotor-Kettenlader von Caterpillar mit hydrostatischem Antrieb ist das Modell 943. Er wird 1980 vorgestellt. Einige der Vorteile: Bessere Sicht für den Fahrer auf die Schaufel, der Motor ist ein natürliches Gegengewicht zur Schaufel, Z-Kinematik und gegenläufiges Antreiben der Ketten verbessert die Manövrierbarkeit des Laders.

In 1992 the production of the 80 hp and 25,900 lb Caterpillar 943 track loader was stopped. It had been attached with a 1.5 yd³ bucket.

1992 wurde die Produktion des 80 PS starken 11.750 kg schweren Caterpillar-Kettenladers 943, der mit einer 1,15 m³-Schaufel ausgerüstet war, eingestellt.

A Caterpillar 951B (79H) is attached with a Zeppelin cab, built from 1967 to 1971. When I took this picture the track loader was already operating for more than 21 years.

Ein mit Zeppelin-Fahrerhaus ausgerüsteter Caterpillar 951B (79H), gebaut von 1967 bis 1971. Als ich diese Aufnahme machte, war der Kettenlader schon mehr als 21 Jahre im Einsatz.

In 1971 the revised version of the Caterpillar 951 was presented, the C-series (86J) with more power (95 hp), a higher weight of 27,200 lb, and the bucket carried 1.75 yd³.
In 1981 the production of the 951C model came to its end.

1971 kam die Weiterentwicklung der Caterpillar 951, die C-Serie (86J) mit mehr Leistung, 95 PS, höherem Einsatzgewicht von nun 12.338 kg und einer 1,34 m³-Schaufel auf den Markt.
1981 wurde die Produktion der 951C eingestellt.

The second rear engine track loader model is the Caterpillar 953, introduced in 1981. This Cat 953 is attached with a skellet bucket to sive rocks out of the soil. It was used in a recultivation project on a vineyard near Stuttgart/Germany in 1991.

Das zweite neue Heck-Motor-Kettenlader-Modell war 1981 der Cat 953, ausgerüstet mit einer Skelettschaufel zum Aussieben von Gesteinsbrocken. Eingesetzt wurde dieser 953 bei einer Weinberg-Rekultivierung im Jahr 1991 in der Nähe von Stuttgart.

The Caterpillar track loader 953 is powered by a Cat 3204 4-cylinder turbo engine with 112 hp at 2400 r.p.m. The hydrostatic drive train allows a variable travel speed up to 6.4 mph, forward and reverse.

Der Caterpillar Kettenlader 953 wird angetrieben durch einen Cat 3204 4-Zyl.-Turbo-Motor mit 112 PS bei 2.400 U/min. Der hydrostatische Fahrantrieb ermöglicht eine stufenlose Regelung der Fahrtgeschwindigkeit bis zu 10,4 km/h vorwärts und rückwärts.

This Cat 953 is attached with a Dima 3-shank ripper and was in the program until 1985. Successor is the Cat 953B (5MK) with a new Cat 3116T 6-cylinder turbo engine rated at 121 hp and larger buckets up to 2.41 yd^3. It was built between 1992 and 1996.

Dieser Caterpillar 953 ist mit einem 3-Zahn-Dima-Aufreisser ausgerüstet und blieb bis 1985 im Programm. Nachfolger wurde der Cat 953B (5MK) mit neuem Cat 3116T 6-Zyl.-Turbo-Motor mit 121 PS und größeren Schaufeln von 1,6-1,85 m^3. Er wurde von 1992 bis 1996 gebaut.

In 1997 a new "Caterpillar" hatches out of its cocoon."A new star is born". The Caterpillar track loader 953C with 122 hp has a totally new cab with more glass and a sloped engine hood for a better overview to all sides.

Aus ihrem Kokon schlüpft eine neue Raupe. "A new star is born". Auffälligste Neuerung des 1997 vorgestellten 122 PS-starken Kettenladers 953C ist das neue Fahrerhaus mit noch mehr Glasfläche für eine bessere Sicht nach allen Seiten und die abgeschrägte Motorhaube.

Equipped with an open cab for the export this new Caterpillar 953C is standing on the yard of the Caterpillar-plant in Grenoble/France. Caterpillar France is responsible for the design work, independent from the mother-plant in the USA, together with operating companies from over the world. A new machine is planned.

Mit einem offenen Fahrerhaus für den Export steht dieser neue Caterpillar 953C auf dem Hof der Caterpillar-Fabrik in Grenoble/Frankreich. Caterpillar France hat die totale Designkontrolle, unabhängig vom Mutterwerk in den USA. Zusammen mit Fahrern, Händlern, Betreibern aus aller Welt und einem Team von Ingenieuren bis hin zum Service-Mann wird jeder in die Planung eines neuen Gerätetyps mit einbezogen.

In 1966 Caterpillar introduced the new 955K (61H) with 115 hp. It was replaced by the Cat 955L (85J) with 130 hp and a weight of 33,800 lb in 1971. The picture shows a 955L (13X) of the last series with a ROPS cab and a bucket with 2.25 yd³ capacity.

1966 wurde der neue Caterpillar 955K (61H) mit 115 PS vorgestellt, abgelöst wurde er 1971 durch den Cat 955L (85J) mit 130 PS und einem Einsatzgewicht von 15.330 kg. Das Bild zeigt eine 955L (13X) aus der letzten Serie mit Überrollschutz-Fahrerhaus und einer 1,72 m³ fassenden Schaufel.

A new painted and overhauled Caterpillar 955L (13X). The planetary power shift transmission with three gears forward and three gears reverse, allows the loader a max. speed of 6 mph in the third forward gear . The production stopped in 1981.

Neu lackiert und generalüberholt: Eine Caterpillar 955L (13X). Durch das Planeten-Last-Schaltgetriebe mit drei Vor- und drei Rück-wärtsgängen erreicht der Lader im dritten Vorwärtsgang max. 9,7 km/h. Die Produktion wurde 1981 eingestellt.

In 1981 the Caterpillar 953 was offered. At the same time the Cat 963 (6Z) was put on the market. It replaced the old 955L (13X). Attached with a rake this Caterpillar 963 with 150 hp clears the construction site on a highway project from tree stumps.

Zeitgleich mit dem Caterpillar 953 kam auch der Cat 963 (6Z) 1981 auf den Markt. Er löst den alten 955L (13X) ab. Ausgerüstet mit einem Roderechen ent-fernt der 150 PS-starke Caterpillar Kettenlader 963 Trasse einer Autobahnbaustelle.

With a 2.6 yd³ bucket the Caterpillar 963 (21Z00235) built in 1984, is the appropriate track loader for midsize construction sites. Because of the hydrostatic drive train the loader reaches a travel speed of 6.27 mph in both directions. Lifting, dumping and lowering the bucket needs only 12 sec., this means a short truck loading time.

Mit der 2 m³-Schaufel ist der Caterpillar 963 (21Z00235), Baujahr 1984, der richtige Kettenlader für mittlere bis große Baustellen. Dank seines hydrostatischen Antriebs erreicht er vor- wie rückwärts eine Fahrtgeschwindigkeit von 10,1 km/h. Ein Arbeitstakt aus Heben, Abkippen und Senken der Schaufel dauert gerade mal 12 Sekunden. Dies ermöglicht ein schnelles Beladen der Lkws.

A Caterpillar 963 (21Z) with an operating weight of 40,490 lb is clearing tree stumps on a highway project. This Cat was built from 1982 to 1995.

Ein Caterpillar 963 (21Z), gebaut von 1982 bis 1995 mit einem Einsatzgewicht von 18.370 kg führt Rodungsarbeiten auf einer Autobahntrasse aus.

In 1995 Caterpillar offered the new 963B (9BL) with 162 hp and a weight of 43,270 lb. A 3-shank ripper adds 1,314 lb to the operating weight, an airconditioner another 238 lb.

1995 wird der neue Caterpillar 963B (9BL) mit 162 PS und einem Gewicht von 20.000 kg vorgestellt. Das Einsatzgewicht erhöht sich um 596 kg, wenn ein Aufreisser mit drei Zähnen angebaut wird. Mit der Klimaanlage kommen nochmals 108 kg hinzu.

When I was visiting the Caterpillar-plant in Grenoble/France, I took a picture of a new Caterpillar 963B (9BL) with ROPS cab.

Während einer Besichtigungstour durch das Caterpillar-Werk in Grenoble/France konnte ich diesen neuen Caterpillar 963B (9BL) mit ROPS-Fahrerhaus fotografieren.

This Cat 963B (9BL) gives the needed pushing power to a Cat 637D scraper.

Ein Cat 963B (9BL) leistet die nötige Schubhilfe für einen Cat 637D Scraper.

The Caterpillar 963C out of a sales brochure from 1999

Der Caterpillar 963C aus einem Verkaufsprospekt von 1999

This Caterpillar 977K (46H) with 170 hp and an operating weight of 42,000 lb was built from 1966 to 1978. The 977K is equipped with a Cat 5-shank ripper.

Von 1966 bis 1978 wurde dieser Caterpillar 977K (46H) mit 170 PS und einem Dienstgewicht von 19.100 kg gebaut. Ausgerüstet ist der 977K mit einem Cat-Aufreisser, der mit max. fünf Zähnen bestückt werden kann.

This Caterpillar 977K (46H) with a 2.5 yd³ bucket is standing in front of lake Thun. It works on a road project in Switzerland.

Der Caterpillar 977K (46H) ist mit einer 1,9 m³ fassenden Schaufel ausgerüstet und steht vor einer Traumkulisse, dem Thunersee.

Without any problem this Caterpillar 977L (14X) is loading a DJB truck, used on a train project in Switzerland. In the L-series the engine output grew up to 190 hp, and the weight rose to 48,010 lb.

Mühelos lädt dieser Caterpillar 977L (14X) einen DJB-Dumper auf einer Eisenbahntrassen-Baustelle in der Schweiz. Bei der L-Serie wurde die Motorleistung auf 190 PS und das Gewicht auf 21.780 kg angehoben.

This Caterpillar 977L (64X881) loads 3-axle road trucks with 3-passes. It is equipped with a Caterpillar ROPS cab and a ripper.

Mit drei Ladespielen lädt dieser 977L (64X881) 3-Achs-Kipper. Er ist ausgerüstet mit Cat-ROPS-Fahrerhaus und einem Heckaufreisser.

In 1982 the biggest rear engine track loader, the Caterpillar 973 (26Z/32Z), deserted the factory. It is powered by a Cat 3306 DI-T 6-cylinder turbo engine, rating at 210 hp. This unusual picture shows a modern track loader which is loading an old German Magirus-Deutz 250D 25 AK 6x6 dump truck from the sixties.

Der größte Heck-Motor-Kettenlader, der Cat 973 (26Z/32Z), wurde 1982 vorgestellt. Der Cat 3306 DI-T Motor mit sechs Zylindern und Turbo-Aufladung leistet 210 PS. Ein außergewöhnliches Bild: Einer der modernsten Heck-Motor-Kettenlader lädt einen alten Magirus-Deutz 250D 25 AK 6x6-Muldenkipper aus den sechziger Jahren.

This Cat/DJB D350C truck and a Caterpillar 973 are used to load top soil in a gypsum mine. Equipped with a 4.18 yd³ bucket the loader weighs 63,945 lb.

Dieser Cat/DJB D350C Dumper und ein Caterpillar 973 werden zum Abtrag der Deckschichten in einem Gipsbruch eingesetzt. Ausgerüstet mit einer 3,2 m³-Schaufel wiegt der Lader 29.000 kg.

A 1991 Caterpillar 973 piles top soil on an airport project near Stuttgart/Germany.
Ein Caterpillar 973 von 1991 schiebt bei einem Flughafenprojekt in Stuttgart Humus ab.

This Caterpillar 973 works on a road project in Switzerland. You can identify this newer Cat-loader by the top of the cab, it's black now.

Auf einer Straßenbaustelle in der Schweiz steht dieser neuere Caterpillar 973 mit jetzt schwarzem Fahrerhausdach.

This Caterpillar 973 returned into the workshop for a routine check.
For more than 40 years the Eberhard Company, located near Zurich/Switzerland, is well-known for its pioneer work in civil engineering. A lot of interesting ideas for earthmoving equipment are developed, build and tested there.

Für einen routinemäßigen check kam dieser Cat 973 in die firmeneigene Werkstatt zurück. Die Firma Eberhard aus der Nähe von Zürich/Schweiz zeichnet sich durch mehr als 40 Jahre lange Pionierleistungen im Tiefbau aus. Viele neue Ideen für Baumaschinen werden in der eigenen Werkstatt entwickelt, selbst gebautund in der Praxis getestet.

The 983 (38K) is the biggest Caterpillar track loader. It is used for the toughest work: Demolition, loading slag, loading rocks, excavation, and other tough loading operations. Caterpillar's D343 turbo engine rated 275 hp at 2060 r.p.m. The operating weight goes from 75,980 lb and buckets are available up to 4.57 to 5.62 yd^3.

Der 983 (38K) ist der größte Caterpillar-Kettenlader für die schwersten Einsätze: Für Abbrucharbeiten, für das Ausräumen von Schlacke, das Laden von Fels, für Aushubarbeiten und für weitere Einsätze. Caterpillars D343 Turbo-Motor leistet bei 2.060 U/min. 275 PS, das Gewicht beträgt 34.460 kg und Schaufeln werden von 3,5 bis 4,3 m^3 angeboten.

A Caterpillar 983B (58X) works in one of the toughest jobs, as a block handler. He replaced the old 983, built from 1969 to 1978.The picture shows a lot of this powerful 78,530 lb track loader. Produced from 1978 to 1982 this type is the heaviest track loader ever built by Caterpillar.

Ein glücklicher Tag für mich. Ein Caterpillar 983B (58X) im Schwersteinsatz als "block handler". Er löst die von 1969 bis 1978 gebaute 983 ab. Das Bild allein sagt schon alles über diesen kraftvollen Kettenlader aus. Mit 35.620 kg ist der 983B noch heute der schwerste Cat-Kettenlader, der je gebaut wurde. Dieser wurde in der Zeit von 1978 bis 1982 produziert.

Equipped with an additional 2,293 lb counter weight, this Caterpillar 983B (58X) moves the heaviest rock blocks in a quarry near Würzburg/Germany. The biggest visible difference to the Caterpillar 983 (38K) is the new Cat ROPS cab. I took these pictures back in 1999.

Ausgerüstet mit einem 1.040 kg schweren Zusatzheckgewicht hebt der Caterpillar 983B (58X) die schwersten Felsblöcke. Eingesetzt wird der Kettenlader in einem Steinbruch in der Nähe von Würzburg. Äußerlich der einzige Unterschied zur alten Caterpillar 983 (38K) sind das neue Cat ROPS-Fahrerhaus und die verstärkte Aufnahmeplatte am Laderahmen für den Hubzylinder. Die Bilder entstanden 1999.

Track Type Tractor

Kettendozer

Caterpillar is considered to be the pioneer of crawlers with the greatest experience. Today the company is the market leader. Because of that it was not surprising when Caterpillar introduced the world's biggest and strongest track type tractor, the D9 with a weight of 59,535 lb in 1954. The first design was shown as a wooden D9 mock-up model in 1950. And five complete versions were developped and cancelled, before the D9 was produced in 1954. Nine happy contractors were allowed to test the first preproduced D9 - they were enthusiastic about this engine. But not one of the five D9 was sold. Caterpillar used the experience of the contractors and operators and built the biggest and best dozer ever built in the factories of Caterpillar.

In the mid of the sixties contractors looked for a bigger track type tractor than the D9H. Therefore Caterpillar produced the DD9H and the Cat SxS D9H. The DD9H consisted of a one by one coupled D9H. They needed only one operator on the front track type tractor. This type was attached with an inside push blade to push the biggest Caterpillar scraper. The SxS D9H consisted of two side by side coupled D9H with a 24' width dozer blade. It also was operated by only one person, sitting on the left tractor. Several engineers and development teams worked very hard on a new concept for track type tractors. In 1971 a Cat D9G dozer was attached with the elevated sprocket design undercarriage, for to test all possible components. In 1973 the technicians got the 'go' to start with the production of a D10. In July the first prototype X-1 was finished and there were built three more prototypes until 1975. Until 1977 ten pilot models were built and tested on Caterpillar's proving ground and on construction sites. Each of the prototype track type tractors clocked up more than 5.000 hours. In 1978 the decision was made to build the D10 in series. This new drive concept with the top mounted drive train was later built in each tractor, down to the smallest D4H. The decisive advantage was the free running top mounted drive train, that ran far from rock and mud and without the shock loades of the push arms. The time to change components in service or repair dropped to a minimum. The blade moved closer to the track type tractor. The new track roller frame with four oscillated bogies helped to increase more track on the ground for a better traction. You can say the new Caterpillar D10 nearly doubled the output of a Cat D9H.The current top model is the Caterpillar D11R CD, rated 850 at hp and with a weight of 246,500 lb.

Caterpillar gilt als Pionier des Kettenantriebs mit der größten Erfahrung und ist heute der Marktführer auf diesem Sektor. Daher war es nicht verwunderlich, als Cat 1954 den weltgrößten und stärksten Kettendozer vorstellte, die D9 mit einem Gewicht von 27.000 kg. Die ersten Entwürfe wurden als Holzmodell 1950 gefertigt. Fünf verschiedene Versionen wurden entworfen und wieder verworfen bis dann 1954 die ersten D9 ausgeliefert wurden. Neun Unternehmer durften die ersten Vorserien der Cat D9 testen und sie waren begeistert. Aber keine der neuen Maschinen durfte verkauft werden. Caterpillar nutzte die Erfahrung der Unternehmer und Fahrer, um die D9 weiter zu verbessern: Sie sollte der beste und größte Kettendozer werden, der die Fabrikhallen von Caterpillar verläßt.

Bereits Mitte der 60er Jahre war klar, daß man einen größeren Kettendozer als die D9H benötigen würde. Die Antwort darauf war die Cat DD9H und die Cat SxS D9H. Die DD9H besteht aus zwei hintereinander gekoppelten D9H, die aber nur ein Fahrer auf dem vorderen Kettendozer bedient. Dieser Typ ist mit einem innenliegenden Push-Schild für das Schieben der größten Caterpillar Scraper ausgerüstet. Die SxS D9H besteht aus zwei nebeneinander gekoppelten D9H mit einem 7.320 mm breiten Planierschild. Auch sie wird nur von einem Fahrer auf dem linken Traktor bedient. Verschiedene Ingenieure und Entwicklungsteams arbeiteten schon 1970 an einem neuen Konzept für Kettendozer. 1971 wurde eine Cat D9G Kettendozer mit Delta-Laufwerk ausgerüstet,

um alle möglichen Komponenten zu testen. 1973 kam das Okay für die D10 und im Juli war der erste Prototyp X-1 fertig gestellt. Es wurden noch drei weitere bis 1975 gebaut. Bis 1977 wurden zehn Pilotmodelle gebaut und auf dem Caterpillar-Versuchsgelände sowie auf Baustellen getestet. Jeder der zehn Prototypen hatte schon mehr als 5.000 Betriebsstunden auf dem Zähler, als man sich entschloß, die D10 1978 in Serie zu fertigen. Dieses Antriebskonzept mit dem nach oben verlegten Endantrieb wurde nach und nach bis zur kleinsten Cat D4H eingeführt. Entscheidende Vorteile sind, daß der Antrieb nicht mehr den Stoßbelastungen der beiden Schubarme und der Schmutzbelastungen ausgesetzt ist. Auch die Aus- und Einbauzeit bei Service oder Reparatur ist auf ein Minimum gesunken. Das Schild konnte näher am Kettendozer angebracht werden. Mit dem Laufrollenrahmen mit vier Hauptpendelträgern verbessert sich die Traktion deutlich, man kann sagen, die neue Cat D10 leistet fast das doppelte einer D9H. Das aktuelle Topmodell ist die Caterpillar D11R CD mit 850 PS und einem Einsatzgewicht von 111.800 kg.

This Caterpillar D3 LGP (6N) is attached with a fully adjustable hydraulic angling and tilt blade. It was built from 1972 to 1979 with an operation weight of 11,925 lb and a 62 hp engine.

Eine Caterpillar D3 LGP (6N) ist mit dem voll hydraulischen Schwenk- und Kippschild ausgestattet. Sie wurde von 1972 bis 1979 mit einem Gewicht von 5.410 kg und 62 PS Motorleistung gebaut.

The derivative edition of the Caterpillar D3 was introduced in 1979. The picture shows a Cat D3B (3YC). Until 1987 it was in the dealer's sales lists. Successor was the D3C (5KG) (from 1987-1990), and the D3C II (5KG) (from1990-1993). The current model is the Cat D3C III/D3C III Hystat with hydrostatic drive train. With a joystick you steer, change the direction and speed. And shift up and down. With 77 hp and a weight of 15,681 lb the dozer carries a blade with 1.65 yd^3 capacity.

Die Weiterentwicklung der bekannten Caterpillar D3 kam 1979. Das Bild zeigt eine Cat D3B (3YC). Sie stand bis 1987 in der Verkaufsliste der Händler. Nachfolger wurde die D3C (5KG) (von 1987-90) und die D3C II (5KG) (von 1990-93). Das aktuelle Modell ist die Cat D3C III/D3C III Hystat mit hydrostatischem Antrieb. Mit einem Joystick wird der Dozer gelenkt, die Fahrtgeschwindigkeit reguliert und gewählt sowie geschaltet. Der 7.112 kg schwere Kettendozer ist mit einem 1,26 m^3-Schild ausgerüstet, die Leistung beträgt nun 77 PS.

The Caterpillar D4D (83J) with 75 hp is equipped with a Zeppelin cab. It is used to pull a roller. The forerunner was the Cat D4C (39A)/(40A), built between 1959 and 1963. The Cat D4D (78A-83J) was in the sales program from 1963 to 1977.

Mit einem Zeppelin-Fahrerhaus ausgerüstet, wird diese Caterpillar D4D (83J) mit 75 PS zum Ziehen einer Anhängerwalze eingesetzt. Die D4D löst die D4C (39A)/ (40A) ab, die von 1959 bis 1963 gebaut wurde . Die Cat D4D (78A-83J) blieb von 1963 bis 1977 im Verkaufsprogramm.

This Caterpillar D4D (83J) is equipped with a Zeppelin hard top cab, a Cat No.4 ripper and a 4A angling blade. The weight increases to 14,332 lb. The successor is the new D4C (1RJ) (from 1987-1990) and the D4C II (from 1990-1993) The current model is the Cat D4C III/D4C III Hystat with 82 hp and an operating weight of 17,529 lb. It carries a dozer blade with 2.19 yd³ capacity.

Diese Caterpillar D4D (83J) ist mit einem neueren Zeppelin Fahrerhaus mit festem Dach, einem Cat-Aufreisser No.4 und einem Schwenkschild 4A ausgerüstet. Sie wiegt nun 6.500 kg. Nachfolger wird die neue D4C (1RJ) (von 1987 bis 90), und die D4C II (von 1990 bis 93). Das aktuelle Modell ist die Cat D4C III/D4C III Hystat. Der 7.950 kg schwere Kettendozer ist mit einem 1,68 m³-Schild ausgerüstet, die Leistung beträgt nun 82 PS.

This is a Caterpillar D4E LGP (low ground pressure) (27X/28X). The visible difference between the new E-series and the old D-series is Caterpillar's new ROPS (Roll over Protective Structure) cab, sloped engine hood and the angular fuel tank with 7.92 US gallons more capacity than the old D4D with 54.95 US gallons.

Ein Caterpillar D4E LGP (low ground pressure) (27X/28X). Das auffälligste Merkmal der neuen E-Serie ist Caterpillars ROPS (Roll over Protective Structure)-Fahrerhaus, abgeschrägte Motorhaube und ein eckiger Diesel-Tank mit 30 l größerem Fassungsvermögen als bei der D4D mit 208 l Inhalt.

Caterpillar's revolutionary drive system was used on the Cat D10 (84W) for the first time in 1978. On a flatbed trailer you can see a 1998 Cat D4H III LGP with ripper. The first Cat D4Hs were delivered from 1985 to 1990, the successor, the D4H II was delivered from 1990-1992 and the D4H III from 1992-1998.

Caterpillars revolutionäres Antriebskonzept wird erstmals in der "Ur"-D10 (84W) verwendet. Auf dem Tieflader steht ein 98er Modell einer Cat D4H III LGP mit Aufreisser. Von 1985 bis 1990 wurden die ersten Cat D4H ausgeliefert, Nachfolger wird die D4H II (von1990-92) und die D4H III (von1992-98).

640 in³ displacement boosted the 6-cylinder Cat D333 diesel engine to 93 hp. It is found in an early Cat D5 (81H-84H), attached with a Zeppelin cab and 5S blade. This 23,924 lb heavy dozer was built in 1967 for only one year.

Aus 10,5 l Hubraum leistet der 6-Zyl.-Cat D333 Diesel-Motor 93 PS. Eingebaut in eine frühe Cat D5 (81H-84H) mit Zeppelin-Fahrerhaus und 5S-Schild. Gebaut wurde dieser 10.850 kg schwere Dozer 1967.

Caterpillar's new D5B (23X) with a ROPS cab was built from 1977 to 1982. The current model is the Cat D5C III/D5C III Hystat. with 92 hp and an operatig weight of 20,402 lb. The dozer carries a 2.52 yd³ blade.

Caterpillars neue D5B (23X) mit ROPS-Fahrerhaus wurde von 1977 bis 1982 gebaut. Das aktuelle Modell ist die Cat D5C III/D5C III Hystat. Mit einem Einsatzgewicht von 9.253 kg und einem 1,93 m³-Schild leistet der Kettendozer 92 PS.

A Caterpillar D5H with elevated sprocket, with 120 hp and an operating weight of 26,922 lb is used to build a new road. The first Cat D5Hs were built from 1985 to 1990.

Eine neue Umgehungsstraße wird gebaut. Zum Einsatz kommt eine Caterpillar D5H mit Delta-Laufwerk mit 120 PS und einem Gewicht von 12.212 kg. Die ersten Cat D5Hs wurden von 1985 bis 1990 gebaut.

A Caterpillar D5H II LGP from the Boskalis Oosterwijk b.v. Company, a world wide operating contractor for special marine projects. This 120 hp and 35,700 lb heavy dozer works on a dike-job near Rotterdam /the Netherlands. It was built from 1990 to 1996.

Eine Caterpillar D5H II LGP der Firma Boskalis Oosterwijk b.v., einem weltweit tätigen Spezialunternehmen für den Wasserbau und die Landgewinnung. Der 120 PS starke und 16.200 kg schwere Dozer wird in Rotterdam/Niederlande für das Befestigen der Deiche eingesetzt. Er wurde von 1990 bis 1996 gebaut.

You can find the latest Cat D5M LGP, attached with an open ROPS cab in the Caterpillar plant in Grenoble/France. Caterpillar/France was etablished in 1960. They build track loaders, track type dozers and hydraulic excavators. The Cat dozer D5M LGP is powered by a Cat 3116 turbo engine rated at 121 hp. With an operating weight of 27,783 lb the dozer carries a 2.65 yd^3 blade.

In der Caterpillar-Fabrik in Grenoble/ Frankreich steht die neue Caterpillar D5M LGP, ausgerüstet mit einem offenen ROPS-Fahrerhaus für den Export. Gegründet wurde Caterpillar/France 1960. Es werden Kettenlader, Kettendozer und Hydraulikbagger hergestellt. Der Cat-Dozer D5M LGP hat eine Schildkapazität von 2,03 m^3 und ein Gewicht von 12.600 kg. Er wird angetrieben von einem Cat 3116 Turbo-Motor mit 121 PS.

If you ordered a track type tractor back in 1967 you had to order the blade, the ripper and the hydraulic controls separately. The picture shows a Caterpillar D6B (37A/44A) built from 1959 to 1967 with an output of 75 hp. The tractor weighed 18,280 lb + No.6S blade 3,520 lb + No.163 hydraulic controls 400 pounds meant 22,200 lb operating weight.

Bis 1967 mußte man bei einem Kettendozer auch das Planierschild, den Heckaufreisser und die Hydraulikanlage gesondert bestellen. Das Bild zeigt eine Caterpillar D6B (37A/44A), gebaut von 1959 bis 1967, mit 75 PS. Das Gewicht des Traktors: 8.291 kg + No.6S Schild 1.596 kg + No.163 Hydraulikanlage 180 kg = 10.067 kg Einsatzgewicht.

This Caterpillar D6C (10K) is equipped with a 6A angling blade and a typical North American canopy. It slopes the berth of the ferry boat across the Yukon river. In the back you can see Dawson City, the legendary gold rush town. The 30,600 lb heavy Cat D6C with 140 hp was built until 1976.

Im Yukon Territory steht diese Caterpillar D6C (10K), mit 6A-Schwenkschild und dem typischen nordamerikanischen Überrollschutzdach. Sie wird eingesetzt, um die Anlegestelle für die Fähre über den Yukonfluss zu unterhalten. Im Hintergrund sieht man Dawson City, die berühmte Goldgräberstadt. Mit 140 PS und 13.880 kg Gewicht wurde die Cat D6C bis 1976 gebaut.

A Caterpillar D6C with a European style cab and a 6A angling blade is dozing top soil.

Eine Caterpillar D6C mit einem europäischen Fahrerhaus und einem 6A-Schwenkschild ausgestattet, schiebt Muttererde ab

From 1977 to 1986 this Caterpillar D6D
LGP (6X) was built. I saw this D6D LGP
with 6S blade and a ROPS cab on a road
project in Anchorage/Alaska. The 6-cylin-
der turbo engine with a displacement of
640 in³ rated at 140 hp.

Von 1977 bis 1986 wird die Caterpillar
D6D LGP (6X) gebaut. Auf einer Straßenbaustelle in Anchorage/Alaska, sah ich
diese D6D LGP mit 6S-Schild und ROPS-
Fahrerhaus. Der 6-Zyl.-Turbo-Motor mit
10.5 l Hubraum leistet 140 PS.

This Caterpillar D6D (4X) is pulling a disc
harrow on a road project.

Auf einer Straßenbaustelle zieht diese
Caterpillar D6D (4X) eine Scheibenegge,
um das geschüttete Erdmaterial mittels
Kalkzugabe zu stabilisieren.

You hardly find this new Caterpillar D6E
in Germany. It is for sale on a shipyard in
Rotterdam. The 33,875 lb heavy dozer is
attached with a 4.27 yd³ 6S blade and is
powered by a Cat 3306 turbo engine
with 155 hp.

Diese neue Caterpillar D6E wird normalerweise nur für den Export gebaut und
ist in Deutschland so gut wie nie zu
sehen. Sie steht im Hafengelände von
Rotterdam und wartet auf einen neuen
Besitzer. Der 15.363 kg schwere Kettendozer ist mit einem 6S-Schild mit 3,27 m³
ausgerüstet. Sie wird angetrieben durch
einen Cat 3306 Turbo-Motor mit 155 PS.

This 1997Caterpillar D6M LGP operates with a loser equipment for fine grading. It belongs to the Eberhard Company of Switzerland.

Die Firma Eberhard Bau AG rüstete dieses 97er Modell der Caterpillar D6M LGP mit einem Laser aus für das Feinplanieren von großen Flächen.

In 1985 Caterpillar introduced its first D6H. This model is often seen on midsize construction projects, and is well-known by the contractors. The blade capacity ranges from 3.19 to 5.33 yd³ and the Cat 3306 DIT 6-cylinder turbo engine rates at 165 hp and the dozer weighs 37,367 lb. It was replaced by the Cat D6H II in 1990.

1985 wurde Caterpillars erste D6H vorgestellt. Ein Modell, das sehr populär bei vielen mittleren und auch großen Bauunternehmern ist und daher häufig auf Baustellen angetroffen wird. Mit einer Schildkapazität von 2,44 m³ bis 4,08 m³ und dem Cat 3306 DIT 6-Zyl.-Turbo-Motor mit 165 PS wiegt der Dozer 16.950 kg. Er wurde 1990 durch die Cat D6H II abgelöst.

This Caterpillar D6H works on a landfill near Stuttgart/Germany. It is equipped with a 11,8 yd³ 6SU landfill blade, front and back stricher bars and a full coverage of the gearbox.

Ausgerüstet mit einem 9 m³ Müllverteilschild 6SU mit Abstreifern vorn und hinten und einer kompletten Getriebeabdeckung am Heck, arbeitet diese Cat D6H auf einer Mülldeponie in der Nähe von Stuttgart.

The Eberhard Company combined a roll-on / roll-off system for carrying 20 yd³ silos with a Caterpillar VFS 70 (Versatile Flotation System). This trailer is able to carry a maximum load of 70,008 lb and is mainly used in agriculture.

Die Firma Eberhard Bau AG hat diesen Hakenabroller mit 15 m³ Silo selbst entwickelt und gefertigt. Aufgebaut ist er auf ein Caterpillar VFS 70 (Versatile Flotation System) Chassis. Dieser Hänger ist ausgelegt für max. Lasten bis zu 31.750 kg und wird hauptsächlich in der Landwirtschaft verwendet.

On the June 15th, 1999 it was the first time the trailer left the workshop. The mounted Perkins engine powers a hydraulic pump, so that the trailer can lift and lower the silo without any help. This 4-axle truck loaded the silo and moved it to the first job site.

Am 15. Juni 1999 kam der Hänger zum ersten Mal aus der Werkstatt. Durch den aufgebauten Perkins-Motor, der die Hydraulikpumpe antreibt, können jederzeit unabhängig das Silo oder eine Pritsche auf- und abgesetzt werden. Die Silos werden mit einem 4-Achs-Lkw auf die Baustelle gebracht.

Here the enormous size of the trailer can seen. Each track frame allows an oscillation of 17° degrees up and down. We can see the engine, the fuel tank and the electrical switchboard.

Jeder Laufrollenrahmen des Hängers kann um 17° von der Horizontalen nach oben oder unten pendeln. Man kann den Motor, den Tank und den Schaltschrank für die Elektrik erkennen.

Ready for use is the new Caterpillar VFS 70 chassis with lime silo. Martin Eberhard, is operating and testing the new system himself. This Caterpillar D6H LGP is equipped with two exhaust catalysts for reducing environment pollution.

Erster Einsatz des neuen Caterpillar VFS 70 mit Kalksilo. Martin Eberhard testet das neue System bei einem Probelauf. Diese Cat D6H LGP wurde mit zwei Abgaskatalysatoren ausgerüstet. Dies ist Eberhards aktiver Beitrag zum Umweltschutz.

The silo on the Caterpillar VFS 70 is filled with lime directly from a road truck. The D6H pulls the silo next to a Wirtgen WR 2500 Recycler. Without stopping the mixing process the lime can be pumped from the VFS silo into the Wirtgen Recycler. A few months ago Eberhard replaced the D6H with a Cat 95E Challenger.

Der Caterpillar VFS 70 mit dem Silo wird direkt von einem Straßen-Lkw mit Kalk beladen. Dann macht sich der "Cat-Zug" auf den Weg ins Gelände, wo er dann während der Fahrt den Kalk in eine Wirtgen WR 2500 Bodenfräse umpumpt.

This Caterpillar D6H II LGP belongs to the Boskalis Oosterwijk b.v. contractor from the Netherlands. It is attached with a 4.83 yd³ capacity blade and 182 hp. This 44,100 lb dozer spreads sand for a marine project.

Ein Caterpillar D6H II LGP des niederländischen Unternehmens Boskalis Oosterwijk b.v. mit einem 3,7 m³ fassenden Schild und 182 PS. Eingesetzt wird dieser 20.000 kg schwere Kettendozer an einem Spülfeld.

The latest Caterpillar D6R XL was introduced in 1996 (XL means a longer track to the front) for a better fine dozing. This Cat D6R XL with 40,351 lb is attached with special lifting loops, mounted by the Cat dealer Geveke from the Netherlands. The dozer is lifted with a crane into a ship to doze the load, so that it can be unloaded with a big clameshell crane.

Die neue Caterpillar D6R XL wurde 1996 eingeführt (XL, d. h. verlängertes Laufwerk nach vorn) für ein besseres Feinplanieren. Diese Cat D6R XL mit 18.300 kg wurde durch den niederländischen Cat-Händler Geveke mit speziellen Ösen zum Anheben ausgerüstet. Der Kettendozer arbeitet im Bauch eines Schiffes und schiebt die Ladung an einen Punkt, an dem sie mit großen Greifern gelöscht werden kann.

Because of the Caterpillar undercarriage with long life sealed and lubricated pins, bushings and rollers, this Cat D6R LGP can work on a water project, without any danger for the natural environment. The picture was taken on the coast near Rotterdam in the Netherlands.

Dank des abgedichteten Caterpillar-Laufwerks mit long life geschmierten Laufrollen und Buchsen, kann die Cat D6R LGP ohne Gefahr für die Umwelt im Wasserbau eingesetzt werden. Das Bild entstand an der niederländischen Küste in der Nähe von Rotterdam.

A "super" Caterpillar D6R LGP with special selfcleaning shoes and a modificated cab. You can order the Cat D6R with two different steering systems: differential steer or finger tip control steer.

Eine "Super" Caterpillar D6R LGP mit speziellen selbstreinigenden Bodenplatten und Spezial-Fahrerhaus. Die Cat D6R kann wahlweise mit Differentiallenkung oder Fingerhebellenkung bestellt werden.

"Back to the roots". The Caterpillar D7 (3T) with 108 hp is attached with No.7A blade and No.46 hydraulic controls. It was built between 1954 and 1955. The tractor weighs 25,952 lb + 6,024 lb of the 7A blade + 0,663 lb of the hydraulic control means an operating weight of 32,640 lb. A few drops of oil and this parked dozer will come to live again.

"Back to the roots". Eine Caterpillar D7 (3T) aus den Jahren 1954 bis 1955 mit 108 PS, ausgerüstet mit No.7A-Bulldozer und No.46 Hydrauliksystem. Der Traktor wiegt 11.770 kg + 2.732 kg für das 7A-Schild + 301 kg für die Hydraulik = Einsatzge-wicht von 14.803 kg. Mit ein paar Hand-griffen ist dieser Bulldozer, der in Canada abgestellt wurde, wieder einsatzbereit.

The Caterpillar D339 4-cylinder turbo engine with a displacement of 830 in³ boosted 160hp into the Cat D7E (48A). The complete weight of the track type tractor with blade and hydraulic controls goes up to 39,017 lb. It was built from 1961 to 1969. You could choose between two transmissions: power shift or direct drive.

Der Caterpillar D339 4-Zyl.-Turbo-Motor mit 13,6 l Hubraum leistet 160 PS in der Cat D7E (48A). Das komplette Gewicht des Kettendozers mit Schild und Hydraulikanlage beträgt 17.695 kg. Er wurde von 1961 bis 1969 gebaut und mit zwei Getrieben angeboten: Power shift oder direct drive.

This Caterpillar D7F (94N) rated at 180 hp works on a US military airport where a new runway is build by US pioneers. Equipped with a 7S blade and a No.7 ripper the weight of this Cat goes up to 48,510 lb.

Auf einem US-Militärflugplatz wurde diese Caterpillar D7F (94N) mit 180 PS von US-Pionieren bei dem Bau einer neuen Rollbahn eingesetzt. Mit einem 7S-Planierschild und einem No.7-Aufreisser wiegt die Cat 22.000 kg.

A Caterpillar D7F (94N) is attached with a multi shank parallelogram ripper. It reached a max. penetration of 2'42". It works on a road project in Portugal. The Cat D7F was built from 1969 to 1974. I took this picture in 1997. After approx. 25 years this track type tractor runs as good as on its first working day.

Die Caterpillar D7F (94N) ist ausgerüstet mit einem Mehrzahn-Parallelogrammaufreißer, der eine max. Reißtiefe von 740 mm erreicht. Sie arbeitet auf einer Straßenbaustelle in Portugal. Gebaut wurde die Cat D7F von 1969 bis 1974. Das Bild entstand 1997.

In 1976 Caterpillar introduced the new D7G (92V/91V). The most evident difference to the old D7F model is the restyled, angular, hydraulic tank and the new ROPS cab. The picture shows a Cat D7G (92V) with power shift transmission and the new ROPS cab with tinted glass. It was in the sales lists until 1986.

1976 wurde die neue Caterpillar D7G (92V/91V) vorgestellt. Auffälligste äußerliche Merkmale sind das neue ROPS-Fahrerhaus und der neue quadratische Hydrauliköltank, gegenüber der alten länglichen Tankform der D7F. Das Bild zeigt eine Cat D7G (92V) mit Power shift-Getriebe und neuem ROPS-Fahrerhaus mit getönten Scheiben, sie bleibt im Verkaufskatalog bis 1986.

This Caterpillar D7G (92V) with a 12'49" width 70 blade works in a big Swiss gravel pit. The dozer weighs 51,597 lb and is equipped with a multi shank ripper. It pushes the gravel downhill to the loading station. The Cat D7G with 200 hp is still built for export.

In einer großen Schweizer Kiesgrube arbeitet diese Caterpillar D7G (92V) mit einem 7U-Schild, das 3.810 mm breit ist. Der 23.400 kg schwere, mit einem Mehrzahnaufreißer ausgerüstete Kettendozer schiebt mit seinen 200 PS den Kies hinunter zur Verladestation. Die Cat D7G wird auch weiterhin für den Export gebaut.

From 1985 to 1990 the Caterpillar D7H was built. The picture shows a Cat D7H (79Z02038) built in 1988 with 215 hp and an operating weight of 61,343 lb and a blade capacity of 10.85 yd³. It is equipped with Caterpillar's unique differential steering, which allows continuous power to both tracks even in tight turns.

Von 1985 bis 1990 wird die Caterpillar D7H gebaut. Das Bild zeigt eine D7H (79Z02038), Baujahr 1988, mit 215 PS und 27.820 kg Gewicht sowie einer Schildkapazität von 8,3 m³. Sie ist ausgerüstet mit Caterpillars einzigartiger Differentiallenkung, d. h. beide Ketten werden kraftschlüssig angetrieben.

This Caterpillar D7H (79Z) first ripps the soil to improve a higher efficiency when dozing the material later.

Eine Caterpillar D7H (79Z) lockert den Boden durch Aufreißen. Dies erhöht die Produktivität beim späteren Abschieben des Materials.

You don't often find such an exceptional Caterpillar, the D7H II LGP with 230 hp and an operating weight of 68,452 lb. It works in a gravel pit and was built between 1991 and 1996.

Ein seltenes Modell: Eine Caterpillar D7H II LGP mit 230 PS und einem Gewicht von 31.044 kg arbeitet in einer Kiesgrube. Sie wurde von 1991 bis 1996 gebaut.

This Caterpillar D7H II works on a highway project in France . Noticeable is the big rear mounted plow/ripper to mix the soil-lime mixture to stabilize the underground. In 1996 the current Cat D7R model came to the market. You can choose between three different undercarriage versions: Standard, XR and LGP with different track shoes.

Auf einer Autobahnbaustelle in Frankreich wurde diese Caterpillar D7H II eingesetzt. Mit dem pflugähnlichen Aufreißer erreicht man ein besseres Vermengen der Böden, die zuvor mit Kalk behandelt wurden. 1996 wird die aktuelle Cat D7R vorgestellt. Es stehen drei Laufwerke zur Auswahl: Standard, XR und LGP mit jeweils verschiedenen Bodenplatten.

Near Chicken/Alaska a gold miner used this Caterpillar D8D,G (15A) built from 1955 to 1957 rated at 191 hp. Attached with a No.8U blade 8,427 lb, + No.46 hydraulic controls 654 lb + No.8 ripper 6.773 lb + D8 tractor 35,963 lb. The result is a complete operating weight of 51,819 lb. The picture was taken in 1992 after an approx. 36 year working time of this dozer.

Bei einem Goldgräber in der Nähe von Chicken/Alaska wird diese Caterpillar D8D,G (15A) verwendet, gebaut von 1955 bis 1957 mit 191 PS. Ausgerüstet mit dem No.8U-Bulldozer 3.822 kg + No.46 Hydrauliksystem mit 297 kg + No.8 Aufreisser 3.072 kg = 7.191 kg + Traktor D8 16.310 kg ergibt 23.501 kg. Die Aufnahme entstand 1992, der Cat-Bulldozer war dann schon ca. 36 Jahre im Einsatz.

A Caterpillar D8 is to see in the Yukon Territory in Canada. It was built from 1955 to 1957.

Eine Caterpillar D8 steht im Yukon Territory Kanadas, gebaut von 1955 bis 1957.

This Caterpillar D8H (46A) with a multi shank ripper and an 8S blade works on a highway project in Southern Germany. It was built from 1958 to 1974 with a Cat D342 6-cylinder turbo engine rated at 270 hp with 1280 r.p.m. It is the right dozer for the big jobs with 72,765 lb.

Auf einer Autobahnbaustelle in Süddeutschland wurde diese Caterpillar D8H (46A) mit hydraulisch verstellbarem Aufreißer und 8S-Schild verwendet. Gebaut wurde dieser Typ von 1958 bis 1974 mit einem Cat D342 6-Zyl.-Turbo-Motor mit 270 PS bei 1.280 U/min. Mit 33.000 kg sicherlich kein Leichtgewicht aber der richtige Kettendozer für große Arbeitsflächen.

This Caterpillar D8H (46A) was overhauled in 1991. It is pushing a scraper on a road construction project in Stuttgart/Germany. Those days many of these dozers were equipped with a Kelley single shank ripper.

Dieser Caterpillar D8H (46A) wurde 1991 neu überholt und schiebt einen Scraper auf einer Straßenbaustelle in Stuttgart. Viele dieser Kettendozer wurden damals mit einem Kelley-Einzahn-Aufreisser ausgerüstet.

Please, have a seat on an operator`s station of a Caterpillar D8H (46A). On the left there is the power shift transmission lever with three forward and three reverse gears. In the middle, in front of the operator, you find the two steering clutches, and on the left there is the start lever for the gasoline starting engine. On the right you find the dashboard and the trottle lever. The lever on the right is for rising and lowering the blade and tilting function. Both big pedals in the middle are the break pedals and close to the right is the decelerator.

Bitte nehmen Sie Platz auf dem Fahrersitz einer Caterpillar D8H (46A). Zur Linken das Powershift-Getriebe mit drei Vor- und drei Rückwärtsgängen, in der Mitte die beiden Lenkkupplungen, links davon ist der Starterhebel für den Benzinmotor. Rechts davon der Gashebel für den Diesel und das Armaturenbrett. Zur Rechten der lange Hebel ist für das Heben und Senken des Schildes. Die beiden großen Pedale in der Mitte sind die Bremspedale, das kleinere Pedal rechts daneben ist das Gasreduzierpedal.

This Caterpillar D8H (46A), attached with a No.8D single shank ripper, ripps soil in Portugal.

In Portugal reisst diese Caterpillar D8H (46A) mit einem No.8D Einzahn-Aufreisser den Boden auf.

The Cat D8K (76V/77V) was the last Caterpillar D8 with the old undercarriage design. This Cat D8K (77V) was built from 1974 to 1982. It was powered by a 300 hp Cat D342 turbo engine with 6-cylinder and a displacement of 1244 in³. It stands near an airport in Alaska. Attached with an 8U blade the weight goes up to 83,150 lb.

Die letzten D8 von Caterpillar mit dem alten Laufwerk waren die Cat D8K (76V/77V). Diese Cat D8K (77V) wurde von 1974 bis 1982 gebaut, angetrieben durch einen 300 PS starken Cat D342 Turbo-Motor mit 6 Zylindern und 20,4 l Hubraum. Sie steht in der Nähe eines Flughafens in Alaska. Ausgestattet mit einem 8U-Schild wiegt sie 37.710 kg.

This 1984 Cat D8L (53Y02323) rated at 335 hp. It works on a highway project in Southern Germany. It was built between 1982 and 1986 with a weight of 82,243 lb.

Eine Cat D8L (53Y02323) Baujahr 1984 mit 335 PS arbeitet auf einer Autobahnbaustelle in Süddeutschland. Sie wurde gebaut von 1982 bis 1986 mit einem Gewicht von 37.305 kg.

This Caterpillar D8L runs in a Swiss quarry. Attached with an 8U blade and a single-hank ripper. We can see the four oscillated bogies which are mounted on the track roller frame. This allows more track on the ground and the results are a better traction and a higher productivity of the track type tractor.

In einem Steinbruch in der Schweiz wird diese Caterpillar D8L benötigt, ausgestattet mit einem 8U-Schild und einem Einzahn-Aufreisser. Man kann gut die vier Hauptpendelträger erkennen, die am Laufrollenrahmen montiert sind. Dies ermöglicht eine bessere Anpassung des Laufwerkes an den Untergrund. Somit ergibt sich eine höhere Traktion und damit auch eine höhere Produktivität des Kettendozers.

This Caterpillar D8L works on a highway project in France mixing soil and lime. It is attached with a special ripper/plow. The Cat D8L is powered by a Cat 3408 V8 turbo engine with a displacement of 1098 in³.

Mit einem Spezialaufreißpflug ist diese Caterpillar D8L ausgerüstet, sie vermischt den mit Kalk versetzten Boden auf einer Autobahnbaustelle in Frankreich. Die Cat D8L wird angetrieben durch einen Cat 3408 V8-Turbo-Motor mit 18 l Hubraum.

On a construction site in Whitehorse/ Canada this Caterpillar D8L dozer pushes a fleet of Cat 631D scraper. The Cat D8L (7JC) was built from 1984 to 1990, and the (7YB) was produced from 1985 to 1992.

Auf einer Scraper-Baustelle in Whitehorse/Kanada wird dieser Caterpillar D8L Kettendozer für das Schieben von Cat 631D Scrapern eingesetzt. Die Cat D8L (7JC) wurde von 1984 bis 1990, die (7YB) von 1985 bis 1992 gebaut.

The first Caterpillar D8N (9TC) was introduced in 1987. With 285 hp and an operating weight of 81,236 lb it was a little bit smaller than the Cat D8L. The Cat D8N is to be assigned between the old D8K and the D8L. This Caterpillar D8N dozes 11.37 yd³ of earth with the 8 SU blade. The production stopped in 1992.

Die ersten Caterpillar D8N (9TC) wurden 1987 vorgestellt. Mit 285 PS und einem Gewicht von 36.842 kg wurde dieser Typ etwas kleiner als die Cat D8L. Einzuordnen ist die Cat D8N zwischen der alten D8K und der D8L. Diese Caterpillar D8N schiebt mit ihrem 8 SU-Schild 8,7 m³ Erde. Das Produktionsende kam 1992.

This Caterpillar D8N (5TJ) with a blade capacity of 15 yd³ and a multi shank ripper is used to doze and ripp pumice stone. The latest Caterpillar model was introduced in 1996. It is the Cat D8R. Powered by a Cat 3406C 6-cylinder turbo engine rated at 310 hp and an operating weight of 82,894 lb.

Diese Caterpillar D8N (5TJ) mit einer Schildkapazität von 11,7 m³ und einem Mehrzahn-Aufreißer wird zum Schieben und Reißen von Bimsstein verwendet. Das neueste Modell wurde 1996 vorgestellt: Die D8R, angetrieben von einem Cat 3406C 6-Zyl.-Turbo-Motor mit 310 PS und mit einem Gewicht von 37.594 kg.

The D9 (18A) was the world`s biggest dozer when introduced in 1955, with 17'11" length, 9'93" width and a height of 8'75". Powered by a Cat 6-cylinder turbo engine rated at 286 hp, the D9 was built until 1956. The Caterpillar D9D (19A/34A) was built from 1955 to 1961, the D9E (49A/50A) from 1959 to 1960. The picture shows an early D9G (66A) with 385 hp and a Kelley ripper. It works in the high mountains of Switzerland.

Caterpillars D9 (18A) war der weltgrößte Bulldozer mit 5.460 mm Länge, 3.030 mm Breite und einer Höhe von 2.670 mm, als er im Jahr 1955 vorgestellt wurde. Angetrieben von einem Cat 6 Zyl.-Turbo-Motor mit 286 PS wurde die D9 bis 1956 gebaut, die Caterpillar D9D (19A/34A) von 1955 bis 1961, die D9E (49A/50A) von 1959 bis 1960. Das Bild zeigt eine frühe D9G (66A) mit 385 PS und einem Kelley-Aufreißer im Hochgebirge in der Schweiz.

This early Caterpillar D9G (66A) is attached with a No.9U blade, No.193 hydraulic control and a No.9 ripper. The total operating weight goes up to 87,007 lb. In this picture you can see the front mounted hydraulic tank in the lower part of the radiator.

Diese frühe Caterpillar D9G (66A) ist ausgestattet mit dem No.9U-Schild, der Hydraulikanlage No.193 und einem No.9-Aufreißer. Das Gesamteinsatzgewicht beträgt 39.459 kg. Auf dem Bild kann man gut den Hydrauliktank erkennen, der im unteren Teil des Kühlers vorgebaut wurde.

This Caterpillar D9G (66A) pusher is attached with a 9C cushioned push blade. It is just getting a new undercarriage.

Eine Caterpillar D9G (66A) pusher mit einem gefederten Schubschild 9C bekommt gerade ein neues Laufwerk montiert.

A more modern Caterpillar D9G (66A) is attached with a Zeppelin cab. If it`s nice in the summer the operator can remove the canopy curtains to have an open cab. The hydraulic tank is now mounted on the right side of the tractor.

Eine modernere, mit einem Zeppelin-Fahrerhaus ausgestattete D9G (66A). Bei gutem Wetter im Sommer kann der Fahrer die Plane entfernen und hat somit ein offenes Fahrerhaus. Der Hydrauliktank wurde nun auf der rechten Traktorseite aufgebaut.

The Kelley KR9-1 single shank ripper weighs 10,165 lb and has a maximum penetration of 6'98". This Caterpillar D9G (66A) ripps heavy soil. It helps to reduce the cycle time when dozing the soil downhill.

Der Kelley KR9-1 Einzahn-Aufreißer wiegt 4.610 kg und hat eine max. Eindringtiefe von 2.130 mm. Diese Caterpillar D9G (66A) reißt einen schweren Boden, durch das Aufreißen wird das spätere Abschieben erleichtert.

A D9G tandem arrangement, mechanically coupled for one man operation, is available for applications requiring full tractor potential in tandem pushloading. The Quad-Track arrangement provides high production capacity, simple operational characteristics and ease of transport.

FEATURES:

The D9G Quad-Track arrangement provides:

... 100% power at contact with scraper. No wait time for positioning a second tractor.

... Faster return speeds on rough surfaces due to the shock absorbing characteristics of the weight transfer cylinder on the tractor coupling.

... Less traffic in the cut where shuttle pushloading by two tractors is hampered.

... Reduced operator fatigue by eliminating the close and constant coordination required between operators on separate tractors in conventional tandem pushloading.

... Excellent transportability by trailering each D9G separately.

This is a sales information from 1964. Bigger construction jobs need bigger machines. The first prototype of the Quad D9 was built by a Caterpillar dealer in San Leandro/California, the Peterson Tractor and Co. It was carried out under the direction of R. A. "Buster" Peterson. This Cat worked on a dam project near Orinda/California in 1963. Ten units where built between 1963 and 1967. Later some more Cat D9 were converted to Quad D9s. Peterson also offered a special side by side D9.

Eine Verkaufsinformation aus dem Jahr 1964, immer größere Bauprojekte verlangten nach immer größeren Maschinen. Der erste Prototyp wurde von einem Caterpillar-Händler in San Leandro/Kalifornien, gebaut. Die Firma Peterson Tractor & Co. baute unter der Leitung von R. A. "Buster" Peterson 1963 den ersten Quad D9. Diese Maschine wurde eingesetzt bei einem Dammprojekt in der Nähe von Orinda/Kalifornien. Von 1963 bis 1967 wurden insgesamt zehn Stück gebaut und einige Cat D9 wurden nachträglich umgerüstet zu einer Quad D9, auch eine side-by-side-Cat D9 war von Peterson erhältlich.

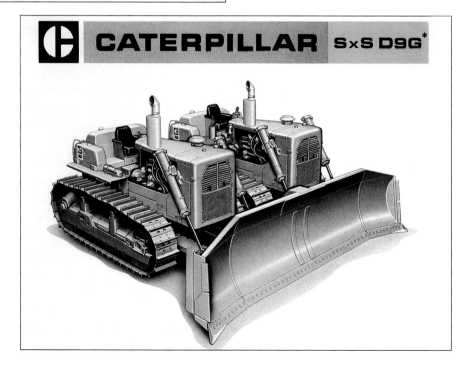

In 1968 Caterpillar took over the idea and built its own DD9G and SxS D9G, the "super" D9 with a whooping output to 770 hp and a weight Quad 175,200 lb, SxS 190,000 lb. Both types were in the sales lists until 1974. The successor, the SxS D9H, was built from 1974 to 1977, and the DD9H from 1974 to 1980.

1968 nahm Caterpillar die Idee der DD9G und der SxS D9G auf und produzierte diese "Super"-D9 mit 770 PS und einem Gewicht von Quad-79.470 kg, bzw. SxS-86.200 kg. Beide Typen bleiben bis 1974 im Verkaufsprogramm. Nachfolger wurde die SxS D9H von 1974 bis 1977 und die DD9H von 1974 bis 1980.

This Caterpillar D9H (90V) with 410 hp and an operating weight of 72,400 lb works without a cab on a project in Germany.

Ohne Fahrerhaus arbeitet diese Caterpillar D9H (90V) mit 410 PS und 32.840 kg auf einer Autobahnbaustelle in Deutschland.

Equipped with a Zeppelin cab and a Cat single shank ripper this Caterpillar D9H (90V) pushes earth on a steep downhill grade . The picture was taken on a big vineyard recultivation job in Germany in 1991.

Ausgerüstet mit einem Zeppelin-Fahrerhaus und Caterpillars Einzahn-Aufreißer schiebt diese D9H (90V) Erde eine steile Böschung hinunter. Das Bild entstand 1991 bei einer großen Weinbergrekultivierung in Deutschland.

On a cold day in December 1999 I took this picture of a Caterpillar D9H (90V) removing top soil.

An einem kalten Tag im Dezember 1999 konnte ich diese Caterpillar D9H (90V) beim Abschieben von Muttererde fotografieren.

Caterpillar's last developement of the D9H (90V) with ROPS cab and tinted glass. It works in a gravel pit in Switzerland.

Caterpillars letzte Entwicklungsstufe der D9H (90V) mit ROPS-Fahrerhaus und getönten Scheiben. Sie arbeitet in einer Kiesgrube in der Schweiz.

Here you can visualize the size of the Caterpillar D9L (14Y). It was built from 1980 to 1986. The 114,656 lb heavy dozer is powered by a Cat 3412 DIT V12 turbo engine with 460 hp and a displacement of 1647 in^3.

Man kann hier gut die Größe der neuen Cat D9L (14Y), die von 1980 bis 1986 gebaut wurde, erkennen. Der 52.055 kg schwere Kettendozer wird von einem 460 PS starken Cat 3412 DIT V12-Turbo-Motor mit 27 l Hubraum angetrieben.

The new styled undercarriage with four oscillated bogies mounted on the roller frame allows higher push and ripping power for this Caterpillar D9L (14Y). There is more track on the ground and less slippage than any other tractor.

Das mit vier Pendelgestellen ausgerüstete Laufwerk der Caterpillar D9L (14Y) erlaubt höhere Schub- und Reißleistung dank besseren Bodenschlusses gegenüber anderen Kettendozern.

This Caterpillar D9L (14Y) is straightening the legendary Alaska Highway between Delta Junction and Tok, formerly called Alcan military highway.

Die Caterpillar D9L (14Y) begradigt den legendären Alaska-Highway zwischen Delta Junction und Tok.

In Belgium this Caterpillar D9L (14Y) was equipped with a Balderson cushion push blade and used on the TGV railroad project near Brussels. The cushioned blade, type BDI 9-11'6C is 11'54" wide, 5'6" high, and weighs 14,500 lb.

In Belgien wurde diese Caterpillar D9L (14Y) mit einem gefederten Balderson-Schubschild bei der TGV-Neubaustrecke in der Nähe von Brüssel eingesetzt. Das Schubschild des Types BDI 9-11'6C hat eine Weite von 3.524 mm, eine Höhe von 1.715 mm und wiegt 6.575 kg.

The little bit smaller successor of the Caterpillar D9L was the D9N (1JD) with 370 hp and an operating weight of 96,196 lb. It was built between 1986 and 1995.

Der etwas kleinere Nachfolger der D9L wurde die D9N (1JD) mit 370 PS und einem Einsatzgewicht von 42.816 kg. Sie wurde von 1986 bis 1995 gebaut.

A very rare picture: A Cat D9N (1JD) pulls a Cat 637D scraper. The soil in this area was too muddy so that the track type tractor was required for pulling.

Eine äußerst seltene Aufnahme: Eine D9N (1JD) zieht einen Cat 637D Scraper. Der an dieser Stelle zu nasse Boden erfordert das Ziehen des Scrapers durch einen Kettendozer.

The original fuel tank was replaced by a round style gas tank. This Caterpillar D9N (1JD) was rebuilt with a gas engine and an exhaust catalyst.

Der Original-Kraftstofftank wurde entfernt und durch einen runden Gastank ersetzt. Die Caterpillar D9N (1JD) wird jetzt gasbetrieben und besitzt einen Katalysator.

In 1995 the Caterpillar D9R with a maximum blade capacity of 21.45 yd³ was introduced.

1995 wurde die Caterpillar D9R mit einem max. Schildfassungsvermögen von 16,4 m³ vorgestellt.

From 1987 to 1993 the Caterpillar D10N (2YD) with 520 hp and an operating weight of 147,232 lb was built. The blade capacity reached 27.33 yd³.

Von 1987 bis 1993 wurde die Caterpillar D10N (2YD) mit 520 PS und einem Einsatzgewicht von 66.772 kg gebaut. Die Schildkapazität erreicht 20,9 m³.

A new painted Caterpillar D10N (2YD), belonging to a French contractor, attached with a Balderson BDI 10-11'6C cushion push blade with a weight of 13,483 lb. Often these track type tractors are called "push Cats" or "inside pushers".

Eine neu lackierte Caterpillar D10N (2YD) eines französischen Bauunternehmers mit einem Balderson BDI 10-11'6C-Schubschild, das 6.115 kg wiegt. Oft werden diese Kettendozer als "push Cat" oder "inside pusher" bezeichnet.

This beautiful Caterpillar D10N (2YD) inside pusher is painted with the French national colours.

Diese wunderschöne Caterpillar D10N (2YD) inside pusher ist in den Nationalfarben Frankreichs lackiert.

In 1995 I took pictures of this Caterpillar D10N (3SK). It works in a pumice stone and lava quarry near Koblenz/Germany. This type (3SK) was built between 1993 and 1996.

1995 konnte ich diese Caterpillar D10N (3SK), die in einem Bims- und Lavabruch in der Nähe von Koblenz arbeitet, fotografieren. Der Typ (3SK) wurde von 1993 bis 1996 gebaut.

A nearly new D10N (3SK) pusher is working on a French highway project.

Eine neue D10N (3SK) pusher begrüßt mich auf einer Baustelle in Frankreich.

This Caterpillar D10R inside pusher was built in 1999. A standard Cat D10R with 578 hp, a 28,71 yd³ blade and a single-shank ripper weighs 145,009 lb.

Dies ist eine Caterpillar D10R »inside pusher«, Baujahr 1999. Eine Standard D10R mit 578 PS, einem Schildfassungsvermögen von max. 22 m³ und einem Einzahn-Aufreißer wiegt 65.764 kg.

The big test for the first Caterpillar D10 took place on a road project near the Yellowstone National Park in 1977. Everybody was fascinated when he saw the biggest track type tractor of the world with an operating weight of 175,526 lb and its powerful Cat V12 twin turbo engine rated at 700 hp. The D10 attracted nearly as many people as Yellowstone Park.

Getestet wurde die erste Caterpillar Ur-D10 bei einem Straßenprojekt in der Nähe des Yellowstone National Parks 1977. Man sagte, daß sie die zweitgrößte Touristenattraktion im Westen Montanas sei. Es kamen viele Leute, um diesen größten Kettenbulldozer mit einem Gewicht von 79.619 kg und einem Cat V12-Bi-Turbo-Motor mit 700 PS zu sehen .

My parents didn`t spare any effort in showing me the great machines. So we visited a Caterpillar D10 (84W511), when I was about 15 or 16 years old. I was so very nervous, that I could hardly sleep the night before. Some units of measurement of the D10 (84W): length 33'41", width 17'99", height 14'98". The fuel tank has a capacity of 383 US gallons. Thanks to the new developped driving concept the D10 (84W) is much more efficient and economical than the older D9.

Für meine Eltern war kein Weg zu weit. So besuchten wir eine Caterpillar D10 (84W511). Ich war damals 15 oder 16 Jahre alt. Vor lauter Aufregung schlief ich in der vorherigen Nacht nicht viel. Mit großen Augen stand ich am nächsten Morgen vor der D10. Einige Maße der D10 (84W): Länge 10.187 mm, Breite 5.486 mm, Höhe 4.569 mm. Der Kraftstofftank faßt allein schon 1.450 l. Dank des neuen Antriebkonzeptes leistet die neue Cat D10 (84W) das Doppelte wie eine Cat D9, und das bei besserer Wirtschaftlichkeit.

The dashboard of a Caterpillar D10 with all the gauges, lights and switches looks quite futuristic. The fully adjustable suspension seat angled 15° to the right. This allows an ideal seat position for the operating and a high visibility to the ripper and the blade.

Seiner Zeit schon weit voraus: Das Armaturenbrett der D10 mit Anzeigen, Lampen und Schaltern. Der Schwingsitz wurde um 15° nach rechts gedreht, dies ermöglicht eine optimale Sitzposition des Fahrers, der eine gute Sicht auf den Aufreißer und das Schild hat.

On August 23rd, 1979 the biggest track type tractor, the Caterpillar D10, arrived at the port of Basel by ship. From there it was transported to Langenthal with a flatbed trailer.The Swiss Cat dealer Ammann completed the track type tractor and handed it over to the Eberhard Bau AG near Zurich. The Cat's first job site was on the N20 highway project north of Zurich. The picture was taken in a clay pit in Switzerland near Lausanne.

Der größte Caterpillar Kettendozer D10 wurde am 23. August 1979 in Basel per Schiff angeliefert und per Lkw weiter nach Langenthal transportiert. Nach der Komplettierung durch den Cat-Händler Ammann wird der Kettendozer an die Firma Eberhard Bau AG in Zürich übergeben. Erstmals wurde dieser bei dem Bau der Nordumfahrung Zürichs N20 eingesetzt. Das Bild entstand in einer Tongrube in der französischen Schweiz nahe Lausanne.

A professional driver is needed to operate those big machines. Karl Ziegelmaier is one of them. He is an experienced Cat dozer operator. He controls his Caterpillar D10 (84W01120) smooth and efficiently. He works in a big quarry for the cement industries.

Karl Ziegelmaier hat eine große Berufserfahrung als Cat Dozerfahrer. Für die besten Maschinen benötigt man auch einen Profi, wie ihn. Er bedient seine Caterpillar D10 (84W01120) sehr wirtschaftlich und arbeitet in einem großen Steinbruch für die Zementindustrie.

Both vehicles are diesel powered. A Ford (GFJ) with 109 in³ displacement rated at 60 hp and a Caterpillar D10 (84W0179) with 1787 in³ displacement and 700 hp. This Cat D10 still works every day in a quarry for the cement industries.

Beide Fahrzeuge sind dieselangetrieben. Ein Ford (GFJ) mit 1,8 l Hubraum und 60 PS und eine Caterpillar D10 (84W0179) mit 29,3 l Hubraum und 700 PS. Die Cat D10 arbeitet noch heute in einem Steinbruch für die Zementindustrie.

The second generation of the Caterpillar D10 (84W/76X) was built from 1978 to 1986. The later versions set apart from the former ones because of the two exhaust pipes and the turbo chargers, were moved away from the Cat, rebuilt and new painted by Zeppelin. This Cat D10 is waiting for the next job.

Die zweite Generation der Caterpillar "Ur"-D10 (84W/76X) wurde von 1978 bis 1986 gebaut. Man kann beide sehr gut unterscheiden, die etwas neuere Version hat zwei Auspuffanlagen, und die Turbo-Lader wurden von dem Fahrerhaus weg nach vorne verlegt. Eine von Zeppelin generalüberholte und neu lackierte Cat D10 wartet auf den nächsten Einsatz.

With the new Caterpillar D10 (84W/76X) you are able to rip rock that was considered too hard for a Cat D9. The costs for blasting are eliminated. Because of the high mounted final drive the durability and the lifespan increased. The final drive runs free from any shocks from the both push arms and larger rocks.

Mit der neuen Caterpillar "Ur"-D10 (84W/76X) kann man jetzt Fels reißen, welches vorher mit der Cat D9 nur schwer oder gar nicht abgebaut werden konnte. Das Sprengen entfällt in den meisten Fällen. Dank des nach oben verlegten Antriebs erhöht sich die Lebensdauer auf ein Vielfaches. Es treten keine Stoßbelastungen mehr durch die Schubarme und durch große Felsbrocken auf.

You can see a Caterpillar D10 (84W) (1:50 scale model) on the original push arm. That`s unique! A Caterpillar D10 (84W) (1:50) scale model is pushing rocks on an original track shoe of a Cat D10 (84W).

Man kann gut das Modell der Caterpillar D10 (84W) im Maßstab 1:50 auf dem Schubarm erkennen. Das gibt es nur einmal: Ein 1:50 Modell einer Caterpillar D10 (84W) schiebt Fels auf der Originalkette einer Cat D10 (84W).

In 1986 Caterpillar introduced the D11N (74Z). It is a refined and improved model of the first Cat D10 (84W/76X). The power is unchanged and the operating weight went up to 215,040 lb. The blade capacity increased to 42.11 yd³.

1986 stellte Caterpillar die D11N (74Z) vor, eine Weiterentwicklung der "Ur"-D10 (84W/76X). Die Leistung blieb unverändert, das Gewicht beträgt je nach Ausrüstung bis zu 97.524 kg, das Schild hat ein Fassungsvermögen von 32,2 m³.

In October 1988 the world`s first and largest Caterpillar track type tractor, the D11N with impact ripper, came to Europe. The Swiss contractor Eberhard bought the 770 hp and 224,910 lb heavy Caterpillar dozer, at a price of 1.7 Mio Swiss Franc.

Im Oktober 1988 kam der erste und auch weltgrößte Caterpillar-Kettendozer, die D11N mit Impact Ripper, nach Europa. Die Schweizer Baufirma Eberhard kaufte den 770 PS starken und 102 t schweren Caterpillar-Kettendozer für 1,7 Mio. Schweizer Franken.

It is 6.30 am (1993) near Porrentruy in the district Jura in Switzerland. Kurt Huber, the operator of the Caterpillar D11N Impact, works on the motor highway N16 jobsite. This day I am allowed to go with him. He works with his Caterpillar D11N dozer on a 1.86 miles section, where he moves within the next two and a half years approximately 784,800 yd³ of the exceptional hard Jura Lime Rock with a hardness up to 21,337 lb/in². First he walks around his track type tractor for a check-up. He looks for possible leacks of the hydraulic system, controls track rollers, track shoes, final drive, the bulldozer blade and of course the impact ripper for weals and cracks or damaged screws. Everything looks good. After the control of oil and water Kurt starts the engine. It runs by idle speed for the warm up – now it is 7.00 am. The impact ripper is permanently used for the very hard rock, to detach the material. A standard D11N has a penetration force up to 59,900 lb, the D11N Impact has an impact force up to 450,000 lb at the teath. Because of his long time experience with Cat D9 and Cat D10 track type tractors Kurt works with his D11 so skillfully, that he rips downhill, and afterwards pushes the material onto a pile. Then a Cat 245 excavator loads it into a Cat 769C truck, which hauls it to the dumpside. I can hear the deep sound from the Cat V8 engine, the typical noise of the tracks and the permanent tack-tack-tack from the hydraulic impact ripper. Now it is 9.00 am – the typical noise of the impact ripper dies away. Kurt drives with his D11 to the side. I ask

him, "What's up?" He answers, that the ripper tip is too stub so that he has to change the 0.176 lb heavy ripper teath. After half an hour Kurt stars again, but before he greases the ripper carefully. Now he works without a break until 12.00 am. After lunch at 1.00 pm Kurt mounts another new ripper and work goes on till 5 pm. A fuel truck comes to the side and Kurt is joking: "...now we must have a few gallons of diesel...". The fuel clock stops at 251 gallons. Kurt changes the ripper teath a last time for this day, greases up and the Cat V8 runs on idle speed for a few minutes, then the sound dies away. "Now, I think, I'll call it a day..."

Es ist 6.30 Uhr am Morgen (1993), in der Nähe von Porrentruy im Kanton Jura in der Schweiz. Ich begleite Kurt Huber, den Fahrer des Caterpillar D11N Impact einen Tag lang auf der Autobahnbaustelle N16. Er arbeitet mit seinem D11N Dozer auf dem etwa 3 km langen Teilstück, auf dem in den nächsten eineinhalb Jahren ungefähr 600.000 m³ Felsaushub des besonders harten Jurakalkfels mit einer Härte von 1.500 kg/cm² abgebaut werden. Als erstes kontrolliert Kurt seinen Kettendozer auf eventuelle Undichtigkeiten des Hydrauliksystems, kontrolliert Laufrollen, Kettenplatten, Antrieb, Planierschild und natürlich den impact ripper (Schlagaufreißer) auf Risse oder beschädigte Schrauben. Es scheint alles in Ordnung zu sein. Nachdem er den Öl- und Wasserstand kontrol-

liert hat, lässt Kurt die D11 warmlaufen. Inzwischen ist es 7 Uhr. Durch den sehr harten Fels wird der Impact Ripper ständig benötigt, um das Material überhaupt lösen zu können. Eine Standard-D11 hat eine Reißkraft von 267 KN, die D11 Impact hat dagegen etwa 2.000 KN. Durch seine langjährige Erfahrung mit Cat D9 und D10 Kettendozern setzt Kurt die D11 so geschickt ein, daß er hangabwärts aufreißt und danach das gelöste Felsmaterial auf ein Depot schiebt, auf dem es dann mit einem Cat 245 auf Cat 769C Muldenkipper geladen und abtransportiert wird. Man hört den tiefen Sound des Cat V8-Motors, das typische Ächzen und Knarren der Kettenplatten und das ständige tack, tack, tack des hydraulischen Schlagaufreißers. Es ist 9 Uhr und das typische Geräusch des Rippers verstummt, Kurt fährt mit seiner D11 zur Seite. Als ich ihn fragte, was los sei, antwortete er, der Aufreißzahn sei zu stumpf. Er müsse einen neuen 80 kg schweren Zahn mit einem Kollegen montieren. Nach etwa einer halben Stunde geht es dann weiter, zuvor wird der Aufreißer sorgfältig abgeschmiert. Nun wird ohne Unterbrechung bis 12 Uhr gearbeitet. Nach der Mittagspause um 13 Uhr wird erneut ein neuer Aufreißzahn montiert und es geht weiter bis 17 Uhr. „Jetzt müssen wir ein wenig Diesel tanken", scherzt Kurt. Bei 950 l bleibt die Uhr stehen. Es wird ein letztes Mal für heute der Aufreißzahn gewechselt und abgeschmiert. Ruhig brummt der Cat V8 vor sich hin, bis er nach ein paar Minuten verstummt. „So, jetzt habe ich Feierabend."

Kurt Huber began his career on a Cat D9E with cable operated blade in Saudi Arabia in 1976. For two years he worked on different earthmoving machines: The Cat 988 and 983. After he had returned to Switzerland, he operated the Cat D9G and on September 19th, 1979 he changed onto the biggest dozer, the Cat D10. He worked with this machine until 1988. On September 1st, 1988, he got the biggest of all, the Cat D11N impact. Only three units were ever built. This super track type tractor made it possible to rip rock, you had not been able to rip before. Because of that, many construction jobs could be finished earlier than planned.

1976 begann Kurt Huber seine Karriere auf einer Cat D9E mit Seilschild in Saudi Arabien, wo er zwei Jahre verschiedene Großgeräte Cat 988 und 983 fuhr. Zurück in der Schweiz ging es dann weiter mit der D9G und am 19.September 1979 bekam er den größten Kettendozer, die Cat D10, auf der er bis 1988 arbeitete. Dann kam die größte von allen, die Cat D11N Impact. Es wurden nur drei Stück von dieser "Super" D11 gebaut. Mit diesem Kettendozer konnte Kurt Huber so manchen Fels reißen, der als unreißbar galt und manche Baustelle schneller abwickeln, als es der Terminplan vorsah.

This Caterpillar D11N (74Z) was built in 1991. It works in a quarry for the cement industries. It is powered by a Cat 3508 V8 twin turbo engine with a displacement of 2104 in^3 rated 781 hp at 1800 r.p.m.

Eine Caterpillar D11N (74Z), Baujahr 1991, arbeitet in einem Steinbruch. Angetrieben durch einen Cat 3508 V8-Bi-Turbo-Motor mit 34,5 l Hubraum leistet sie 781 PS bei 1.800 U/min.

This Caterpillar D11N works in a quarry. Equipped is this D11N (4HK) with the redesigned fuel tank and the computerized monitoring system (CMS). Continuously it watches all machine systems and informs the operator before any damage happens.

Ausgerüstet ist diese D11N (4HK) Version mit der neuen konischen Tankform und einem computergestützten Überwachungssystem (CMS), das den Fahrer frühzeitig über Störungen der Maschinenfunktionen informiert.

In this picture you can see the size of a Caterpillar D11N (4HK). The height from the ground to the roll over bar goes up to 15".

Man kann sich bei dem Bild dieses Caterpillar D11N (4HK) gut die Größe vorstellen. Vom Boden aus bis zum Überrollbügel sind es 4.586 mm.

This Caterpillar D11N (4HK) is equipped with a special air cleaner for the cab. It works on a reclamation job in a uranium mine. Noticeable is the additional upper track roller and the big SU blade, attached with wear plates. Both aren`t standard.

Mit einer speziellen Schutzbelüftung für das Fahrerhaus wird diese Caterpillar D11N (4HK) in einem Uranbergwerk zu Rekultivierungsarbeiten eingesetzt. Man beachte die nicht serienmäßige Stützrolle am Laufwerk und das mit Verschleißstreifen bestückte SU-Schild.

The first introduction of the Cat D11R (8ZR) with 770 hp was in 1996. In 1997 power was raised up to 850 hp and the blade capacity went up to 45 yd³. A brand-new Cat D11R, built in 1998. It is used on a reclamation job in Eastern Germany.

Vorgestellt wurde die erste Caterpillar D11R (8ZR) im Jahr 1996 mit 770 PS. Ab 1997 hat sie eine Leistung von 850 PS und die Schildkapazität beträgt nun 34,4 m³. Eine fast ganz neue Cat D11R, Baujahr 1998, in einer Uranmine in Ostdeutschland.

Some months ago I was visited by an eleven year old boy, who is as interested in Caterpillar machines. He had never seen a real Caterpillar D11R CD before, but that`s the unmistakable mythos around Caterpillar. At home the boy had a brochure of a Cat D11R CD. He made this drawing as a gift for my collection. The painting shows Caterpillar's top model the D11R CD with 850 hp and an operating weight of 239,550 lb.

Vor ein paar Monaten besuchte mich ein elf Jahre alter Junge, der sich für Caterpillar Maschinen interessiert. Er hatte noch nie eine D11R CD im Original gesehen. Aber genau das ist der unverwechselbare Mythos, der Caterpillar umgibt. Der Junge hatte zu Hause einen Prospekt dieser D11R CD und machte sich daran, sie für mich abzumalen, um mir das Bild für meine Sammlung zu schenken. Die Zeichnung zeigt Caterpillars Topmodell, die D11R CD mit 850 PS und einem Einsatzgewicht von 111.800 kg.

The first Caterpillar Challenger 65 (7YC) was built between 1987 and 1990 with 270 gross horsepower and an operating weight of 31,000 lb. Normally the Challenger is used in agriculture, but this CH 65 was modified by the Cat-dealer Geveke from the Netherlands. It is used by the Dutch coastguard.

Der erste Caterpillar Challenger 65 (7YC) wurde von 1987 bis 1990 gebaut mit einer Nennleistung von 270 PS bei einem Gewicht von 14.061 kg. Eigentlich wird der Challenger in der Landwirtschaft verwendet, aber dieser CH 65 wurde durch den niederländischen Cat-Händler Geveke umgerüstet für den Einsatz bei der Küstenwache.

On the Bauma exhibition in Munich I saw my first Cat Challenger in 1989. It was a white coloured CH 65. In 1991 the CH 65B (7YC) was introduced with 285 gross hp. In 1993 the CH 65C (2ZJ) with the same power was offered. In 1995 the CH 65D (2ZJ) followed with an operating weight of 32,875 lb and a gross hp up to 300 hp. The current Challenger model, the CH 65E, has now 310 gross hp.

Den ersten Cat Challenger habe ich 1989 auf der Baumaschinenmesse in München gesehen, den CH 65, und er war weiß lackiert. 1991 wurde der CH 65B (7YC) vorgestellt mit einer Nennleistung von 285 PS. 1993 kam der Challenger 65C (2ZJ), ebenfalls mit 285 PS und 1995 der Challenger 65D (2ZJ) mit einem Einsatzgewicht von 14.909 kg und einer Leistung von 300 PS. Der aktuelle Challenger ist der 65E mit 310 PS.

In 1997 the joint venture with the German ag.-machinery manufacturery Claas and Caterpillar Inc. started. Claas sells and maintains the complete Caterpillar range 35, 45, 55 and the bigger E-series 65, 75, 85 and 95, painted in the typical Claas colors green and grey. The picture shows a Claas Challenger 35 with 210 gross hp.

1997 begann die Zusammenarbeit zwischen dem deutschen Landmaschinenhersteller Claas und Caterpillar. Die komplette Caterpillar Challenger-Reihe 35, 45, 55 und die größere E-Serie 65, 75, 85, 95 werden in den Claasfarben grün und grau in Europa von Claas vertrieben und gewartet. Das Bild zeigt einen Claas Challenger 35 mit 210 PS Nennleistung.

An original Caterpillar Challenger 45 with 240 gross hp and an operating weight from 22,000 lb to 25,500 lb. For each type you can choose between five different rubber belts from 16 to 32 inches.

Ein Original Cat-Challenger 45 mit 240 PS Nennleistung und 9.977 bis 11.564 kg Einsatzgewicht. Es stehen für jeden Typ fünf verschiedene Laufbandbreiten von 406 mm bis 813 mm zur Verfügung.

This Claas Challenger 45 is at work. Equipped with a 16 forward gears transmission the Challenger reaches a top speed of 17.8 mph and 9.7 mph in the 11th reverse gear.

Der Claas Challenger 45 mit 16-Gang-Vorwärtsgetriebe erreicht eine max. Geschwindigkeit von 28,6 km/h und 12,7 km/h im 11. Rückwärtsgang.

The biggest Challenger of the small line is the 55. It is equipped with a Caterpillar 3126 6-cyl. turbo engine with a displacement of 439 in³ rated at 270 gross hp.

Der größte Challenger in der kleinen Klasse ist der 55. Ausgerüstet mit einem Caterpillar 3126 6-Zyl.-Turbo-Motor mit einem Hubraum von 7,2 l und einer Nennleistung von 270 PS.

This is a Claas Challenger 75E with 340 gross hp and an operating weight of 31,972 lb. The first Cat CH 75 (4CJ) was introduced in 1991 and was replaced by the CH 75C (4KK) in 1993. The Cat CH 75D (5AR) was built between 1996 and 1997 with 330 gross hp and an operating weight of 32,800 lb.

Ein Claas Challenger 75E mit einer Nennlei-stung von 340 PS und einem Gewicht von 14.500 kg. Der erste Cat CH 75 (4CJ) wurde 1991 vorgestellt, abgelöst durch den CH 75C (4KK) 1993. Der CH 75D (5AR) wurde zwischen 1996 und 1997 gebaut mit einer Nennleistung von 330 PS und einem Gewicht von 14.878 kg.

Ready for the first field trip: a Claas Challenger 75E from '98. With 10 forward and 2 reverse gears the CH 75E reaches a top speed of 18 mph. This model is attached with special self cleaning driving wheels.

Fertig für den ersten Einsatz auf dem Feld: Ein 98er Claas Challenger 75E. Mit zehn Vorwärtsgängen und zwei Rück-wärtsgängen erreicht er eine Höchstge-schwindigkeit von 29 km/h. Dieses Modell wurde mit selbstreinigenden Antriebsrädern ausgerüstet.

The first Caterpillar Challenger 85C (9TK) was introduced in 1993 with 355 gross hp, followed by the Challenger 85D (4GR), which was built between 1996 and 1997 with 370 gross hp. The picture shows the current Claas Challenger 85E with 340 gross hp and an operating weight of 33,985 lb. The biggest Cater-pillar/Claas Challenger model is the CH 95 rated at 410 gross hp.

Der erste Caterpillar Challenger 85C (9TK) wurde 1993 vorgestellt mit einer Nennleistung von 355 PS, gefolgt vom Challenger 85D (4GR), gebaut von 1996 bis 1997 mit 370 PS Nennleistung. Das Bild zeigt den aktuellen Claas Challenger 85E mit 340 PS und einem Gewicht von 15.413 kg. Der größte Caterpillar/Claas Challenger ist der CH 95 mit einer Nenn-leistung von 410 PS.

This Claas Lexion 480 combine is equipped with Caterpillar's MTS (mobil track system) and is powered by a Mercedes Benz OM441LA V6 turbo engine with 375 hp. If this combine is sold under Caterpillar trade mark, it is powered by a Cat 3176C 6-cylinder turbo engine rated at 365 hp.

Ein Claas Lexion 480 Mähdrescher mit Caterpillars Mobil Track System wird angetrieben von einem Mercedes Benz OM441LA V6-Turbo-Motor mit 375 PS. Wird der Lexion 480 Mähdrescher unter dem Namen Caterpillar verkauft, treibt ihn der Cat 3176C 6-Zyl.-Turbo-Motor mit 365 PS an.

A picture from a 1998 sales brochure. Caterpillar sells and maintains the Claas Lexion combines in the USA under its own trade marke.

Eine Abbildung aus einem Verkaufsprospekt von 1998. Caterpillar vertreibt die Claas Lexion Mähdrescher-Serie unter ihrem eigenen Warenzeichen in Amerika.

Excavators

Caterpillar introduced his first four types of hydraulic excavators in 1976, the Cat 225, 235, 245 and last but not least the smallest, the Cat 215. For operators as well as with contractors the 200-series was a very popular series. The operator cab was spacious and all operator instruments could be reached easily and comfortably by the operator. The contractor estimated the 200-series with durability and fast cycle times. All Caterpillar booms and sticks were stress relieved, this reduced residual stress after welding and increased lifetime. Critical welding points were controlled previously with X-ray or ultrasonics. In 1963 Caterpillar and Mitsubishi Ltd. began their joint venture in Japan and later they developed a new line of hydraulic excavators. After 1987 the company, now named Shin Caterpillar Mitsubishi Ltd., produced hydraulic excavators. They built the following models: E70, E110, E120, E140, E180, E200B, E240, E300, E450 and E650. A further step to grow the product line of hydraulic excavators was the joint venture with the German company Eder. They developped and built wheeled and tracked excavators for the European market. In spring 1992 Caterpillar presented its new 300-series, the World Class Performers, the 320 and 325 hydraulic excavators. In the same year the first mining shovel, the Cat 5130 with 397,000 lb, came on the market. The next model which followed in 1994, was the 701,190 lb heavy 5230 mining shovel. Caterpillar began with the production of backhoe loaders in the UK in 1985. After only ten years, in January 1995, Caterpillar had already built 50,000 backhoe loaders. Today the Caterpillar hydraulic excavator line spans 24 standard models with an operation weight from 3,682 lb up to 702,292 lb.

Hydraulikbagger

Caterpillar stellte 1976 seine ersten vier Hydraulikbagger vor, den Cat 225, 235, 245 und zuletzt den kleinen 215. Die 200er Serie ist bei Fahrern und Unternehmern gleichermaßen beliebt. Das Fahrerhaus wurde großzügig und geräumig gestaltet, und alle Bedienhebel sind für den Fahrer übersichtlich und bequem zu erreichen. Der Bauunternehmer schätzte die 200er Serie wegen der Langlebigkeit und Schnelligkeit. Alle Caterpillar-Ausleger und -Löffelstiele sind spannungsfrei geglüht, somit wird ein hohes Maß an Festigkeit und Langlebigkeit gewährleistet. Die kritischen Schweißstellen werden zuvor geröntgt oder mit Ultraschallgeräten sorgfältig kontrolliert. 1963 begannen Caterpillar und Mitsubishi Ltd. in Japan ein joint venture, um Hydraulikbagger zu entwickeln und zu bauen. Ab 1987 wurden die ersten Hydraulikbagger produziert und die Firma hieß nun Shin Caterpillar Mitsubishi Ltd. Es wurden folgende Modelle gefertigt: E70, E110, E120, E140, E180, E200B, E240, E300, E450 und E650. Ein weiterer Schritt, um Caterpillars Produktpalette an Hydraulikbaggern zu vergrößern, war die Zusammenarbeit mit der deutschen Firma Eder. Dort wurde eine Reihe von Rad- und Kettenbaggern für den europäischen Markt entwickelt und gebaut. Im Frühjahr 1992 präsentierte Caterpillar seine neue 300-Serie, die World Class Performers, den 320 und 325 Hydraulikbagger. Im gleichen Jahr stellte man den ersten großen Minenbagger mit 174 t, den Cat 5130, vor. Ihm folgte 1994 der 318 t schwere 5230 Hydraulikbagger. 1985 begann Caterpillar mit dem Bau von Baggerladern in England, nach nur zehn Jahren wurde im Januar 1995 der 50.000ste Baggerlader gefeiert. Heute umfaßt die Caterpillar Hydraulikbagger-Serie insgesamt 24 Grundmodelle mit einem Einsatzgewicht von 1.670 bis 318.500 kg.

225·235·245
EXCAVATORS
designed and built by
CATERPILLAR

On the 1998 Bauma exhibition in Munich Caterpillar presented its smallest hydraulic excavator: the 301.5 with 17.7 hp and an operating weight of 3,609 lb. It is so small, that it fits in a garden house.

1998 auf der Bauma in München wird Caterpillars kleinster Hydraulikbagger präsentiert: Der 301.5 mit 17,7 PS und einem Gewicht von 1.637 kg. Er ist so klein, daß er in ein Gartenhaus passt.

The Caterpillar mini excavators 301.5 and 302.5 are built under same high quality standards as the bigger Cat hydraulic excavators. The 302.5 is powered by a Cat engine with 22.9 hp and has an operating weight of 6,028 lb.

Für die Caterpillar Minibagger 301.5 und 302.5 gelten die gleichen hohen Qualitätsstandards wie für die größeren Cat-Hydraulikbagger. Der Cat 302.5 wird von einem Cat Motor mit 22,9 PS angetrieben und das Einsatzgewicht beträgt 2.734 kg.

In 1963 Caterpillar started a joint venture with Mitsubishi Ltd. in Japan. The first hydraulic excavators were offered in 1987 and the company was renamed Shin Caterpillar Mitsubishi Ltd. The picture shows the smallest excavator of this line, the Cat E70 (3BG09058) with 52 hp and a weight of 14,300lb. It was built until 1989. The successor was the Cat E70B. It was produced until 1994. Caterpillar built the following models: E70, E110, E120, E140, E180, E200B, E240, E300, E450, and E650.

1963 begann Caterpillar mit Mitsubishi Ltd. die Zusammenarbeit in Japan. Ab 1987 wurden die ersten Hydraulikbagger produziert und die Firma hieß nun Shin Caterpillar Mitsubishi Ltd. Das Bild zeigt den kleinsten Hydraulikbagger, den Cat E70 (3BG09058) mit 52 PS und einem Gewicht von 6.500 kg. Gebaut wurde er bis 1989, der Nachfolger wurde der Cat E70B bis 1994. Es wurden folgende Caterpillar Modelle gefertigt: E70, E110, E120, E140, E180, E200B, E240, E300, E450 und E650.

Here you can see at a fleet of new Caterpillar 307 with 54 hp and an operating weight of 16,760 lb. They were built between 1994 and 1997 and they were afterwards replaced by the current Cat model, the Cat 307B.

Bei einem Händler steht eine ganze Flotte neuer Caterpillar 307 mit 54 PS und einem Gewicht von 7.600 kg. Sie wurden gebaut zwischen 1994 und 1997 und abgelöst durch das aktuelle Modell, den Cat 307B.

On a construction site in Anchorage/Alaska I saw this Caterpillar E120B with 84 hp and an operation weight of 25,578 lb. The E120B was built between 1990 and 1992. The first Cat E120 was introduced in 1987 and was in the sales lists until 1989. Between the Cat E70 and the Cat E120 is the Caterpillar E110 with a weight of 23,600 lb.

Auf einer Baustelle in Anchorage/Alaska habe ich diesen Caterpillar E120B mit 84 PS und einem Einsatzgewicht von 11.600 kg entdeckt. Gebaut wurde der Cat E120B von 1990 bis 1992. Der erste Cat E120 wurde 1987 vorgestellt und blieb bis 1989 im Verkaufsprogramm. Zwischen dem Cat E70 und dem E120 liegt der E110 mit 10.700 kg.

The Caterpillar E120B is in the same operating weight-class as the Cat 311 from the new 300-series. It was built between 1993 and 1996 and it was replaced by the Cat 311B. The picture shows a Cat 312 with an offset-boom. In 1998 Caterpillar introduced the new 312B with a weight of 28,665 lb.

In der gleichen Gewichtsklasse wie der Caterpillar E120B liegt der Cat 311 aus der neuen 300-Serie. Er wurde von 1993 bis 1996 gebaut und wird abgelöst durch den Cat 311B. Hier ein 312, 1998 wurde der neue 312B mit 13.000 kg vorgestellt.

The first Caterpillar 315 was introduced in 1994 and was built until 1997. The picture shows a `99 model from the Swiss Cat dealer Ammann. The Cat 315B L is an excavator in the 16-tons class and rated at 132 hp. The L stands for a longer undercarriage. The 315 was followed by the Cat 317 with 99 hp in the 17-tons class. It was built from 1995 and was replaced by the current Cat 317B model in 1998. The next bigger current model is the Cat 318B in the 18-tons class.

Der erste Caterpillar 315 wurde 1994 vorgestellt und bis 1997 gebaut. Das Bild zeigt ein 99er Modell des Schweizer Cat-Händlers Ammann. Der Cat 315B L ist ein Hydraulikbagger der 16 t-Klasse mit 132 PS. Das L steht für ein längeres Laufwerk. Es folgte der Caterpillar 317 mit 99 PS in der 17 t-Klasse, er wurde gebaut ab 1995 und 1998 durch den 317B ersetzt. Der nächstgrößere ist der aktuelle Cat 318B in der 18 t-Klasse.

In 1984 the joint venture with a German excavator manufacturer, the Eder Company, began. They built a line of wheeled and tracked excavators for Europe: the models 205, 211 and 213. The picture shows a Cat 213B LC with a weight of 39,932 lb and an output of 110 hp. In 1990 the new B-series came up and all models were in the sales lists until 1992.

1984 begann die Zusammenarbeit mit einem namhaften deutschen Baggerhersteller, der Firma Eder. Dort werden eine Reihe von Rad- und Kettenbaggern für Europa gebaut: die Modelle 205, 211 und 213. Mit diesen Modellen füllte man die Lücken in der 200-Serie. Das Bild zeigt einen 213B LC mit 18.110 kg Einsatzgewicht und 110 PS. Von 1990 an wurde die B-Serie gebaut und alle Modelle blieben bis 1992 im Verkaufsprogramm.

This is the Caterpillar 215 (96L) with 85 hp and an operating weight of 38,480 lb. It was the fourth new excavator from the 200-series from Cat and it was introduced in 1976.

Das ist der Caterpillar 215 (96L) mit 85 PS und einem Gewicht von 17.450 kg. Er war der vierte neue Bagger der 200-Serie von Cat und wurde 1976 vorgestellt.

Attached with the new cab this Caterpillar 215 works on a demolition job site with a concrete pulverizer.

Schon mit dem neuen Fahrerhaus ausgestattet wird dieser Caterpillar 215 mit einem Betonbeißer auf einer Abbruchbaustelle eingesetzt.

A nearly brand-new Caterpillar 215B LC (9YB), with 105 hp and an operating weight of 40,806 lb. The B-series was built between 1984 and 1987. As a standard this Cat model 215B LC is equipped with the wide adjustable undercarriage. The LC (long undercarriage) gives the excavator an excellent lift capacity when he is moving heavy loads.

Ein fast neuer Caterpillar 215B LC (9YB) mit 105 PS und einem Einsatzgewicht von 18.510 kg. Gebaut wurde die B-Serie von 1984 bis 1987. Der Cat 215B LC verfügt als Standardausrüstung über ein in der Breite verstellbares Laufwerk. Das längere LC-Laufwerk verleiht dem Hydraulikbagger eine bessere Standsicherheit beim Heben schwerster Lasten.

In 1987 the improved Caterpillar 215C LC (4HG) with 115 hp and an operating weight of 43,150 lb was put on the market. It is powered by a Cat 3304 DIT 4-cylinder turbo engine with a displacement of 427 in³.

1987 wurde der überarbeitete Caterpillar 215C LC (4HG) mit 115 PS und einem Gewicht von 19.570 kg vorgestellt. Er wird angetrieben durch einen Cat 3304 DIT 4-Zyl.-Turbo-Motor mit 7 l Hubraum.

The picture was taken in summer 1992. Two Caterpillar 215D LC (9TF) were standing on a big job site. The power of the D-series was increased to 125 hp. The customer can choose between two booms and three sticks.

Das Bild entstand im Sommer 1992. Zwei Caterpillar 215D LC (9TF) stehen auf einer großen Baustelle. Die Leistung beträgt bei der D-Serie 125 PS. Der Kunde kann zwischen zwei Auslegervarianten und drei Löffelstielen wählen.

This Cat 219 LC (5CF) is just been loaded onto a flatbed trailer. The top model is the Cat 219D LC (5XG) with a weight of 49,300 lb and a power of 140 hp.

Ein Caterpillar 219 LC (5CF) wird gerade auf einen Tieflader verladen. Das Top-Modell, der Cat 219D LC (5XG) brachte es auf 22.400 kg Einsatzgewicht und auf eine Leistung von 140 PS.

A Caterpillar EL180 with 118 hp and an operating weight of 43,659 lb. It is 1,543 lb heavier than the standard version E180. In 1987 it was replaced by the Cat E/EL200B with its modern styled cab.

Ein Caterpillar EL180 mit 118 PS und 19.800 kg Einsatzgewicht. Er ist um 700 kg schwerer als die Standard-version des Cat E180 und wurde 1987 durch den Cat E/EL200B mit einem moderneren Fahrerhaus abgelöst.

In spring 1992 Caterpillar presented its new 300-series on the Bauma exhibition in Munich: the World Class Performers, the Cat 320 and the 325 hydraulic excavator. They are equipped with a new cab, new undercarriage and a new upper structure, and last but not least the new electronical control system Maestro.

Im Frühjahr 1992 auf der Bauma in München: Caterpillar präsentiert seine neue 300-Serie, die World Class Performers, den Cat 320 und den 325 Hydraulikbagger mit neuem Fahrerhaus, neuem Laufwerk, neuem Oberwagen und dem elektronischen Steuergerät Maestro.

This is a Caterpillar 320 L from the first series, equipped with a special bucket for demolition work, with an operating weight of 44,915 lb, 128 hp and a power mode selector with three levels.

Ein Caterpillar 320 L aus der allerersten Serie, ausgestattet mit einem Spezial-löffel für den Abbruch, 20.370 kg Einsatz-gewicht, 128 PS und einem Leistungs-stufenschalter mit drei Einstellungen.

This is a Caterpillar 320 L works on a pipeline construction site. It is attached with a tilt bucket. The picture shows a 94' model.

Auf einer Pipeline-Baustelle arbeitet dieser Caterpillar 320 L. Er ist mit einem Böschungslöffel ausgestattet. Das Bild zeigt ein 94er Modell.

This Caterpillar 320 L is loading a 4-axle truck in a deep gravel pit. The Cat 320 was built between 1991 and 1996 and then it was replaced by the Cat 320B.

In einer tiefen Kiesgrube lädt dieser Caterpillar 320 L einen Vierachs-Lkw. Der Cat 320 wurde von 1991 bis 1996 gebaut und durch den Cat 320B abgelöst.

A Caterpillar EL240 in British Columbia between '87 and '89. This 50,700 lb heavy excavator was built and is powered by a Cat 3304 4-cylinder turbo engine with a displacement of 427 in^3 and 148 hp. It was replaced by the B-series. The C-series stopped in 1993.

Ein Caterpillar EL240 in British Columbia. Gebaut wurde dieser 23.600 kg schwere Hydraulikbagger von 1987 bis 1989. Er wird angetrieben durch einen Cat 3304 4-Zyl.-Turbo-Motor mit 7 l Hubraum und 148 PS. Von 1989 bis 1992 wurde die B-Serie gebaut, die C-Serie bis 1993.

The Cat 225 (51U) was the first Cat hydraulic excavator with an output of 125 hp and a weight of 50,715 lb. It was offered with a mono boom or a two piece boom and three different sticks: 6'49", 8'00", 10'00".

Der Cat 225 (51U) war der erste Cat Hydraulikbagger mit 125 PS und einem Gewicht von 23.000 kg. Er wurde mit einem ein- oder zweiteiligen Ausleger und mit drei verschiedenen Löffelstielen angeboten: 1.980 mm, 2.440 mm und 3.050 mm.

The Cat 225 (51U) is attached with a two piece boom. Caterpillar booms and sticks are stress relieved. This reduces residual stress after welding and increases the lifetime. Critical welding points are controlled before with X-ray or ultrasonics.

Dieser Cat 225 (51U) ist mit einem zweiteiligen Ausleger bestückt. Da Caterpillar Ausleger und Löffelstiele spannungsfrei glüht, wird ein hohes Maß an Festigkeit und Langlebigkeit gewährleistet. Die kritischen Schweißstellen werden zuvor geröntgt oder mit Ultraschallgeräten sorgfältig kontrolliert.

A newer model of the Cat 225 (51U) with a new cab and increased power of 135 hp.

Eine neuere Ausführung des Caterpillar 225 (51U) mit neuem Fahrerhaus und einer Leistung von nun 135 PS.

This Cat 225 logger works in Fort Saint John in Canada. Finning rebuilts the Cat excavators for forestry-work. It is equipped with engine guards, a cab riser, a bigger cab and a log-loader attachment from the Young Company.

In Kanada steht dieser Caterpillar 225 logger. Finning rüstet auf Kundenwunsch die Caterpillar Hydraulikbagger für den Forstbetrieb um: Auf Wunsch ausgestattet mit einem Motorenschutz, einem höheren und größeren Fahrerhaus sowie einer Ladeeinrichtung der Firma Young.

This Caterpillar 225B LC was built between 1986 and 1989 and weighs up to 57,638 lb. It is powered by a 145 hp Cat engine. The production of the last version of the Caterpillar 225D with 165 hp and an operating weight of 58,873 lb ended in 1991.

Dieser Caterpillar 225B LC wurde zwischen 1986 und 1989 gebaut und wiegt 26.140 kg. Angetrieben wird er von einem 145 PS starken Cat-Motor. Die letzte Version, der Caterpillar 225D mit 165 PS und einem Gewicht von 26.700 kg, wird bis 1991 gebaut.

In Grande Prairie/Alberta I found the Caterpillar FB227, a really rare highlight for European Cat-people. It is equipped with a special undercarriage with a four-way tilt swing mechanism. The advantage is that the cab is kept in level for operating ease and comfort and the unit's centre of gravity is kept close to the centre line of the carrier for a better weight distribution on steep slopes out in the forest. The engine enclosure looks like a tent. It spreads the heat of the engine. This reduces the danger of forestfires. The front mounted feller buncher holds the tree and cuts this with a hydraulic driven discsaw and lays the tree to the side, for later transportation.

In Grande Prairie/Alberta konnte ich den für uns Europäer so seltenen Caterpillar FB227 bestaunen. Ausgestattet mit einem Speziallaufwerk und einem verstellbaren Drehkranz kann sich dieser Baumfäller auf abschüssigem Gelände immer wieder horizontal ausrichten. Die zeltähnliche Motorabdeckung dient einer besseren Wärmeverteilung und vermindert die Brandgefahr im Forst. Mit der Klammer hält der Bagger den Baum fest, sägt ihn dann mit einer hydraulisch angetriebenen Kreissäge ab und legt ihn zur Seite, wo der Baum dann später abtransportiert werden kann.

The Caterpillar 322 L is equipped with a long stick. It loads earth into trucks on a job site in France. It was built from '93 to '96 with 153 hp and an operating weight of 52,800 lb.

Ein Caterpillar 322 L ist mit einem langen Löffelstiel ausgerüstet. Er lädt in Frankreich Erdaushub auf Lkws. Er wurde von 1993 bis 1996 mit 153 PS und einem Gewicht von 23.950 kg gebaut.

The Cat 325 replaced the old Cat 225. On the ICE railroad construction site Frankfurt/Cologne in Germany works this Cat 325 L long reach with an operating weight of 63,592 lb. The maximum reach goes up to 60'5", and the maximum digging deepth to 48'5". Because of the Maestro electronic controls you can work very smooth and exact with this long reach version.

Der 325 löst den alten Cat 225 ab. Auf der ICE-Baustelle Frankfurt/ Köln wird dieser 325 L long reach mit 28.840 kg eingesetzt, um Böschungen zu planieren. Die max. Reichweite beträgt 18.420 mm, die max. Grabtiefe 14.720 mm.

This Caterpillar 325 L is used as a material handler at a transfer station for a landfill in the Netherlands.

Ein Caterpillar 325 L wird als Lademaschine für den Müllumschlag auf einer niederländischen Mülldeponie eingesetzt.

In 1996 the Caterpillar 325 was replaced by the new Cat 325B. The picture shows a Cat 325B L with a straight boom in a quarry. The straight boom was especially developed for use in demolition application.

1996 wurde der Caterpillar 325 durch den neuen Cat 325B abgelöst. Das Bild zeigt einen Cat 325B L mit geradem Ausleger in einem Steinbruch. Diese gerade Form des Auslegers wurde speziell für Abbrucharbeiten entwickelt.

A new Caterpillar 229D (2LJ) with an operating weight of 69,898 lb is used on a demolition site. It is powered by a Cat 3304 DIT 4-cylinder turbo engine with a displacement of 427 in³ and an output of 157 hp. The first Cat 229 units were built between 1986 and 1989 and were replaced by the D-series. The production stopped in 1991.

Ein neuer Cat 229D (2LJ) mit einem Gewicht von 31.700 kg wird als Abbruchbagger eingesetzt. Angetrieben wird er durch einen Cat 3304 DIT 4-Zyl.-Turbo-Motor mit 7 l Hubraum und 157 PS. Die ersten Cat 229 wurden von 1986 bis 1989 gebaut und durch die D-Serie abgelöst. Die Produktion wird 1991 eingestellt.

Near Eagle Plain on the Dempster Highway I saw this Caterpillar EL300B. This heavy excavator with 68,780 lb is powered by a Cat 3306 6-cylinder turbo engine with a displacement of 640 in³ and rated at 206 hp. The first Cat E/EL300 were built between 1987 and 1989 and were replaced by the new B-series. The production ended in 1991. The Cat EL300B is in the same size class as the Cat 231D and the new Cat 330.

In der Nähe von Eagle Plain auf dem Dempster Highway sah ich diesen Cat EL300B. Angetrieben wird der 31.200 kg schwere Kettenbagger durch einen Cat 3306 6-Zyl.-Turbo-Motor mit 10,5 l Hubraum und 206 PS. Die ersten Cat E/EL300 wurden von 1987 bis 1989 gebaut und abgelöst durch die neue B-Serie. Das Produktionsende kam 1991. Der Cat EL300B ist von der Größe mit dem Cat 231D und dem neuen Cat 330 vergleichbar.

The successor of the Caterpillar 229D was the Cat 231D in 1990. It is powered by a 200 hp Cat 3208 V8 turbo engine with a displacement of 634 in³. The operating weight increased up to 75,600 lb, the production end for the Cat 231D/LC came in 1992.

Der Nachfolger des Caterpillar 229D wurde 1990 der Cat 231D. Angetrieben wird dieses Modell von einem 200 PS starken Cat 3208 V8-Turbo-Motor mit 10,4 l Hubraum. Das Einsatzgewicht stieg auf 34.300 kg, das Produktionsende kam 1992.

The Caterpillar 231D LC was the top model with a weight up to 78,100 lb. This Cat 231D LC works in a lava pit near Koblenz/Germany.

Der Caterpillar 231D LC mit 35.500 kg Einsatzgewicht war das Top-Modell. Dieser Cat 231D LC wird in einem Lavabruch in der Nähe von Koblenz eingesetzt.

The demolition of residental and industrial buildings becomes more and more popular. Mostly demolition with drop balls or blasting is forbidden. Buildings could be damaged.The solutions to these problems are the Caterpillar ultra high demolition booms. The Cat 330 LN reaches to a maximum height of 68'5" and has a maximum reach of 45'3". You can attach work tools up to 5,071 lb to the stick without any problem.

Der Abbruch von Wohn- und Industriegebäuden nimmt immer mehr zu. Die Abrißkugel oder das Sprengen ist in den meisten Fällen nicht mehr gestattet, außerdem könnten benachbarte Gebäude beschädigt werden. Die Antwort auf solche Probleme hat Caterpillar mit seinen ultra langen Abbruchauslegern gelöst. Ein Cat 330 LN erreicht eine max. Höhe von 20.900 mm und eine max. Reichweite von 13.800 mm. Arbeitswerkzeuge können bis zu 2.300 kg ohne Probleme an den Ausleger angebaut werden.

This Caterpillar 330 L with an operating weight of 73,889 lb and an output of 222 hp works on a construction site near Cologne/Germany. Noticeable is the bigger counter weight of this version. The Cat 330 was built between 1992 and 1995 and was replaced by the current model, the Cat 330B.

Auf einer Baustelle in der Nähe von Köln arbeitet dieser Caterpillar 330 L mit einem Gewicht von 33.510 kg und einer Leistung von 222 PS. Man beachte das größere Spezialheckgewicht an dieser Version. Der Cat 330 wurde von 1992 bis 1995 gebaut und durch den Cat 330B abgelöst.

One of my best hydraulic excavator pictures: a Caterpillar 235 (64R). After school I went nearly five miles on my bike to the construction site to take this picture. The Cat 235 excavator with 195 hp and an operating weight of 86,700 lb was built from 1973 until 1986.

Eines meiner besten Hydraulikbagger-Bilder: Ein Caterpillar 235 (64R). Für dieses Bild fuhr ich nach der Schule extra noch 8 km mit dem Fahrrad auf die Baustelle. Mit einem Einsatzgewicht von 39.320 kg wurde dieser 195 PS starke Cat 235 Hydraulikbagger von 1973 bis 1986 gebaut.

On a pipeline project in Switzerland you can see this Caterpillar 235C, equipped with a tilt bucket. The Cat 235C was built in two versions: Standard and ME (mass excavator) for a maximum production in heavy truck loading with a 18'6" long ME boom and a 8'3" long ME stick.

Ein Caterpillar 235C, ausgestattet mit einem Schwenklöffel, steht auf einer Pipeline Baustelle in der Schweiz. Der Caterpillar 235C wurde in zwei Versionen angeboten: Standard und ME (mass excavator) für den Massenaushub mit einem 5.660 mm langen ME-Ausleger und einem 2.540 mm langen ME-Löffelstiel.

This Caterpillar 235C, built in 1991, is loading earth into articulated dump trucks of the 30-40 tons class. The production end for the C-series came in 1992.

Ein Caterpillar 235C, Baujahr 1991, lädt Erdaushub auf Dumper der 30- bis 40-t-Klasse. Das Produktionsende für diese C-Serie kam 1992.

This 250 hp Caterpillar 235D is equipped with a long reach boom for the material handling of coal and iron ore. It was the last type of the 235-serie D and was built from 1992 to 1993. The operation weight in the standard version goes up to 108,620 lb. Its North American cousin was the Cat E450 with 101,430 lb and 276 hp.

Für den Materialumschlag von Kohle und Erz wurde dieser 250 PS starke 235D mit einem long reach-Ausleger ausgestattet. Er war der letzte Typ der 235-Serie D, die von 1992 bis 1993 gebaut wurde. Das Gewicht in der Standardversion beträgt nun 49.270 kg. Sein Bruder in Nordamerika heißt Cat E450 mit einem Einsatzgewicht von 46.000 kg und einer Leistung von 276 PS.

I saw my first Caterpillar 235D FS at the Caterpillar plant in Gosselies/Belgium in 1993. This front shovel excavator is mostly used in quarries to load blasted material from the bank. In 1965 Caterpillar established the Gosselies plant, a 242 acres facility. In Gosselies there are three different production lines: one for wheel loaders, one for hydraulic excavators and one for diesel engines.

1993 konnte ich in der Caterpillar-Fabrik in Gosselies/Belgien meinen ersten Cat 235D FS bestaunen. Dieser Hochlöffelbagger wird meistens in Steinbrüchen verwendet, um das gesprengte Material von der Wand zu laden. 1965 gründete Caterpillar das 98 ha große Werk. Davon bedeckt die Fertigungsanlage eine 25 ha große Fläche. In Gosselies werden drei Produktreihen gebaut: Radlader, Hydraulikbagger und Dieselmotoren.

In 1997 one of the latest Caterpillar hydraulic excavators, the Cat 345B was introduced. This Cat 345B L has just been loaded onto a flatbed trailer. The 3176C ATAAC 6-cylinder turbo engine with 294 hp powered this 104,991 lb heavy excavator.

1997 wurde einer der neuesten Caterpillar Hydraulikbagger präsentiert, der 345B. Dieser Cat 345B L wird gerade auf einen Tieflader verladen. Der 3176C ATAAC 6-Zyl.-Turbo-Motor mit 294 PS treibt diesen 47.615 kg schweren Hydraulikbagger an.

In less than two minutes a Caterpillar 345B loads a 35 tons capacity Cat D350E truck. It needs only 5-6 cycles.

In weniger als zwei Minuten lädt ein Cat 345B einen Cat D350E Dumper mit 31,7 t Nutzlast, er benötigt dazu nur 5 bis 6 Ladespiele.

This Cat 350 L ME works on a highway construction site. The new Cat 350 replaced the old Cat 235D back in 1994. The productivity increased up to 22% compared to the old Cat 235D. This was reached by more power on stick and boom and by faster cycle times. The fuel consumption went down 10-13% because of the electronical control of engine and hydraulic system.

Auf einer Autobahnbaustelle arbeitet dieser Caterpillar 350 L ME. Der neue Cat 350 löst den alten Cat 235D im Jahr 1994 ab. Die Produktivität stieg um 22% gegenüber dem alten Cat 235D. Dies wurde erreicht durch eine höhere Kraft an Löffelstiel und Arm und durch schnellere Arbeitsabläufe. Der Kraftstoffverbrauch sank dabei um 10-13% dank der elektronischen Überwachung von Motor- und Hydrauliksystem.

This Caterpillar 350 L is equipped with a straight boom and a concrete pulverizer. It works on a demolition job site in Switzerland. It is powered by a Cat 3306C 6-cylinder turbo engine, with a displacement of 640 in³ and a power output of 290 hp.

Der Caterpillar 350 L ist mit einem geraden Ausleger und einem Betonpulverisierer ausgerüstet und arbeitet auf einer Schweizer Abbruchbaustelle. Angetrieben wird er durch einen Cat 3306C 6 Zyl. Turbo-Motor mit 10,5 l Hubraum und 290 PS.

The Boskalis Oosterwijk b.v. company from the Netherlands uses this Caterpillar 350 L with GPS (global position system) on a canal project. The 115,762 lb heavy hydraulic excavator is equipped with a special stick and stands on a floating barge.

Die Firma Boskalis Oosterwijk b.v. aus den Niederlanden setzt diesen Caterpillar 350 L mit GPS (global position system) bei Nassbaggerarbeiten an einem Kanal ein. Der 52.500 kg schwere Hydraulikbagger ist mit einem Spezialstiel ausgestattet und steht auf einem schwimmenden Ponton.

This 20 year old Caterpillar 245 (82X) hydraulic excavator is still working. Watching this picture you can hardly believe It: still the original painting, the first stick and boom and the original decals. There isn`t any better proof for the durability of Caterpillar's 200-series. The series was introduced in 1974. With 325 hp and an operating weight of 127,890 lb the Cat 245 has been working on many heavy construction sites.

Seit mehr als 20 Jahren im Einsatz ist dieser Caterpillar 245 (82X) Hydraulikbagger. Wenn man das Bild anschaut, glaubt man es gar nicht: Es sind immer noch der erste Lack, Stiel und Arm sowie die erste Beschriftung. Einen besseren Beweis für die Langlebigkeit der 200-Serie, die 1974 vorgestellt wurde, gibt es nicht. Mit 325 PS und einem Gewicht von 58.000 kg war der Cat 245 auf vielen Großbaustellen zu Hause.

On a highway project in Southern Germany works this Cat 245 (84X). It was one of the first Cat 245 hydraulic excavators in the ME-version with 325 hp and a maximum operating weight of 144,967 lb.

Auf einer Autobahnbaustelle in Süddeutschland arbeitet dieser Caterpillar 245 (84X). Er war einer der ersten Cat 245 Hydraulikbagger mit 325 PS und einem max. Einsatzgewicht von 65.745 kg, welcher für den Massenaushub gebaut wurden.

A B-series Caterpillar 245 ME (6MF) is loading 4 axle dump trucks with a loading capacity of 25 tons on an airport project. The B-series was introduced in 1988 with 360 hp and a weight of 143,500 lb. The Caterpillar E650 with 375 hp and an operating weight up to 138,000 lb is in the same class as the Cat 245B. The Cat E650 was in the sales lists from 1987 to 1992.

Einer der ersten Caterpillar 245 ME (6MF) der B-Serie lädt 4-Achs-Muldenkipper mit einer Nutzlast von 25 t bei einem Flughafenprojekt. Die B-Serie wurde 1988 vorgestellt, mit 360 PS und einem Gewicht von 65.200 kg. Der Caterpillar E650 Hydraulikbagger mit 375 PS und einem Gewicht von 62.600 kg ist vergleichbar mit unserem Cat 245B. Der E650 stand von 1987 bis 1992 in der Verlaufsliste der Händler.

This Caterpillar 245B (6MF), equipped with a long boom and stick, works on a canal project. It loads rocks onto a barge with a special grapple.

Dieser Caterpillar 245B (6MF), ausgestattet mit einem langen Arm und Stiel, wird auf einer Kanalbaustelle eingesetzt. Er lädt mit einem speziellen Greifer Steine auf ein Ponton.

This is another Caterpillar 245B, equipped with a La Bounty concrete crusher. It is working in a quarry on a demonstration show.

Ein anderer Caterpillar 245B ist ausgerüstet mit einem La Bounty Beton-pulverisierer und arbeitet während einer Vorführung in einem Steinbruch.

Eberhard used this Caterpillar 245B II (1SJ), equipped with a concrete pulverizer on a demolition job. Noticeable is the one of a hind boom and a stick on this excavator. It was dropped out the sales list in 1992.

Die Firma Eberhard setzt diesen Caterpillar 245B II (1SJ) mit einem Betonpulverisierer bei Abbrucharbeiten ein. Man beachte die speziell angefertigte Arm- und Stielkombination an dem Hydraulikbagger, der bis 1992 gebaut wurde.

The last generation of the Caterpillar 245, a Cat 245D HD (4LK/7ZJ) works on the coast in the Netherlands to protect the dike. The operating weight of this version goes up to 165,154 lb. The Cat 245D is powered by a Cat 3406B 6-cylinder turbo engine with a displacement of 890 in³ and 385 hp. It was built until 1993 and was replaced by the recently introduced Cat 365B excavator.

Die letzte Generation des Caterpillar 245, ein Cat 245D HD (4LK/7ZJ), wird bei der Küstensicherung in den Niederlanden eingesetzt. Das Gewicht geht bei dieser Version bis 74.900 kg. Angetrieben wird der 245D von einem Cat 3406B 6-Zyl.-Turbo-Motor mit 14,6 l Hubraum und 385 PS. Er wurde bis 1993 gebaut und durch den 365B Hydraulikbagger abgelöst.

A Caterpillar 245B FS with 360 hp, a 4.05 yd³ capacity bottom dump bucket and a weight of 149,785 lb loads a Cat 769C truck with 40 tons capacity in only 6-cycles. It is able to reach an hourly production of 600-700 tons/h.

Ein Caterpillar 245B FS mit 360 PS, einer 3,1 m³ fassenden Klappschaufel und 67.930 kg Gewicht lädt einen Cat SKW 769C mit 37 t Nutzlast in nur sechs Ladespielen, es können so 600 bis 700 t/Std. geladen werden. Das Foto entstand in der Nähe von Stuttgart.

Equipped with a 5 yd³ front dump bucket, this Cat 245B II FS weighs up to 160,524 lb.

Dieser Caterpillar 245B II FS ist mit einer 3,8 m³ fassenden Kippschaufel ausgerüstet, das Gewicht beträgt bis zu 72.800 kg.

This brand-new Caterpillar 245B II FS was built in 1992 and works in a quarry near Heilbronn/Germany. Because of the cab riser the operator has a better overview when loading Cat 769C trucks.

Ein neuer Caterpillar 245B II FS, Baujahr 1992, steht in einem Steinbruch in der Nähe von Heilbronn. Durch die Erhöhung des Fahrerhauses hat der Fahrer eine bessere Übersicht beim Laden des Cat 769C Muldenkippers mit 37 t Nutzlast.

The biggest hydraulic excavator of the 300-series is the Cat 375 with a weight of 183,015 lb. It is powered by a Cat 3406C 6-cylinder turbo engine with 890 in³ displacement and a power output of 428 hp. The picture shows a Cat 375 L with straight boom on a demolition site.

Der größte Hydraulikbagger der 300-Serie ist der 375 mit 83.000 kg. Er wird angetrieben durch einen Cat 3406C 6-Zyl.-Turbo-Motor mit 14,6 l Hubraum und 428 PS. Das Bild zeigt einen Cat 375 L mit geradem Ausleger bei Abbrucharbeiten.

Equipped with a special grapple this Caterpillar 375 L works on a dike project in the Netherlands.

Ein mit Spezialgreifer ausgerüsteter Cat 375 L wird bei der Küstensicherung in den Niederlanden eingesetzt.

This Caterpillar 375 L ME, equipped with a 7.3 yd³ bucket, is loading a Cat 773C truck with 60 tons in 5-cycles in less than two minutes.

Ein Caterpillar 375 L ME, ausgerüstet mit einem 5,6 m³ Löffel, belädt einen Cat 773C Muldenkipper mit 53 t Nutzlast in nur fünf Arbeitstakten unter zwei Minuten.

A miniature construction site is set up in a real excavator bucket.

Eine Großbaustelle in Miniaturausführung in einem original Baggerlöffel.

In 1993 Caterpillar introduced the smallest of the 5000-series, the Cat 5080 (8SL) with 428 hp and an operating weight of 184,779 lb. It is similar to the Cat 375, but it is equipped with a front shovel. You can choose between two bottom dump buckets with a capacity from 5.5 yd³ to 6.8 yd³.

1993 wurde der Kleinste der Caterpillar 5000-Serie vorgestellt, der Cat 5080 (8SL) mit 428 PS und einem Dienstgewicht von 83.800 kg. Er ist der Bruder des Cat 375, versehen mit einer Hochlöffelausrüstung. Es stehen zwei Klappschaufeln zur Auswahl mit 4,2 m³ und 5,2 m³.

A remarkable picture: normally a Caterpillar 5080 FS loads trucks in the 40-60 tons-class.

Ein außergewöhnliches Bild: Normalerweise belädt ein Caterpillar 5080 FS Muldenkipper der 40 bis 60 t-Klasse.

This Caterpillar 5130 FS (5ZL) is nearly ready to be used. The hydraulic excavator weighs 395,000 lb and is powered by a Cat 3508 V8-twin turbo engine with a displacement of 2104 in³ and 755 hp.

Es fehlt nicht mehr viel und dieser Cat 5130 FS (5ZL) ist für den ersten Einsatz fertig. Angetrieben wird der 179.000 kg schwere Hydraulikbagger von einem Cat 3508 V8-Bi-Turbo-Motor mit 34,5 l Hubraum und 755 PS.

This is a look inside the cab of a modern Cat 5130 FS excavator.

So sieht es im Fahrerhaus eines modernen Cat 5130 FS Hydraulikbaggers aus.

This Cat 5130B ME works under tough job conditions: Attached with a 13 yd³ bucket it loads unblasted limestone from the bank into a 60-tons 773B truck in only 3-4 cycles. Despite these very hard conditions the production per day goes up to 2000-3500 tons.

Dieser Cat 5130B arbeitet unter härtesten Bedingungen: Ausgerüstet mit einem 10 m³ Löffel lädt er ungesprengten Kalkstein auf einen Cat Muldenkipper 773B (60 t) in nur drei bis vier Arbeitstakten. Die so abgebaute Tagesleistung liegt bei 2.000 bis 3.500 t.

The weight of the new Cat B-series increased up to 401,310 lb and the engine power rose up to 800 hp. The 5130B has enough power to dig unblasted limestone in a quarry in Southern Germany.

Bei der neuen B-Serie des Cat 5130 stieg das Einsatzgewicht und die Motorleistung auf 182.000 kg bzw. 800 PS. Auf das zeitaufwendige Sprengen kann in diesem Steinbruch in Süddeutschland verzichtet werden, der Caterpillar 5130B hat die Kraft, den Kalkstein zu lösen.

This is a picture out of a sales brochure and shows Caterpillar's biggest excavator, the 5230 which was introduced in 1994.

Dies ist ein Bild aus einem Verkaufsprospekt und zeigt Caterpillar's größten Hydraulikbagger. Der 5230 wurde 1994 vorgestellt.

Built by Eder for Caterpillar the Cat 206B FT was the smallest wheel excavator. With 106 hp and an operating weight of 32,854 lb the version FT (fast travel) reached a top speed of 21.7 mph. The production stopped in 1995.

Der Cat 206B FT war der kleinste Radbagger, den die Firma Eder für Caterpillar baute. Mit 106 PS und einem Gewicht bis zu 14.900 kg ist die Version FT (fast travel) bis zu 35 km/h schnell. Das Produktionsende kam 1995.

With an operating weight of 35,500 lb and 113 hp the Caterpillar 212B FT reached a top speed of 19.8 mph. It was in the sales lists until 1995. The next bigger wheel excavators were the Cat 214B with 41,230 lb and a power rating of 135 hp, and the Cat 224B with 49,612 lb and 137 hp.

Mit einem Gewicht bis zu 16.100 kg und 113 PS war der bis zu 32 km/h schnelle Caterpillar 212B FT der nächstgrößere Radbagger von Cat. Er blieb bis 1995 im Verkaufsprogramm. Die beiden nächstgrößeren Radbagger waren der Cat 214B mit 18.700 kg und 135 PS sowie der Cat 224B mit 22.500 kg Einsatzgewicht und 137 PS.

This is Caterpillar's latest wheel excavator generation. The smallest model is the Cat M312 with 114 hp and an operating weight of 31,465 lb. It has the blue angel certificate for low noise and emission.

Das ist Caterpillars neueste Radbagger-Generation. Das kleinste Modell ist der Cat M312 mit 114 PS und einem Gewicht von 14.270 kg. Ihm wurde das Umweltzeichen verliehen, weil der Dieselmotor so lärmarm ist und die Emissionswerte schon heute die zukünftigen europäischen Abgaswerte erfüllen.

Caterpillar wheel excavators made in Germany. They are developed and built in a modern factory in Wackersdorf. Powered is the Cat M315 by a Cat 3054 DITA 4-cylinder turbo engine with a displacement of 243 in³ and 124 hp. The maximum travel speed goes up to 21 mph.

Caterpillar Mobilbagger made in Germany. Sie werden in einer modernen Fabrikationsstätte in Wackersdorf entwickelt und gebaut. Der Cat M315 wird durch einen Cat 3054 DITA 4-Zyl.-Turbo-Motor mit 3,99 l Hubraum und 124 PS angetrieben. Die max. Höchstgeschwindigkeit beträgt 34 km/h.

The customer can choose between two booms, a one-piece boom with 16'56" length and an hydraulically adjustable boom with a maximum 17'18" length. In addition there are five sticks available for a maximum flexibility. The operating weight of a Caterpillar M315 goes up to 34,684 lb.

Es stehen zwei Auslegervarianten zur Verfügung, ein einteiliger Ausleger mit 5.050 mm Länge und ein Verstellausleger mit max. 5.240 mm Länge. Des weiteren kann man unter fünf verschiedenen Löffelstielen wählen, so daß das Gerät für jeden Kunden individuell ausgerüstet werden kann. Das Einsatzgewicht des Cat M315 beträgt bis zu 15.730 kg.

In 1995 Caterpillar introduced the M318 with 140 hp and a weight of 39,491 lb. The picture shows a Cat M318 MH (material handler) with 42,997 lb operating weight. The maximum reach goes up to 34'44" and the max. height to 39'68".

1995 wird der Caterpillar M318 vorgestellt mit 140 PS und einem Gewicht von 17.910 kg. Das Bild zeigt einen Cat M318 MH (material handler) mit 19.500 kg. Die max. Reichweite beträgt 10.500 mm, die max. Höhe 12.100 mm.

The biggest Caterpillar wheel excavator is the M320 with 140 hp and a weight of 42,799 lb. In Switzerland I saw this Cat M320 MH with an operating weight of 49,171 lb. It is powered by a Cat 3116 DIT 6-cylinder turbo engine with a displacement of 402 in³.

Der größte Cat-Mobilbagger ist der M320 mit 140 PS und einem Einsatzgewicht von 19.410 kg. Auf einer Ausstellung in der Schweiz sah ich diesen M320 MH mit 22.300 kg Gewicht, angetrieben durch einen Cat 3116 DIT 6-Zyl.-Turbo-Motor mit 6,6 l Hubraum.

The smallest in the Caterpillar backhoe loader-series is the Cat 416 (5PC). It was built from 1985 to 1990. After many stages of development the current model, the Cat 416C, has a power output of 78 hp and a weight of 14,383 lb. This Caterpillar 426 II (7BC) 4x4 (built from 1990-92) is used in Dawson City/Canada for road maintenance with an operating weight of 16,129 lb and 70 hp. The current model is the Cat 426C/426C IT.

Der kleinste in der Caterpillar-Baggerlader-Serie ist der Cat 416 (5PC).Er wurde von 1985 bis 1990 gebaut. Nach mehreren Entwicklungsstufen leistet das aktuelle Modell, der Cat 416C, 78 PS bei einem Gewicht von 6.523 kg. Dieser Caterpillar 426 II (7BC) 4x4 (gebaut von 1990-92) wird in Dawson City/Kanada für den Unterhalt der Straßen eingesetzt mit einem Gewicht von 7.315 kg und 70 PS. Das aktuelle Modell ist der Cat 426C/426C IT.

This is a Caterpillar 428 II (6TC) 4x4, built in 1991, with 72 hp and an operating weight of 17,199 lb. The front bucket capacity goes up to 1.3 yd³ and with its backhoe you can dig trenches up to 19'7" deepth.

Dies ist ein Caterpillar 428 II (6TC) 4x4, Baujahr 1991, mit 72 PS und einem Gewicht von 7.800 kg. Die Ladeschaufel faßt 1 m³. Mit dem Heckbagger können Gräben bis zu 6 m Tiefe gezogen werden.

A nearly brand-new Caterpillar 428C, sold and serviced by the Spanish Cat dealer Finanzauto. You can attach different buckets, loader forks, brooms, blades, asphalt cutters, these are just some of the choices. The next bigger backhoe loader is the 89 hp Cat 436C with an operating weight of 15,602 lb.

Ein fast neuer Caterpillar 428C, ausgeliefert durch den spanischen Cat-Händler Finanzauto. Es können verschiedene Schaufeln, Palettengabeln, Kehrbesen, Schilde und Asphaltschneider angebaut werden, um nur einige Beispiele zu nennen. Als Sonderausrüstung ist eine Z-Kinematik-Ladeeinrichtung lieferbar. Der nächst größere ist der 89 PS starke Cat 436C mit einem Einsatzgewicht von 7.076 kg.

On the Bauma exhibition in 1995 Caterpillar exhibited the 438B (3KK) Turbo All Wheel Steer backhoe loader. This is the 50000-th backhoe loader built by Caterpillar ten years after its introduction in 1985. One year later Caterpillar showed the Cat C-series, the 89 hp and 16,356 lb heavy Cat 438C backhoe loader. The biggest current backhoe loader is the Caterpillar 446B (6XF) with 95 hp and a weight of 22,907 lb.

Auf der Bauma 1995 wird der Cat 438B (3KK) Turbo All Wheel Steer ausgestellt. Dies ist das Jubiläumsmodell, der 50.000ste Baggerlader, den Caterpillar seit der Markteinführung 1985 baute. Nachfolger wurde die C-Serie mit 89 PS und einem Einsatzgewicht von 7.418 kg. Der größte aktuelle Baggerlader von Caterpillar ist der 446B (6XF) mit 95 PS und einem Gewicht von 10.389 kg.

Trucks   Muldenkipper

Caterpillar introduced his first off-higway truck in 1962 with the model 769, with 35 tons capacity. It was powered by a 400 hp Cat engine and reached a travel speed up to 41.4 mph. Already at that time an oil pneumatic suspension system absorbed haul roads and loading shocks. This allowed the high haul travel speed. It is standard on all Caterpillar trucks. In 1970 Caterpillar introduced the big brother of the 769, the Cat 773, with a load capacity up to 50 tons. A further advantage of Caterpillar trucks are the completly sealed and oil cooled disc brakes. It required no periodic adjustments. The discs are fade resistant even the long steep grade braking and the operator can stop safely at any time. The third new truck was the Caterpillar 777 with a load capacity of 85 tons and a complete new look. In 1992 Caterpillar introduced its 771C Quarry Truck with another transmission and a wider truck body. He reduces the hauling costs to a minimum.

A further milestone in the history of Caterpillar trucks was the introduction of the 240 tons capacity 793 truck in 1990 with a power rated at 2,057 hp. It is the biggest mechanically driven truck all over the world. The biggest of all is the current Caterpillar 797 in the 340 tons up to 360 tons class with a gross vehicle weight of 1,230,000 lb and a power of 3400 hp.

Mit einer Nutzlast von 31,8 t wurde 1962 Caterpillars erster Muldenkipper vorgestellt. Der Cat 769 wird von einem 400 PS starken Cat-Motor angetrieben und erreicht eine Geschwindigkeit von 66,8 km/h. Schon damals gehörte eine ölpneumatische Radaufhängung, welche die Fahrbahnstöße absorbiert und somit die hohen Transportgeschwindigkeiten überhaupt erst zuließ, zur Standausrüstung. 1970 stellte man den großen Bruder des Cat 769, den Cat 773 mit einer Nutzlast von 45,5 t vor. Ein weiterer Vorteil der Caterpillar Muldenkipper ist die vollständig abgedichtete, ölgekühlte Scheibenbremsanlage, die ein sicheres Bremsen auch auf langen Bergabstrecken gewährleistet. Drittgrößter Muldenkipper wird der Cat 777 mit einem ganz neuen Erscheinungsbild und einer Nutzlast von 77 t. 1992 stellte Caterpillar seinen 771C Quarry Truck vor, der mit einem anderen Getriebe und einer größeren Mulde ausgestattet ist. Er reduziert die Transportkosten auf ein Minimum.

Ein weiterer Meilenstein in der Geschichte des Muldenkipperbaus bei Caterpillar war 1990 die Einführung des Cat 793. Mit einer Nutzlast von 218 t und einer Motorleistung von 2.057 PS ist er der größte mechanisch angetriebene Muldenkipper der Welt. Der größte von allen aber ist der aktuelle Muldenkipper 797 in der 340- bis 360 t-Klasse mit einem Gesamtgewicht von 555.990 kg und 3.400 PS.

CATERPILLAR **769**

A sales brochure from 1964 shows Caterpillar's first truck, the 769.

Der Verkaufsprospekt aus dem Jahr 1964 zeigt Caterpillars ersten Muldenkipper, den 769.

DER CATERPILLAR MULDENKIPPER 769

* Caterpillar Dieselmotor mit 400 PS Schwungscheibenleistung und Einspritz-verstellung, - schnellansprechend, robust und wirtschaftlich.

* Caterpillar Power-Shift Antrieb mit Differentialwandler und drei automatischen Schaltstufen in jedem Gangbereich. Spitzengeschwindigkeit 66,8 km/h.

* Caterpillar Öllamellenbremsen zum Halten oder Verzögern des Fahrzeuges,-aussergewöhnlich dauerhaft und vollständig nachstellungsfrei.

* Unabhängige Einzelradaufhängung durch Ölluftzylinder, die Stosslasten beim Beladen und Fahren absorbieren.

* Kippmulde aus hochwertigem Stahl mit Abgasbeheizung, - daher bei allen Materialien sauber entleerbar.

* Fahrersitz mit Luftfederung für gesteigerten Fahrkomfort und höhere Arbeitsleistung.

This original Caterpillar 769 (99F) was built between 1962 and 1967. With a load capacity of 35 tons the truck reaches a travel speed up to 41.5 mph. It is powered by a Cat 6-cylinder diesel engine with a displacement of 892 in³ and 400 hp. After 33 years in a rough quarry this Cat truck was still at work in 1998.

Der Original Caterpillar 769 (99F) wurde von 1962 bis 1967 gebaut. Mit einer Ladekapazität von 31,8 t erreicht der Muldenkipper eine Höchstgeschwindigkeit von 66,8 km/h. Er wird angetrieben durch einen Cat 6-Zyl.-Diesel-Motor mit 14,6 l Hubraum und 400 PS. Dieser Cat-Muldenkipper war 1998 noch im Einsatz, nach mehr als 33 Jahren im harten Steinbruchbetrieb.

This is a very early model of the Caterpillar 769B (99F). The B-series was built between 1967 and 1978. The power increased to 415 hp and and the weight to 61,800 lb. The early models had a ladder at the back of the cab to climb into. But here you can see, that on this Caterpillar 769B truck the ladder is mounted in front near the radiator. Resulted with the new V-shaped dump body is a higher load capacity and lower loading height.

Eine sehr frühe Ausführung des Cat 769B (99F). Gebaut wurde die B-Serie von 1967 bis 1978 mit 415 PS und einem Gewicht von 28.000 kg. Bei früheren Modellen war der Aufstieg hinter dem Fahrerhaus. Auf dem Bild kann man gut erkennen, daß der Aufstieg an diesem 769B Muldenkipper nach vorn neben den Kühler verlegt wurde. Auch die Mulde wurde neu überarbeitet: mit einem V-förmigen Muldenboden ergibt sich eine größere Ladefläche bei niedriger Ladehöhe.

The later Caterpillar 769B (99F) has two ladders in front to climb into the cab: on the left and on the right side of the radiator. The picture shows a fleet of Cat 769B trucks on a highway project in Southern Germany.

Der neuere Caterpillar 769B (99F) besitzt jetzt zwei Aufstiegsmöglichkeiten: jeweils links und rechts vom Motor. Das Bild zeigt Cat 769B Muldenkipper auf einer Autobahnbaustelle in Deutschland.

A Caterpillar 769B (99F) truck. With a length of 25'58" it only needs 52'48" for a full turning cycle. The oil-pneumatic suspension absorbs haul road and loading shocks. This allows a maximum travel speed of 42.8 mph.

Ein Caterpillar 769B (99F) Muldenkipper. Trotz einer Länge von 7.800 mm hat er einen Wendekreis von nur 16.000 mm. Dank ölpneumatischer Aufhängung, die die Stoßbelastung beim Beladen und auf der Transportstrecke absorbiert, können Geschwindigkeiten von max. 69 km/h erreicht werden.

A Caterpillar 769B (99F) on the dump site. Since the introduction of the trucks, Cat has used fully closed, oil-cooled disc brakes, build for a life time.

Ein Caterpillar 769B (99F) auf der Entladestelle. Schon damals wurden serienmäßig vollständig abgedichtete, ölgekühlte Scheibenbremsen verwendet, die für eine lange Lebensdauer ausgelegt waren.

Two Caterpillar 769B (99F) water wagons with a capacity of 7926 US gallons are used to spray water on haul roads to reduce the dust in an iron ore mine in Spain.

Zwei Caterpillar 769B (99F) Wassertanker mit einem Inhalt von 30.000 l werden eingesetzt, um die Staubentwicklung auf der Fahrbahn in einer großen Erzmine in Spanien zu reduzieren.

In 1978 Caterpillar introduced the new 769C (01X) truck. It is powered by a Cat 3408 TA V8 turbo engine with a displacement of 1098 in³ and 450 hp.

1978 wurde der neue 769C (01X) Muldenkipper vorgestellt. Er wird angetrieben durch einen Cat 3408 TA V8-Turbo-Motor mit 18 l Hubraum und 450 PS.

This Caterpillar 245B II FS, equipped with a 5 yd³ shovel, needs only 6-cycles to load a Cat 769C (01X) truck with a capacity of 40 tons.

In sechs Arbeitstakten belädt dieser Cat 245B II FS, mit einer 3,8 m³ Kippschaufel ausgerüstet, den Cat 769C (01X) Muldenkipper mit einer Nutzlast von 37 t.

Two new Caterpillar 769C (01X05416), built in 1990, are equipped with the new body design and sideboard extensions.

Zwei neue Caterpillar 769C (01X05416), Baujahr 1990 sind ausgestattet mit der neuen Muldenform und einer Bordwanderhöhung.

Caterpillar 769C (01X) dumps its 40 tons of limestone into a crusher. With the body fully rised the top reaches 25'19" from the ground. The production stopped when the D-series was introduced in 1996.

Ein Caterpillar 769C (01X) kippt seine 37 t Kalkstein in den Brecher. Bei voll angehobener Mulde sind es vom Boden bis zum Muldenende 7.680 mm. Das Produktionsende kam mit der Einführung der D-Serie 1996.

A picture out of a current sales brochure from Caterpillar Elphinstone shows one of three trucks for the underground mine operation. This 69D with a capacity of 42 tons is powered by a Caterpillar 3408E HEUI V8 turbo engine rated at 510 hp.

Ein Bild aus dem aktuellen Verkaufsprospekt von Caterpillar Elphinstone zeigt einen von drei Muldenkippern für den Untertage-Minenbetrieb. Dieser 69D mit 38 t Nutzlast wird von einem Caterpillar 3408E HEUI V8-Turbo-Motor mit 510 PS angetrieben.

The 40 tons class Caterpillar 769D is powered by a Cat 3408E turbo engine with 503 hp. It is equipped with an automatic Caterpillar planetary power shift transmission which is controlled by an electronical and hydraulical system. The full loaded Cat 769D truck reaches a top speed of 46.7 mph in the 7th gear.

Der Caterpillar 769D mit 37 t Nutzlast und einem 503 PS starken Cat 3408E-Turbo-Motor. Ausgestattet mit einem automatischen Caterpillar Planeten-Last-Schaltgetriebe mit elektronisch-hydraulischer Steuerung erreicht der vollbeladene Cat 769D Muldenkipper im siebten Gang eine Höchstgeschwindigkeit von 75,2 km/h.

A Caterpillar 980G wheel loader loads a Cat 769D truck in 4-5 cycles.

Ein Caterpillar 980G Radlader lädt den Cat 769D Muldenkipper in vier bis fünf Arbeitsspielen.

A 480 hp Caterpillar 771C (3BJ) Quarry Truck: the main difference to the similar Cat 769C is in the bigger and flatter 44 tons capacity dump-body, built with HARDOX 400 BHN steel. The truck is just equipped with a 5-speed transmission and reaches max. 25 mph. That results in really low costs per ton.

Der Caterpillar 771C (3BJ) Quarry Truck: Der Hauptunterschied zum bauartgleichen Cat 769C liegt in der neuen, größeren und flacheren Mulde, die mit HARDOX-400 ausgekleidet ist und nun 40 t faßt. Man beschränkt sich auf ein 5-Gang-Getriebe mit dem max. 40,3 km/h erreicht werden. So werden die niedrigsten Kosten pro Tonne erreicht.

Zeppelins best instructors are giving an interview on the new Cat 771D Quarry Truck at the SteinExpo 1996

Zeppelin's "Top"-Vorführer geben während der SteinExpo 1996 einer Reporterin ein Interview über den neuen 771D Quarry Truck.

A Caterpillar 350 L ME loads a 44 tons capacity Cat 771D truck in 6-7 cycles. Caterpillar's automatic, electronic anti tire slippeach system improves even under the worst underfoot conditions traction and it increases the gradient.

Ein Caterpillar 350 L ME lädt einen Cat 771D Muldenkipper mit 40 t Nutzlast in sechs bis sieben Arbeitsspielen. Caterpillars automatische Antischlupfregelung gewährleistet auch bei schwierigsten Bodenverhältnissen ein Vorwärtskommen und verbessert die Steigfähigkeit.

A Caterpillar 771D and a Cat 350 L ME excavator, with an operating weight of 115,762 lb, are working in a lava quarry near Koblenz/Germany.

Dieses Paar, ein Caterpillar 771D und ein Cat 350 L ME Hydraulikbagger mit einem Einsatzgewicht von 52.500 kg, wird in einem Lavasteinbruch in der Nähe von Koblenz/Deutschland eingesetzt.

Because of the good operator station with an excellent overview you can good manoeuver the Caterpillar 771D Quarry Truck with 503 hp and a width of 14'6" and a length of 27' 53" even in narrow spaces.

Dank eines hervorragend ausgestatteten Fahrerhauses mit einer sehr guten Rundumsicht kann der Caterpillar 771D Quarry Truck mit 503 PS und einer Breite von 4.448 mm sowie einer Länge von 8.700 mm auch auf engstem Raum gut manövriert werden.

CATERPILLAR 773

Truck

This sales brochures from 1975 shows the big brother of the Caterpillar 769.

Ein Verkaufsprospekt von 1975 zeigt den großen Bruder des Caterpillar 769.

Summary of features

50 tons (45.4 t) capacity . . . dual-slope body with V-bottom provides large target, low loading height . . . exhaust heating standard.

Oil-cooled disc brakes resist fading . . . completely sealed and require no periodic adjustment.

Oil-pneumatic suspension absorbs loading and haul road shocks. Four independent, self-contained, Caterpillar-designed-and-built cylinders.

Cat diesel engine delivers 600 flywheel horsepower . . . low loaded-vehicle-weight-to-HP ratio.

Power shift transmission shifts automatically in three speed ranges to give nine forward speeds.

Cat engine

Flywheel horsepower @ 1900 RPM	600
Kilowatts	447

(Kilowatt (kW) is the International System of Units equivalent of horsepower.)

The net power at the flywheel of the vehicle engine operating under SAE standard ambient temperature and barometric conditions, 85° F. (29° C) and 29.38" Hg (99 kPa), using 35 API gravity fuel oil at 60° F. (15.6° C). Vehicle engine equipment includes fan, air cleaner, water pump, lubricating oil pump, fuel pump, air compressor and alternator. Engine will maintain specified power up to 5,000 ft. (1500 m) altitude.   *1 hPa = 0.01 bar*

That was a really fine day in Spain in 1997 when I saw my first Caterpillar 773 (63G). It was built from 1970 to 1978.

Es war für mich ein guter Tag, als ich 1997 meinen ersten Caterpillar 773 (63G) in Spanien gesehen habe. Gebaut wurde dieser Typ von 1970 bis 1978.

This Caterpillar 773B (63W02345), standing loaded with 60 tons in front of the crusher, was built in 1988. The maximum gross vehicle weight goes up to 204,028 lb. It is powered by a Cat 3412 V12 twin turbo engine with a displacement of 1647 in^3 and 650 hp.

Dieser Caterpillar 773B (63W02345), Baujahr 1988, steht mit 60 t beladen vor dem Brecher. Das max. Fahrzeuggewicht beträgt 92.530 kg. Angetrieben wird der Muldenkipper durch einen Cat 3412 V12 Bi-Turbo-Motor mit 27 l Hubraum und 650 PS.

A Caterpillar 773B (63W) is equipped with a water tank with 13210 US gallons capacity. It works in a uranium mine. When the haul roads and the loading area are irrigated with waterthe dust development is reduced drastically, This means more safety for all the operators.

Der Caterpillar 773B (63W) ist mit einem 50.000 l Wassertank ausgerüstet. Er wird in einer Uranmine eingesetzt. Durch das Bewässern der Fahrbahn und des Haufwerkes wird die Staubentrwicklung drastisch reduziert. Das bedeutet bessere Sicht und mehr Sicherheit für die Fahrer.

Two Caterpillar 773B (63W) watertankers cool down the glowing waste rock pile in a uranium mine for better loading by a Cat 992D HL.

Zwei Caterpillar 773B (63W) kühlen das stellenweise glühende Haldenmaterial in einer Uranmine herunter, damit es die Cat 992D HL besser laden kann.

This Caterpillar 245 FS loads a 60 tons class Cat 773B truck in only 6-cycles. You can reach an hourly loadig production of 600-700 tons.

Ein Caterpillar 245 FS lädt einen Cat 773B Muldenkipper der 60 t Klasse in nur sechs Arbeitsspielen. Somit erreicht man eine stündliche Ladeleistung von 600 bis 700 t.

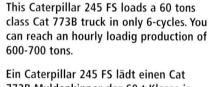

This Caterpillar 5130B needs only 3-4 cycles to load unblasted limestone into a Cat 773B with a capacity of 60 tons. In 1995 the production of the 773B came to its end and it was replaced by the Cat 773D.

Mit nur drei bis vier Arbeitstakten lädt dieser Caterpillar 5130B ungesprengten Kalkstein auf einen Cat 773B mit 55 t Nutzlast. 1995 kam das Produktionsende des Cat 773B. Er wurde ersetzt durch den Cat 773D.

In 1992 Caterpillar introduced its second Quarry Truck, the 775B (7XJ) with 650 hp and a capacity of 65 tons. The picture shows the Cat 775D with 693 hp. It was introduced in 1995.

1992 wurde der zweite Quarry Truck, der Caterpillar 775B (7XJ) mit 650 PS und einer Nutzlast von 60 t vorgestellt. Das Bild zeigt den Cat 775D mit 693 PS. Er wurde 1995 vorgestellt.

Caterpillar's third biggest truck from the seventies was the Cat 777 with 85-tons capacity. It is powered by a Cat D348 V12 twin turbo engine with 870 hp. This Cat 777 (84A) was built in 1984. It clocked up 40 000 hours and transported approx. ten million tons of rock during the last 15 years.

Caterpillars drittgrößter Muldenkipper aus den 70-ern war der Cat 777 mit 77 t Nutzlast. Er wird von einem Cat D348 V12-Bi-Turbo-Motor mit 870 PS angetrieben. Dieser Cat 777 (84A), Baujahr 1984, ist noch heute im Einsatz in einem Steinbruch in Deutschland. Mit 40.000 Betriebsstunden hat er ca. 10 mio/t Fels in den letzten 15 Jahren transportiert.

This Cat 777B (4YC) is transported on a heavy flatbed trailer to its final destination in a big limestone quarry.

Ein Cat 777B (4YC) wird mit einem Schwerlasttieflader auf der Autobahn zu seinem Bestimmungsort in einen großen Kalksteinbruch gebracht.

The transportation weight of this 1991 Caterpillar 777B (4YC), amounts 99,531 lb. For the transportation of the 31,311 lb and 29'48" long dump-body a second flatbed trailer was needed.

Das Transportgewicht dieses Cat 777B (4YC), Baujahr 1991, beträgt 45.139 kg bei einer Breite von 5.064 mm. Für die 14.200 kg schwere und 8.990 mm lange Mulde wurde noch ein zweiter Tieflader benötigt.

I was just in time to take some photos of this excellent Caterpillar 777B (4YC) near Whitehorse/Canada. The trailer was just ready to move.

In der Nähe von Whitehorse/Canada kam ich gerade noch rechtzeitig, um ein paar Bilder von diesem schönen Caterpillar 777B (4YC) zu machen, der Tieflader war bereits startklar für die Weiterfahrt.

With a loading height of 13'66" the Caterpillar 777B (4YC) can be loaded by a 988B HL (high lift) Cat wheel loader.

Mit einer Bordwandhöhe von 4.166 mm kann der Cat 777B (4YC) durch einen Cat Radlader 988B HL (high lift) beladen werden.

Caterpillar offers today a line of three different hauling units to pull big bottom dump trailers. The biggest is the Cat 784C with 1450 hp. (Caterpillar Inc.) Caterpillar bietet heute drei verschiedene Zugmaschinen zum Ziehen großer Hänger an, die zum Boden hin entleeren. Der größte ist der Cat 784C mit 1.450 PS. (Caterpillar Inc.)

A fleet of four Caterpillar 777C (4XJ) trucks is standing idle during the shift change. The Cat was built between 1992 and 1996.

Eine Flotte von vier Caterpillar 777C (4XJ) Muldenkippern stehen beim Schichtwechsel. Sie wurden von 1992 bis 1996 gebaut.

The new Caterpillar 777D with a capacity of 100 tons is loaded with limestone by a Cat 990 HL in 6-7 cycles.

Der neue Caterpillar 777D mit einer Nutzlast von 96 t wird in sechs bis sieben Arbeitstakten von einem Cat 990 HL mit Kalkstein beladen.

The Cat 777D is equipped with a new 972 hp Cat 3508B V8 twin turbo engine with two inlet and exhaust valves per cylinder and an electronic unit injection (EUI). The maximum gross vehicle weight goes up to 355,000 lb. You can reach a considerable top speed of 37.5 mph in the seventh gear.

Der neue Cat 3508B V8-Motor mit 4-Ventil-Technik und elektronischem Hochdruckeinspritzsystem leistet im Caterpillar 777D 972 PS. Das zulässige Gesamtgewicht beträgt 161.028 kg. Im siebten Gang wird eine Geschwindigkeit von 60,4 km/h erreicht.

A sales brochure from 1968 shows one of the three "super" trucks from Caterpillar with a diesel-electric drive train. It was introduced in 1965. In 1969 the developement of diesel-electric powered trucks was stopped.

Der Verkaufsprospekt aus dem Jahr 1968 zeigt einen der drei "Super"-Mulden-kipper von Caterpillar, die 1965 vorge-stellt wurden und mit einem dieselelek-trischen Antrieb ausgerüstet waren. Nach 1969 wurde die Entwicklung für diesel-elektrisch angetriebene Muldenkipper eingestellt.

CATERPILLAR **779**

Low loaded weight/horsepower ratio, high speed hauling and continuous downhill braking capabilities for low cost per ton-mile.

Two optional bodies designed to match material requirements and job application.

85 Ton average capacity bodies with large target area and low center of gravity. Exhaust heated.

960 HP Cat diesel engine featuring dual turbocharging, air-to-air aftercooling, automatic fuel injection timing advance and positive response hydraulic governor.

Cat electric drive, designed specifically for Cat engine, is efficient and simple to operate, easily accessible, and has excellent cooling.

Additional features: oil-cooled non-fade disc brakes, oil-pneumatic suspension, safety hydraulic steering and brake systems, and elimination of all daily grease points.

The first Caterpillar 785 (8GB) with a capacity of 136 tons and an engine power rating of 1290 hp was introduced in 1985. It was replaced by the new B-series in 1992. The picture shows a fully loaded Cat 785B (6HK) with a gross weight of 550,103 lb.

Der erste Caterpillar 785 (8GB) mit einer Nutzlast von 136 t und einer Motor-lei-stung von 1.290 PS wurde 1985 vorge-stellt und blieb bis 1992 im Programm. Das Bild zeigt einen voll beladenen 249.480 kg schweren Cat 785B (6HK).

Caterpillar's biggest loader, the 994, loads a Cat 785B (6HK) in 4-cycles. There are about 25 trucks loaded per hour. So the production amounts 2700-3600 tons per hour. Powered is the Cat 785B (6HK) by a Cat 3512 EUI twin turbo engine with a displacement of 3159 in³ rated at 1290 hp. At the end of 1998 the 785C truck was introduced.

Caterpillars größter Radlader, der 994, lädt einen Cat 785B (6HK) in vier Arbeitstakten. Bei 25 Muldenkipper-Ladungen in einer Stunde beträgt die Stundenleistung 2.700 bis 3.600 t. Angetrieben wird der Cat 785B (6HK) durch einen Cat 3512 EUI Bi-Turbo-Motor mit 51,8 l Hubraum und 1.290 PS. Ende 1998 wird der 785C Muldenkipper vorgestellt.

In 1986 the Caterpillar 789 (9ZC) with 1705 hp and a capacity of 195 tons was introduced. The improved Cat 789B (7EK) came in 1992. The picture shows a fully loaded Cat 789B (7EK) with a gross vehicle weight of 700,131 lb.

1986 wurde der Caterpillar 789 (9ZC) mit 1.705 PS und 177 t Nutzlast vorgestellt, 1992 der überarbeitete Cat 789B (7EK). Das Bild zeigt einen voll beladenen Cat 789B (7EK) mit 317.520 kg Gesamtgewicht.

In a big iron ore mine a Caterpillar 994 loads a 195 tons truck, the Cat 789B (7EK), in 5-6 cycles. It is powered by a Cat 3516 EUI V16 twin turbo engine with a displacement of 4209 in³. The new C-series was offered by the end of 1998.

In einer großen Erzmine lädt der Caterpillar 994 den 177 t-Muldenkipper 789B (7EK) mit fünf bis sechs Arbeitstakten. Er wird angetrieben durch einen Cat 3516 EUI V16-Bi-Turbo-Motor mit 69 l Hubraum. Ende 1998 wurde die neue C-Serie präsentiert.

A fully loaded Caterpillar 789B (7EK) with a gross vehicle weight of 700,131 lb reaches a top speed of 33.8 mph in the sixth gear. The Caterpillar trucks are built in a special plant in Decatur/Illinois.

Mit einem Gesamtgewicht von 317.520 kg erreicht ein vollbeladener Caterpillar 789B (7EK) im sechsten Gang eine Geschwindigkeit von 54,4 km/h. Diese Cat-Muldenkipper werden in einem eigens dafür errichteten Werk in Decatur/Illinois gebaut.

The first "super" truck the Caterpillar 793 (3SJ) was introduced in 1990. In 1992 the Cat 793B (1HL) followed, and the current Cat 793C came in the mid of 1996. The 793 would be the world`s largest mechanical driven truck, but Caterpillar developed an even bigger one, the 797 truck with a Cat 3524BTA engine with 24-cylinder and 4 turbo chargers, the displacement went up to 7137 in^3 and the power output was 3400 hp. With a loading capacity of 340-360 tons and a gross vehicle weighed up to 1,230,000 lb this Caterpillar "super" truck is the biggest in the world. (Caterpillar Inc.) It has broken the capacity record held by the Terer Titan since 1972.

Der erste "Super"-Muldenkipper wurde 1990 mit dem Caterpillar 793 (3SJ) vorgestellt. 1992 folgte der Cat 793B (1HL) und Mitte 1996 kam der Cat 793C. Der 793 wäre der größte mechanisch angetriebene Muldenkipper der Welt, hätte Caterpillar nicht noch einen größeren, den 797 entwickelt. Mit einem Cat 3524BTA mit 24-Zyl.und 4 Turboladern sowie 117 l Hubraum leistet der Motor 3.400 PS. Mit einer Nutzlast von 340 bis 360 t und einem Gesamtgewicht von 555.990 kg ist Caterpillars "Super"-Muldenkipper 797 wieder der größte mechanisch angetriebene Muldenkipper der Welt. (Caterpillar Inc.) Er hat damit den seit 1972 vom Terer Titan gehaltenen Nutzlast Rekord gebrochen.

Articulated Trucks

With Caterpillar's introduction of the DW15 and DW20 wheel tractors, the history of the articulated trucks began. These early articulated dump trucks of course didn't have the same look as their successors today. The Athey Company developed special one axle rear dumps, which were connected to the hitch of the Caterpillar DW15 and DW20 wheel tractors. Caterpillar introduced his first articulated DW21 scraper in 1951, which was the basic for building further articulated trucks. The Cat 621, 631 und 651 scrapers could be changed to an Athey rear dump PR621 with 30 tons, PR631 with 40 tons as the biggest PR651 with 60 tons capacity.

The DJB Engineering Ltd. company from Peterlee, UK, was established in 1973 on an area of 296,010 ft^2 and began to build modern looking articulated dump trucks. In 1975 DJB introduced its first ADT (articulated dump truck), the D250, followed one year later by the D300. Each ADT was equipped with Caterpillar engines, transmissions and axles. The DJB trucks often were sold and serviced by the Caterpillar dealers. In 1985 Caterpillar acquired the DJB Engineering Ltd Company. Today Caterpillar builds 2-axle and four 3-axle articulated dump trucks in the Peterlee plant. Because of the low loading height you can load the trucks with different loading tools. Even smaller loaders can load the ADT without problems. Articulated dump trucks are mainly used on earth moving sites. Because of the articulation, the 6x4 or all wheel drive an articulated dump truck can run on soft or muddy ground without boging down. The most efficient hauling distance (one way) for the ADT is between 300 ft and 4.000 ft, for off-highway trucks 300 ft and 26.000 ft.

Mit Caterpillars Einführung der DW15 und DW20 Radtraktoren beginnt auch die Geschichte der Caterpillar Dumper. Natür-lich sahen die damaligen Dumper etwas anders aus als heutzutage. Die Firma Athey entwickelte spezielle Ein-Achs-Hinterkipper, die man an der Kupplung des Caterpillar DW15/20 Radtraktors anhängen konnte. Als Caterpillar 1951 seinen ersten knickgelenkten Scraper DW21 vorstellte, war das Pendant für den weiteren Dumperbau geschaffen. Mit der Einführung der Cat 621, 631 und 651 Scraper konnte man statt des Scrapers Athey Hinterkipper PR621 mit 30 t, PR631 mit 40 t oder den größten PR651 mit 60 t Nutzlast bestellen.

Die Firma DJB Engineering Ltd. wurde 1973 in Peterlee/Großbritannien gegründet. Auf einer Fläche von 27.500 m^2 wurden die ersten knickgelenkten Dumper, wie wir sie heute kennen, gebaut. 1975 stellte DJB den D250 vor, ihm folgte ein Jahr später der D300. DJB baute in alle Dumper Motoren, Getriebe und Achsen von Caterpillar ein. Oft wurden die ersten DJB Dumper von den Caterpillar-Händlern vertrieben und gewartet. 1985 übernahm Caterpillar die Firma DJB Engineering Ltd. zu 100 Prozent. Heute werden zwei 2-Achs- und vier 3-Achs-Dumpermodelle im Caterpillar Werk in Peterlee gebaut. Durch eine niedrige Ladehöhe können die Caterpillar Dumper durch verschiedenste, auch kleinere Ladegeräte, problemlos beladen werden. Haupteinsatzgebiet des Dumpers sind Erdbaustellen, wo sie dank Knicklenkung, 6x4 oder Allradantrieb auch bei sehr nassem oder schlammigem Untergrund eingesetzt werden können, ohne gleich steckenzubleiben. Die wirtschaftlichste Transportentfernung (einfach) des Dumpers liegt zwischen 100 m und 1.200 m, die des Starr-Rahmen-Muldenkippers von 100 m bis 8.000 m.

A Caterpillar rear dump 613A (71M) with 15.7 yd³ capacity and a length of 27'35" works on a tunnel project in Switzerland. The tractor unit Cat 613 with 150 hp was built from 1969 to 1976.

Ein Hinterkipper 613A (71M) mit 12 m³-Mulde und einer Länge von 8.340 mm auf einer Tunnelbaustelle in der Schweiz. Die Traktoreinheit Cat 613 mit 150 PS wurde von 1969 bis 1976 gebaut.

An Athey model PR621 (43H/23H) rocker with 30 tons capacity is powered by a Cat V8 turbo engine with a displacement of 902 in³ and 300 hp. This type was built from 1965 to 1974.

Ein Athey PR621 (43H/23H) Rocker mit 30 t Nutzlast wird von einem Cat V8 Turbo-Motor mit 14,8 l Hubraum und 300 PS angetrieben. Dieser Typ wurde von 1965 bis 1974 gebaut.

This Athey PR621 (43H/23H) rocker is still working in a gravel pit in Switzerland. With a gross vehicle weight of 121,936 lb, equipped with an 8 gear power shift transmission, the PR621 reaches a top speed of 31 mph.

Dieser Athey PR621 (43H/23H) Rocker wird in einem Kieswerk in der Schweiz eingesetzt. Mit 55.300 kg Gesamtgewicht erreicht der PR621, ausgestattet mit einem 8-Gang-Getriebe, eine Höchstgeschwindigkeit von max. 50 km/h.

This Athey PR631 rear dump with 360 hp
has a 11'74" width and a 15'31" long
dump body with a capacity of 40 tons. He
can easily be loaded by a big shovel. The
complete "train" is 36'08" long and
weighs empty 64,013 lb.

Ein Athey PR631 Hinterkipper mit
360 PS und 40 t Nutzlast kann dank seiner 3.580 mm breiten und 4.670 mm langen Mulde problemlos durch einen großen Hochlöffelbagger beladen werden.
Der komplette Zug ist 11.000 mm lang
und wiegt leer 29.000 kg.

You can see the enormous size of this
Athey PR631 in comparison with the
service wagon. The turning cycle with
raised dump body is only 30'.

Man kann nun die Größe des Athey
PR631 im Vergleich zu dem Servicewagen
gut erkennen. Der Wendekreis mit
angehobener Mulde beträgt gerade
mal 9.140 mm.

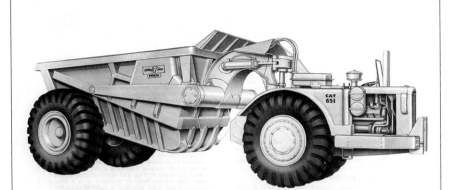

60 TON CAPACITY REAR DUMP *Athey* **PR651 REAR DUMP**

FOR CATERPILLAR* 651 TWO WHEEL TRACTOR

A sales brochure of the Athey Company product line shows the biggest rear dump, the PR651, with an empty weight of 87,615 lb.

Ein Verkaufsprospekt der Firma Athey zeigt den größten Hinterkipper PR651 aus der Produktlinie mit einem Leergewicht von 39.735 kg.

NEW ATHEY FEATURES
60 TON CAPACITY BODY
HIGH STRENGTH STEEL
CONSTRUCTION

NEW CATERPILLAR FEATURES
560 HP (MAXIMUM) ENGINE
POWER SHIFT TRANSMISSION

NEW SPEED, PERFORMANCE AND HANDLING EASE

The smallest DJB was the D22 dump truck with 20 tons capacity, powered by a Cat 3306T turbo engine with a displacement of 640 in³ and the power rated up to 235 hp. The picture was taken on a tunnel project in the Switzerland in 1996.

Der kleinste DJB war der D22 Dumper mit 18 t Nutzlast. Er wird angetrieben durch einen Cat 3306T 6-Zyl.-Turbo-Motor mit 10,5 l Hubraum und 235 PS. Das Bild entstand 1996 auf einer Tunnelbaustelle in der Schweiz.

Two DSD D22 dump trucks are standing on a construction site. They are equipped with the transmissions of the Cat 980B. That allows a top speed of 27.3 mph in the fourth gear. The DJB D22 was built between 1980 and 1982.

Zwei DJB D22 Dumper stehen auf einer Baustelle. Mit dem Getriebe, das von der Cat 980B stammt, kann eine max. Geschwindigkeit von 44 km/h im vierten Gang erreicht werden. Der DJB D22 wurde von 1980 bis 1982 gebaut.

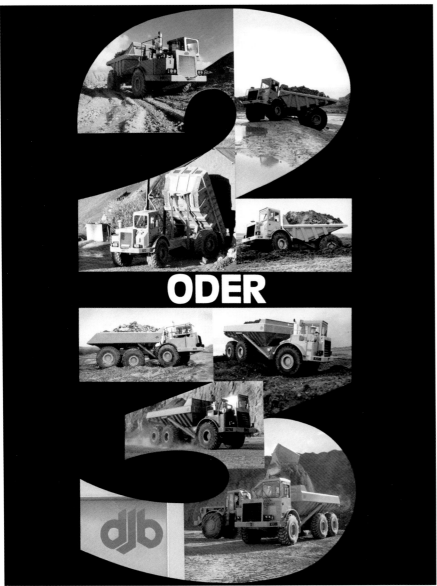

ODER

This is a sales brochure from the DJB Engineering Ltd Company. It was established in Peterlee/U.K. in 1973.

Ein Verkaufsprospekt der Firma DJB Engineering Ltd., die 1973 in Peterlee/Großbritannien gegründet wurde.

DJB D25 with 235 hp was built between 1979 and 1980. The construction nearly had been identical with the DJB D22 dump truck. Successor was the B-series. The picture shows a Caterpillar D25C (9YC00011) dump truck with 260 hp and 25-tons capacity. It was built in 1988. The C-series was built from 1985 to 1989.

1980, nach nur einem Jahr, kam das Produktionsende für den DJB D25 mit 235 PS, der fast baugleich mit dem DJB D22 war. Nachfolger wurde die B-Serie. Das Bild zeigt einen Caterpillar D25C (9YC00011) Dumper, Baujahr 1988, mit nun 260 PS und 22,7 t Nutzlast. Gebaut wurde die C-Serie von 1985 bis 1989.

This Caterpillar D25C dump truck works in an underground gypsum mine. The current model is the Cat D25D with 260 hp.

Dieser Caterpillar D25C Dumper wird in einer Untertagemine für die Gipsgewinnung eingesetzt. Das aktuelle Modell ist der Cat D25D mit 260 PS.

This Caterpillar D30D with a capacity of
30 tons works in the Netherlands. It is
powered by a Cat 3306 6-cylinder turbo
engine with 300 hp. The former model
was the Cat D30C (7ZC). It was in the
sales lists from 1985 to 1989. The next
bigger dump truck was the DJB D35 with
255 hp and a load capacity of 35 tons. It
was built between 1981 and 1983. After
the takeover by Caterpillar in 1985 the
D35C/D35 HP was built until 1989.

In den Niederlanden arbeitet dieser
Caterpillar D30D mit einer Nutzlast von
27,5 t. Er wird angetrieben von einem
Cat 3306 6-Zyl.-Turbo-Motor mit 300 PS.
Vorgänger war der Cat D30C (7ZC), er
stand von 1985 bis 1989 in der Verkaufsliste. Der nächstgrößere Dumper, der DJB
D35 mit 255 PS und einer Nutzlast von
31,8 t, wurde von 1981 bis 1983 gebaut.
Nach der Übernahme von Caterpillar
1985 wurde der D35C/D35 HP noch bis
1989 hergestellt.

A new Caterpillar D40D (2JJ) with 385 hp
and a capacity of 40 tons, built in 1993.
The fully loaded Caterpillar D40D dump
truck weighs up to 141,781 lb and reaches a travel speed of 34.4 mph. The
32'02" long dump truck has a tight turning circle of only 24'6". It was built
from 1989 to 1994.

Ein neuer Caterpillar D40D (2JJ), Baujahr
1993, mit 385 PS und einer Nutzlast von
36,3 t. Der vollbeladene Cat D40D Dumper wiegt 64.300 kg und erreicht im vierten Gang eine Höchstgeschwindigkeit
von 55,4 km/h. Der 9.765 mm lange
Dumper hat einen Wendekreis von nur
7.500 mm und wurde von 1989 bis 1994
gebaut.

A sales brochure from Caterpillar Elphinstone shows one of the two current
dump trucks for underground mining. This
490 hp AD40 II is built for a capacity of
48 tons. The whole truck is only 8'85"
high but 34'25" long.

Ein Verkaufsprospekt von Caterpillar
Elphinstone zeigt einen der zwei Dumper
für den Untertagebetrieb. Dieser 490 PS
starke AD40 II ist für eine Nutzlast von
44 t ausgelegt. Die Fahrzeughöhe beträgt
nur 2.700 mm bei einer Länge von
10.443 mm.

The biggest 2-axle dump truck from
DJB was the model D44 with 450 hp and
a capacity of 44 tons. For more than
13 years this DJB D44 has been working
in a limestone quarry in Switzerland.
It is loaded by a Cat 988F II.

Der größte 2-Achs-Dumper von DJB war
der D44 mit 450 PS und einer Nutzlast
von 40 t. Seit mehr als 13 Jahren ist
dieser DJB D44 in einem Kalksteinbruch
in der Schweiz in Betrieb. Er wird von
einem Cat 988F II beladen.

The DJB D44 is powered by a Caterpillar
3408TA V8 turbo engine with a displacement of 1098 in³. Because of an hydraulic
suspension system the dump truck reaches a top speed of 30 mph. It was built
from 1981 to 1986 and was replaced by
the Cat B-series, which was in the sales
lists until 1987.

Der DJB D44 wird von einem Caterpillar
3408TA V8-Turbo-Motor mit 18 l Hubraum
angetrieben. Dank des hydropneumati-
schen Dämpfungssystems werden Geschwindigkeiten von 48 km/h erreicht.
Er wurde von 1981 bis 1986 gebaut und
durch die Cat B-Serie abgelöst.

The DJB D250 with 235 hp and a load capacity of 27.5 tons was the first dump truck built by DJB Engineering Ltd in 1975. Today this DJB D250 is still at work as a water wagon for a big company in the Netherlands. The production stopped in 1978. Successor was the DJB 275/275B, built until 1982.

Der DJB D250 mit 235 PS und einer Nutzlast von 25 t war der erste Dumper, den DJB Engineering Ltd. 1975 vorstellte. Mit einem Wassertank ausgerüstet ist dieser DJB D250 noch heute bei einer niederländischen Firma im Einsatz. Die Produktion dieses Typs wurde 1978 eingestellt. Nachfolger wurde der DJB 275/275B. Er wurde bis 1982 gebaut.

Successor of the DJB D250 was in 1985 the Caterpillar D250B (5WD) with 218 hp and a capacity of 25 tons. You could order two different versions, 6x6 all-wheel drive or 6x4 permanent four-wheel drive. The D-series was built from 1992 to 1994.

Nachfolger des DJB D250 wurde 1985 der Caterpillar D250B (5WD) mit 218 PS und 22,7 t Nutzlast. Angeboten wurden zwei Versionen: 6x6 Allradantrieb oder 6x4 Vierradantrieb. Von 1992 bis 1994 wurde die D-Serie gebaut.

In 1995 the model changed from the D-series to the E-series. This Caterpillar D250E works in the Netherlands. It hauls coal and iron ore. It is powered by a Cat 3306 6-cylinder turbo engine with 279 hp and equipped with an automatic power shift transmission it reaches a top speed of 31.5 mph. in the fifth shift.

1995 erfolgte der Modellwechsel von der D-Serie zur E-Serie. Dieser Caterpillar D250E wird für den Kohle- und Erzumschlag in den Niederlanden eingesetzt. Angetrieben von einem Cat 3306 6-Zyl.-Turbo-Motor mit 279 PS wird mit dem automatischen Planeten-Last-Schaltgetriebe im fünften Gang eine Geschwindigkeit von 50,9 km/h erreicht.

A Caterpillar 375 ME hydraulic excavator loads a Cat D250E dump truck with 25 tons capacity in 3-cycles. The current model is the Cat D250E II.

Ein Caterpillar 375 ME Hydraulikbagger lädt einen Cat D250E Dumper mit 22,7 t Nutzlast in drei Ladespielen. Das aktuelle Modell ist der Cat D250E II.

The second new dump truck model in 1976 was the DJB D300 with 255 hp and a capacity up to 33 tons. It was in the sales lists until 1978. This Caterpillar D300B (4SD) with 260 hp and a capacity of 30 tons works on the Alaska Highway in British Columbia/Canada.

Das zweite neue Dumper Modell 1976 war 1976 der DJB D300 mit 255 PS und 30 t Nutzlast. Er blieb bis 1978 im Programm. Dieser Cat D300B (4SD) mit 260 PS und einer Nutzlast von 27,2 t arbeitet in British Columbia/Kanada.

From 1985 to 1991 the Caterpillar dump truck D300B (4SD) was built. Because of the frame articulation and a permanent all-wheel drive the dump truck reaches a good traction in poor surface conditions.

Von 1985 - 1991 wurde der D300B (4SD) gebaut. Dank der Rahmen- Knicklenkung und des permanenten Allradantriebs ist auch bei schlechten Bodenverhältnissen eine gute Traktion gewährleistet.

A Caterpillar D300B (4SD) is equipped with a 65 yd³ container. In 1992 Caterpillar introduced the new D-series with now 285 hp.

Ein Caterpillar D300B (4SD), ausgestattet mit einer 50 m³ Mulde. Caterpillar stellt 1992 die neue D-Serie mit 285 PS vor.

In 1995 Caterpillar introduced the new E-series dump trucks with an ergonomically designed cab. This 295 hp Cat D300E is equipped with a specially built roll-on/roll-off system. It can change the different containers very fast to haul them to the different dump sites.

1995 wurde die neue E-Serie von Caterpillar mit einem ergonomisch gestalteten Fahrerhaus und rippenfreier Kippmulde vorgestellt, um nur einige Merkmale der neuen Generation aufzuzählen. Dieser 295 PS starke Cat D300E ist mit einem speziellen Hakenabrollsystem ausgestattet. So können verschiedenste Mulden aufgenommen und zur Entladestelle transportiert werden.

This Caterpillar D300E dump truck shows the construction of the roll-on/roll-off system. Only 11.5 sec. are needed to rise the fully loaded dump body and another 9 sec. to lower the body. This is the fastest dump time in its class.

An diesem D300E Dumper kann man gut die Unterkonstruktion des Hakenabrollsystems erkennen. In nur 11,5 sec. ist die voll beladene Mulde angehoben und in 9 sec. wieder gesenkt. Das ist die schnellste Zeit in dieser Klasse.

A Cat D300E is equipped with a tailgate. The load capacity reaches 30 tons. It is powered by a Cat 3306 turbo engine with a displacement of 640 in^3 and 295 hp. The current model is the Cat D300E II.

Ein Caterpillar D300E, ausgerüstet mit einer Heckklappe. Die Nutzlast beträgt 27,2 t. Angetrieben wird dieser Cat Dumper durch einen Cat 3306 Turbo-Motor mit 10,5 l Hubraum und 295 PS. Das aktuelle Modell ist der Cat D300E II.

The successor of the DJB D300 was the DJB D330 dump truck, introduced in 1978. In France I had the chance to take a photo of this DJB D330 with 255 hp and a loading capacity of 33 tons. That type was replaced by the DJB D330B in 1980, and it was built until 1983.

Der Nachfolger des DJB D300 war der DJB D330 Dumper, vorgestellt im Jahr 1978. In Frankreich konnte ich diesen DJB D330 Dumper mit 255 PS und einer Nutzlast von 30 t fotografieren. Abgelöst wurde er im Jahr 1980 durch den DJB D330B, der bis 1983 gebaut wurde.

The first DJB D350 was introduced in 1978 and was in the sales lists until 1980. An overhauled DJB D350B dump truck with 255 hp and a loading capacity of 35 tons is to be seen in a shipyard in Rotterdam/Netherlands. It was built between 1980 and 1983.

Der erste DJB D350 wurde 1978 vorgestellt und blieb bis 1980 in der Verkaufsliste. Hier ein überholter DJB D350B im Rotterdamer Hafen. Von 1980 bis 1983 wurde der 255 PS starke Dumper mit einer Nutzlast von 32 t gebaut.

This is another DJB D350B dump truck. It works on a construction site in the Netherlands. By request DJB offeres special dump trucks for underground mining, water wagons, pipe carriers, quarry dump trucks and U-frame trucks.

Ein anderer DJB 350B Dumper wird auf einer Baustelle in den Niederlanden eingesetzt. Auf Wunsch bietet DJB auch Spezialdumper für den Untertagebergbau, Wasserwägen, Röhrentransporter, Steinbruch-Dumper und U-Rahmen-Dumper an.

One of the first DJB D350C (8XC) is equipped with tire chains. It runs in a gypsum quarry in Germany. The DJB/Caterpillar version of the D350C was built between 1985 and 1989.

Einer der ersten DJB D350C (8XC), ausgestattet mit Reifenschutzketten, wird in einem Gipssteinbruch in Deutschland eingesetzt. Die DJB / Caterpillar-Version des D350C wurde von 1985 bis 1989 gebaut.

The picture shows a Caterpillar D350D (9RF00085) on the dump site on a big construction site in Germany. It was built in 1990. It is 21'38" from the ground to the peak of the risen dump body.

Das Bild zeigt einen Caterpillar D350D (9RF00085), Baujahr 1990, auf der Entladestelle einer Großbaustelle in Deutschland. Vom Boden bis zur angehobenen Muldenoberkante sind es 6.520 mm.

Powered is the D350D (9RF) with a Cat 3306 6-cylinder turbo engine with a displacement of 640 in³ and 285 hp. The load capacity reaches 35 tons. If desired you can order a wide gauge version with 10'82".

Angetrieben wird der D350D (9RF) von einem Cat 3306 6-Zyl.-Turbo-Motor mit 10,5 l Hubraum und 285 PS. Die Nutzlast beträgt 31,8 t. Als Option steht eine Breitspurausführung mit 3.300 mm zur Verfügung.

On a landfill in the Netherlands runs this Caterpillar D350D (9RF), equipped with a 91.5 yd³ waste body. The Cat 325 MH hydraulic excavator needs about two minutes to fill it up.

Auf einer niederländischen Mülldeponie wird dieser Caterpillar D350D (9RF) mit einer 70 m³ fassenden Mulde eingesetzt. Sie wird in nur zwei Minuten von einem Cat 325 MH Hydraulikbagger beladen.

With 340 hp and a load capacity of 35 tons the Caterpillar D350E was introduced in 1995. The picture was taken on a big construction site of the French contractor Muller. The current model is the Cat D350E II.

Mit 340 PS und einer Nutzlast von 31,7 t wurde der Cat D350E 1995 vorgestellt. Das Bild entstand auf einer Großbaustelle der französischen Baufirma Muller. Das aktuelle Modell ist der Cat D350E II.

The first Caterpillar D400 (IMD) was built between 1985 and 1989. On a construction site works this new D400D (8TF00361), built in 1991.

Der erste Caterpillar D400 (IMD) wurde von 1985 bis 1989 gebaut. Auf einer Baustelle arbeitet dieser neue Cat D400D (8TF00361), Baujahr 1991.

This 385 hp Caterpillar D400D (8TF) with a load capacity of 40 tons is 34.4 mph fast. The production end for the D-series came in 1995.

Mit einer Nutzlast von 36,3 t ist dieser 385 PS starke Caterpillar D400D (8TF) 55,4 km/h schnell. Das Produktionsende für die D-Serie kam 1995.

Successor of the popular D-series was
the E-series, introduced in1996. It was
refined in 1999. The picture shows the
current Caterpillar D400E II with 405 hp
and a body capacity of 40 tons. It
was loaded by a Cat 345B L ME.

Nachfolger der beliebten D-Serie wurde
1996 die E-Serie, die im Jahr 1999 überarbeitet wird. Das Bild zeigt den D400E II
mit 405 PS und 36,3 t Nutzlast. Er wird
durch einen Cat 345B L ME beladen.

The Caterpillar 972G wheel loader loads
a Cat D400E II in 5-cycles.

Der Caterpillar Radlader 972G lädt einen
Cat D400E II in fünf Arbeitstakten.

The Cat D400E II is the biggest current
articulated dump truck. The biggest DJB
dump truck was introduced in 1978. It
was the D550 with 450 hp and a loading
capacity of 55 tons. It was replaced by
the Cat D550B (8SD) with 460 hp in 1986.
The production stopped in 1987.

Der Cat D400E II ist der größte aktuelle
knickgelenkte Dumper. Der größte DJB
Dumper wurde 1978 vorgestellt, der
D550 mit 450 PS und einer Nutzlast von
50 t. Er wurde abgelöst vom Cat D550B
(8SD) mit 460 PS im Jahr 1986. Das
Produktionsende kam 1987.

Wheel Dozer

Raddozer

Wheel dozers are on principle modified models of wheel loaders, equipped with a dozer blade and a redesigned front end. Caterpillar's first wheel dozer was the No.668 with 300 hp. It was introduced in 1956 and it was based on the Cat DW20 wheel tractor. In 1963 Caterpillar introduced its first modern looking wheel dozers, the 824 and the 834. Wheel dozers are mainly used on big construction job sites to level the dump area, in coal power plants, on stock pile sites for coal and iron ore and in big mines for the maintenance of the pit floor around the shovels and the haul roads. In 1981 the Tiger Engineering Pty. Ltd company from Australia built a wheel dozer that was based on the Caterpillar 992C wheel loader. Until 1993 they built more than 45 units of the Tiger 690B, C and D-series. It was the world's largest mechanical driven wheel dozer. In 1994 the Tiger 590 wheel dozer was introduced. It based on the Caterpillar 990 wheel loader. It was followed by the Tiger 790G wheel dozer in 1996, founded on the Cat 992G. Caterpillar acquired the Tiger company in 1997. Today Caterpillar offers a line of five wheel dozer models: the 814F, 824G, 834B, 844, and the biggest, the 854G.

Raddozer sind im Prinzip eine modifizierte Ausführung eines Radladers, ausgerüstet mit Planierschild und geändertem Vorderwagen. Caterpillars erster Raddozer war der No. 668 mit 300 PS. Er wurde 1956 vorgestellt und basiert auf dem Cat DW20 Radtraktor. 1963 stellte Caterpillar die Raddozer 824 und 834, vor. Raddozer werden hauptsächlich auf großen Erdbaustellen zum Planieren der Entladestelle, in Kohlekraftwerken, auf Umschlag-plätzen für Kohle und Erz oder in großen Minen für den Unterhalt der Ladestelle und Fahrt-wege eingesetzt. Die Firma Tiger Engineering Pty Ltd. aus Australien baute 1981 auf der Basis des Caterpillars 992C einen Raddozer. Bis 1993 baute man insgesamt mehr als 45 Einheiten dieses weltgrößten, mechanisch angetriebenen Raddozer Tiger 690B-, C-, D-Serie. 1994 wurde auf der Basis des Caterpillar Radladers 990 der Tiger 590 Raddozer vorgestellt, es folgte 1996 der Tiger 790G, der auf der Basis des Cat 992G gebaut wird. Caterpil-lar übernahm 1997 die Firma Tiger und bietet heute fünf Raddozer-Modelle an: Den 814F, 824G, 834B, 844 und den größten, den 854G.

Caterpillar 814F wheel dozer. The former model was the Cat 814B (16Z) with 216 hp and a weight up to 46,137 lb. It was built until 1995. (Caterpillar Inc.)

Caterpillar Raddozer 814F. Das Vorgängermodell, der Cat 814B (16Z) mit 216 PS und einem Einsatzgewicht von 20.927 kg, wurde bis 1995 gebaut. (Caterpillar Inc.)

TWO NEW WHEEL-TYPE TRACTORS JOIN CATERPILLAR'S GROWING FAMILY OF CONSTRUCTION AND MINING EQUIPMENT

824 250 HP 62,000 Lb.

834 360 HP 90,000 Lb.

A sales brochure shows the first two wheel dozers from Caterpillar, introduced in 1963.

Ein Verkaufsprospekt zeigt die ersten beiden Raddozer, die Caterpillar 1963 vorstellt.

The Caterpillar wheel dozer 824 (29G) was replaced in 1965 by the Cat 824B (36H) with 300 hp and an operating weight of 73,480 lb. This Cat 824B is equipped with a Zeppelin cab and works on a highway construction site in Germany.

Der Caterpillar Raddozer 824 (29G) wurde 1965 durch den Cat 824B (36H) mit 300 PS und einem Gewicht von 33.330 kg abgelöst. Dieser Cat 824B ist mit einem Zeppelin-Fahrerhaus ausgerüstet und arbeitet auf einer Autobahnbaustelle in Deutschland.

This Caterpillar 824B (36H) with a new cab worked on the TGV-railroad project near Brussels/Belgium in 1995. The Cat wheel dozer is equipped with a 3-shift transmission. It allows a maximum travel speed of 18.5 mph. in both directions.

Dieser Caterpillar 824B (36H) wurde 1995 in der Nähe von Brüssel/Belgien beim Bau der TGV-Schnellbahnstrecke eingesetzt. Der Cat Raddozer ist mit einem 3-Gang-Getriebe ausgerüstet, das in beiden Fahrtrichtungen eine Geschwindigkeit von 29,8 km/h ermöglicht.

This 1996 picture was taken on the highway construction site of the A39 in Dole-Bourg En Bresse/France. This Caterpillar 824B (36H) has been working for more than 20 years on innumerable construction sites. The production ended in 1978.

Dieses Bild entstand 1996 auf der Autobahnbaustelle A39 Dole-Bourg En Bresse/Frankreich. Dieser Caterpillar 824B (36H) ist seit mehr als 20 Jahren auf unzähligen Großbaustellen im Einsatz. Die Produktion wurde 1978 eingestellt.

In 1978 Caterpillar offered the wheel dozer 824C (85X) with 315 hp and a weight of 66,975 lb. The Cat 824C is powered by a Cat 3406 DI-T 6-cyl. turbo engine with a displacement of 890 in³.

1978 wurde der Raddozer Cat 824C (85X) mit 315 PS, 30.380 kg Gewicht und dem Cat 3406 DI-T 6-Zyl.-Turbo-Motor mit 14,6 l Hubraum vorgestellt.

The Caterpillar 824G wheel dozer was introduced in 1996. (Caterpillar Inc.)

Der Caterpillar 824G Raddozer wurde 1996 vorgestellt. (Caterpillar Inc.)

The biggest wheel dozer was the Cat 834 (43E). It was built between 1963 and 1974 with 400 hp and a weight of 88,800 lb. Equipped with an S blade the length amounts 26'33" and the width 12'3". You can also get a push blade and a push block which have good suspension.

Der größte Raddozer war der Caterpillar 834 (43E), er wurde von 1963 bis 1974 mit 400 PS und einem Gewicht von 40.300 kg gebaut. Mit S-Schild beträgt die Länge 8.030 mm und die Breite 3.750 mm, als Sonderausrüstung können ein gefedertes Schubschild und auch ein gefederter Schubblock bestellt werden.

The picture shows the current version of the Caterpillar 834B wheel dozer, equipped with a U blade. Powered is the 102,212 lb heavy wheel dozer by a Cat 3408E V8 turbo engine with a displacement of 1098 in³ and 450 hp.

Das Bild zeigt die aktuelle Version des Cat 834B Raddozers, ausgerüstet mit einem U-Schild. Angetrieben wird der 46.355 kg schwere Raddozer von einem Cat 3408E V8-Turbo-Motor mit 18 l Hubraum und 450 PS.

The Tiger Engineering Pty Ltd. company from Australia developed, the Tiger 590 wheel dozer in 1994. It was based on the new Caterpillar 990 wheel loader. Caterpillar acquired the production rights in 1997. In 1998 this new wheel dozer was in the sales lists under Caterpillar`s designation 844. (Caterpillar Inc.)

Die Firma Tiger Engineering Pty Ltd. aus Australien entwickelte 1994 auf der Basis des neuen Caterpillar 990 Radladers einen Raddozer, den Tiger 590. Caterpillar erwarb 1997 die Produktionsrechte und seit 1998 steht der neue Raddozer unter der Caterpillar Bezeichnung 844 in der Verkaufsliste. (Caterpillar Inc.)

The Tiger Engineering Pty Ltd. company from Australia built big wheel dozers based on the Cat 992C wheel loader since 1981. The first type was the 690A/690B. The blade and the hydraulic cylinders are also Caterpillar hardware. The picture shows the Tiger 690B.

Die Firma Tiger Engineering Pty Ltd. aus Australien baut seit 1981 große Raddozer auf der Basis des Caterpillar 992C Radladers. Der erste Typ war der 690A/690B. Schild und Hydraulikzylinder stammen ebenfalls von Caterpillar. Das Bild zeigt einen Tiger 690B.

This Tiger 690B rated at 690 hp and is equipped with a 46,4 yd³.

CDieser Tiger 690B mit 690 PS ist ausgerüstet mit einem 35,5 m³ fassenden Balderson Kohleschild.

A picture out of a sales brochure for the Tiger 690C. In 1992 Tiger introduced the new 690D with 710 hp and the new STIC Control Steering System.

Titelabbildung eines Verkaufsprospekt für den Tiger 690C. 1992 wurde der Tiger 690D mit 710 PS und der neuen Caterpillar STIC-Control-Lenkung vorgestellt.

In 1996 Tiger Engineering company offered the biggest mechanical driven wheel dozer, the 790G with 800 hp. Caterpillar acquired the production rights in 1997 and since 1998 this new wheel dozer is in the sales lists under Caterpillar`s designation 854G. (Caterpillar Inc.)

1996 stellte Tiger Engineering den größten mechanisch angetriebenen Raddozer vor, den 790G mit 800 PS.Caterpillar erwarb 1997 die Produktionsrechte und seit 1998 steht der neue Raddozer unter der Caterpillar-Bezeichnung 854G in der Verkaufsliste. (Caterpillar Inc.)

Compactors   Verdichter

Compactors are based on modificated models of wheel loaders. They are equipped with a dozer blade, a redesigned front end and compactor wheels. In 1970 Caterpillar introduced three types: the Cat 815, 825 and the biggest the 835, rated at 400 hp and with an operating weight of 79,100 lb. Compactors are used on big road/highway construction sites and on dam projects. They have to compact and level a lot of filled earth or rocky material in the shortest possible time. Today Caterpillar offeres two models: the 815F and the 825G with 315 hp. The new Cat 825G uses the same half moon steering wheel with integrated transmission control as the new G-series wheel loader. All new wheel dozers (814F/824G), compactors (815F/825G) and landfill compactor (816F/826G) have the fuel tank on the top of the front end for a better weight distribution.

Verdichter sind im Prinzip eine modifizierte Ausführung eines Radladers, ausgerüstet mit Planierschild, geändertem Vorderwagen und Verdichterwalzen. Caterpillar stellte 1970 drei Typen vor: 815, 825 und den größten, den 835 mit 400 PS und einem Gewicht von 35.900 kg. Eingesetzt werden die Verdichter auf großen Autobahnbaustellen oder bei Staudammprojekten, wo in kürzester Zeit große Mengen geschüttetes Erd- oder Felsmaterial zu planieren und gleichzeitig zu verdichten sind. Heute bietet Caterpillar zwei Modelle an, den Cat 815F und den 825G mit 315 PS. Im neuen Caterpillar 825G wird das gleiche Halblenkrad mit integrierter Getriebeschaltung verwendet wie in der neuen G-Radlader-Serie. Der Kraftstofftank sitzt bei allen neuen Raddozern (814F/824G), Verdichtern (815F/825G) und Müllverdichtern (816F/826G) auf dem Vorderwagen und dient einer besseren Gewichtsverteilung.

The smallest of the three Caterpillar compactors is the Cat 815 (91P) with 170 hp and a weight of 38,200 lb. It was built from 1970 to 1981. The picture was taken in 1995. This Cat 815 (91P) works on the TGV-railroad project in Belgium.

Der kleinste der drei Caterpillar-Verdichter ist der Cat 815 (91P) mit 170 PS und einem Gewicht von 17.300 kg. Er wurde von 1970 bis 1981 gebaut. Das Bild stammt von 1995. Der Cat 815 (91P) arbeitet auf der im Bau befindlichen TGV Schnellbahnstrecke in Belgien.

This Caterpillar 815 (91P) is equipped with a Zeppelin cab. In this picture the Cat is pushing the soil with the blade and simultaneously it is compacting the soil with the tamping wheels.

Der Caterpillar 815 (91P) ist ausgerüstet mit einem Zeppelin-Fahrerhaus. Hier planiert der Cat Erde mit seinem Verteilschild und verdichtet mit den Walzen gleichzeitig das verfüllte Material.

In 1981 Caterpillar introduced the new B-series of the Cat 815 compactor. The operating weight amounts 44,175 lb. Powered is the new Cat 815B (17Z) by a Cat 3306 6-cylinder turbo engine with 216 hp.

1981 wurde die neue B-Serie des Caterpillar-Verdichters 815 vorgestellt. Das Einsatzgewicht beträgt 20.035 kg. Angetrieben wird der neue Cat 815B (17Z) von einem Cat 3306 6-Zyl.-Turbo-Motor mit 216 PS.

A picture out of a sales brochure shows the Caterpillar 815F compactor. It was presented at the end of 1995.

Eine Abbildung des Caterpillar 815F Verdichter aus dem Verkaufsprospekts. Er wurde Ende 1995 vorgestellt.

The Caterpillar 825B (43N) with 300 hp and a weight of 66,300 lb was introduced in 1970 and was in the sales lists until 1978. Two cycles are needed to cover an area of 16' ".

Vorgestellt wurde der Caterpillar 825B (43N) mit 300 PS und einem Gewicht von 30.075 kg 1970. Er blieb bis 1978 im Programm. Bei zwei Übergängen entsteht eine 4.900 mm breite verdichtete Fläche.

Equipped with a planetary-power shift transmission the Caterpillar 825B (43N) can be shifted under full load in all three forward and reverse gears.

Mit dem Planeten-Lastschaltgetriebe kann der Caterpillar 825B (43N) in allen drei Vor- und Rückwärtsgängen unter Volllast geschaltet werden.

The maximum travel speed in the third gear the Caterpillar 825B (43N) amounts 17 mph. This is called high speed compacting. The Cat 825B worked on a highway project in Germany in 1998.

Die max. Geschwindigkeit beträgt beim Cat 825B (43N) im dritten Gang 27,4 km/h. Dies wird als high speed compacting bezeichnet. Dieser Cat 825B wird noch 1998 bei einem Autobahnprojekt in Deutschland eingesetzt.

I saw my first Caterpillar 825B (43N) tamping compactor when I was a 15 year old boy.

Dies war mein erster Caterpillar 825B (43N) tamping Compactor, den ich als Junge mit 15 Jahren sah.

On a big construction site in France this Caterpillar 825B (43N) levels and compacts the dump site.

Auf einer großen Scraper Baustelle in Frankreich wird dieser Caterpillar 825B (43N) zum Planieren und Verdichten eingesetzt.

A new looking Caterpillar 825B (43N) worked on a road construction project in Portugal in 1997.

Ein fast neu aussehender Caterpillar 825B (43N) arbeitete 1997 auf einer Straßenbaustelle in Portugal.

In 1979 Caterpillar introduced the new 825C compactor with 315 hp and an operating weight of 71,442 lb.

1979 wurde der neue Caterpillar 825C Verdichter vorgestellt, mit 315 PS und einem Gewicht von 32.400 kg.

In 1996 I took a photo of this nice Caterpillar 825C belonging to a French contractor in France. This model dropped out of the sales lists in 1995.

In Frankreich konnte ich 1996 diesen schönen Caterpillar 825C eines französischen Bauunternehmers fotografieren. Für dieses Model kam das Produktionsende 1995.

This picture out of a sales brochure shows the current Caterpillar 825G compactor.

Eine Abbildung des Caterpillar 825G Verdichter aus dem aktuellen Verkaufsprospekt.

The Caterpillar 835 (44N) was built between 1970 and 1974. It was the biggest compactor ever offered. In its early production time you could also find it with the designation 834. With 400 hp, a weight of 79,100 lb and speed of 20 mph the Cat 835 (44N) coverages an area of 16'72" in only two passes. I saw my first Cat 835 unit in Belgium in 1995.

Der Caterpillar 835 (44N) wurde von 1970 bis 1974 gebaut und ist der größte Verdichter. In der Anfangszeit wurde er auch mit 834 bezeichnet. Mit 400 PS und einem Gewicht von 35.900 kg verdichtet der 32,2 km/h schnelle Cat 835 (44N) in nur zwei Übergängen eine 5.100 mm breite Fläche. Dieser Cat 835 war der erste, den ich 1995 in Belgien sah.

Landfill Compactors

Müllverdichter

Landfill compactors also are modificated models of wheel loaders. They are equipped with big landfill blades, redesigned front ends, waste chopper wheels, special guards and striker bars to protect the machine from settling waste and to keep it clean. In the seventies Caterpillar introduced two landfill compactors: the 816 and the bigger 826B with 300 hp and an operating weight up to 65,411 lb. The specially developed Cater-pillar chopper wheels chop and compact the waste perfectly. You can order similar wheels to use them on different wheel loader models. In 1993 Caterpillar introduced the 836 landfill compactor, rated at 473 hp and with an operating weight up to 100,000 lb. It is based on the 988 wheel loader. Today you can choose from three models: the 816F, 826G and 836.

Müllverdichter sind ebenfalls eine modifizierte Ausführung des Radladers, ausgerüstet mit Müllverteilschild, geändertem Vorderwagen, Müllverdichterwalzen und speziellen Abdeckungen sowie Abstreifern, die ein Festsetzen des Mülls verhindern. In den 70ern stellte Caterpillar zwei Müllverdichter vor: Den Cat 816 und den größeren, den Cat 826B mit 300 PS und einem Einsatzgewicht von 29.665 kg. Die speziell entwickelten Caterpillar Müllverdichterwalzen zerkleinern und verdichten den Müll optimal. Man konnte ähnliche Walzen auch für verschiedene Radladermodelle erhalten. 1993 stellte Caterpillar auf der Basis des Cat 988 Radladers den 836 Müllverdichter mit 473 PS und einem Einsatzgewicht von 45.360 kg vor. Heute kann man zwischen drei Modellen wählen: Dem 816F, 826G und 836.

The smallest Caterpillar landfill compactor is the 816 (57U) with 170 hp and an operating weight of 40,900 lb.

Der kleinste Caterpillar Müllverdichter ist der 816 (57U) mit 170 PS und einem Gewicht von 18.550 kg.

On a landfill in Germany this Caterpillar 816 (57U) covers an area of 14'76" in only two passes.

Dieser Caterpillar 816 (57U) wird auf einer Mülldeponie in Deutschland eingesetzt. Mit nur zwei Übergängen wird eine 4.500 mm breite Verdichtungsfläche erreicht.

This Caterpillar 816 (57U) is equipped with a 14' width and 6'39" height landfill blade with 19.6 yd³ capacity.

Dieser Caterpillar 816 (57U) ist ausgestattet mit einem 4.270 mm breiten und 1.950 mm hohen Müllverteilschild mit 15 m³ Fassungsvermögen.

In 1981 Caterpillar introduced the new Cat 816B (15Z) landfill compactor. It is powered by a Cat 3306 DI-T 6-cylinder turbo engine with a displacement of 640 in³ and rated at 210 hp.

1981 wurde der neue Caterpillar 816B (15Z) Müllverdichter vorgestellt. Er wird angetrieben durch einen Cat 3306 DI-T 6-Zyl.-Turbo-Motor mit 10,5 l Hubraum und 210 PS.

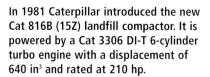

The picture was taken on a landfill in Southern Germany in 1991. It shows a Caterpillar 816B (15Z). The chopper wheels are especially designed for the landfill application, when compaction and traction are very important.

1991 konnte ich diesen Caterpillar 816B (15Z) fotografieren, der auf einer Müll-deponie in Süddeutschland arbeitete. Die Messerwalzen wurden von Caterpillar speziell für den Mülleinsatz konstruiert. Dadurch ergibt sich eine gute Bodenhaf-tung bei gleichzeitig optimaler Verdich-tung und Zerkleinerung des Materials.

The picture shows a new Caterpillar 816B (15Z) landfill compactor. It was replaced by the current Cat 816F by the end of 1995.

Das Bild zeigt einen Cat 816B (15Z) Müllverdichter. Ende 1995 wurde dieser Typ vom aktuellen Cat 816F abgelöst.

A picture out of a sales brochure shows the Caterpillar 816F landfill compactor.

Titelabbildung eines Verkaufsprospekts des Caterpillar 816F Müllverdichter.

In 1978 the new Caterpillar 826C (87X) landfill compactor came to the market. The picture shows a Cat 826C, built in 1991. It is equipped with two different types of chopper wheels.

1978 wurde der neue Caterpillar 826C (87X) Müllverdichter vorgestellt. Das Bild zeigt einen neuen Cat 826C, Baujahr 1991, der mit zwei verschiedenen Messerwalzen ausgerüstet ist.

 **CATERPILLAR** **826B** Landfill Compactor

Summary of features

- **Wheels chop and compact** . . . blades alternate in a staggered-chevron design for best chopper coverage.

- **Center-point articulation** . . . excellent maneuverability. Front and rear drums track, so material is chopped and compacted twice each pass.

- **Protective guarding** . . . helps keep debris from fouling machine components.

- **Reliable Cat power train** . . . Cat D343 diesel delivers 300 flywheel HP. Planetary power shift transmission lets the operator shift on-the-go. Three speeds forward, three reverse.

- **Caterpillar landfill blade** (optional) spreads refuse and cover material . . . strong enough to handle lumber, pipes and appliances.

- **CAT PLUS** . . . from your Caterpillar Dealer . . . the most comprehensive, total product support system in the industry.

Shown with Balderson blade.

Shown with ROPS cab (standard in U.S.A. only), optional landfill blade and lights.

A sales brochure from 1976 shows the biggest available Caterpillar landfill compactor from the seventies. It was introduced in 1972.

Ein Verkaufsprospekt von 1976 zeigt den größten Caterpillar Müllverdichter, der in den 70ern erhältlich war. Er wurde 1972 vorgestellt.

 Caterpillar Engine

Flywheel horsepower @ 2060 RPM 300

The net power at the flywheel of the vehicle engine operating under SAE standard ambient temperature and barometric conditions, 85° F. (29° C) and 29.38" Hg (995 mbar), using 35 API gravity fuel oil at 60° F. (15.6° C). Vehicle engine equipment includes fan, air cleaner, water pump, lubricating oil pump, fuel pump and alternator. Engine will maintain specified flywheel power up to 10,000 ft. (3000 m) altitude.

Caterpillar 4-stroke-cycle Diesel Model D343 with six cylinders, 5.4" (137 mm) bore, 6.5" (165 mm) stroke and 893 cu. in. (14.6 litres) displacement.

Precombustion chamber fuel system with individual adjustment-free injection pumps and valves.

Turbocharged and aftercooled. Parallel manifold porting with two intake and two exhaust valves per cylinder.

Valves directly actuated by overhead camshafts. Stellite-faced valves, hard alloy seats, valve rotators. Variable timing fuel system.

Cam-ground and tapered aluminum alloy pistons with 3-ring design, cooled by oil spray. Steel-backed aluminum bearings. Hi-Electro hardened crankshaft journals. Pressure lubrication with full-flow filtered and cooled oil.

The Caterpillar 826C (87X) landfill compactor has an operating weight of
76,990 lb. It is powered by a 315 hp Cat
3406 turbo engine. This Cat 826C is
equipped with chopper wheels. It works
on a landfill in Switzerland.

Der neue Caterpillar 826C (87X) Müllverdichter hat ein Einsatzgewicht von
34.920 kg. Angetrieben wird er von
einem 315 PS starken Cat 3406 Turbo-
Motor. Dieser Cat 826C, mit Messerwalzen ausgestattet, arbeitet auf einer
Schweizer Mülldeponie.

This Cat 826C (87X) has new designed
plus tip wheels. It works on a big landfill
in Switzerland.

Mit Caterpillars neuen Plus-Tip-Walzen
ausgestattet, arbeitet dieser Cat 826C
(87X) Müllverdichter auf einer großen
Mülldeponie in der Schweiz.

In the Netherlands I discovered this
pretty painted Caterpillar 826C (87X).
The length of the landfill compactor amounts
26'06", the width 14'66" and the height
from the ground to the top of the blade
6'45".

In den Niederlanden fand ich diesen
schön lackierten Caterpillar 826C (87X).
Die Länge des Verdichters beträgt 7.946
mm, die Breite 4.470 mm und vom Boden
bis Schildoberkante sind es 1.969 mm.

A picture out of a sales brochure shows the current Caterpillar 826G landfill compactor. It was introduced in 1996.

Titelabbildung eines Verkaufsprospekts des aktuellen Caterpillar 826G Müllverdichters. Er wurde 1996 vorgestellt.

A picture out of a sales brochure shows the biggest current Caterpillar 836 landfill compactor. This was already introduced in 1993.

Titelabbidung eines Verkaufsprospekts des größten aktuellen Caterpillar 836 Müllverdichters. Er wurde 1993 vorgestellt.

Motor Graders

Motorgrader

The history of the graders began, with the production of automobiles and the need for good roads. The Russel Company was etablished in Stephen/Minnesota in 1903. They built different horse-pulled graders. In 1920 Russel introduced the first motor grader of the world, called the Motor Hi-Way Patrol No.1. In 1926 Russel built the Motor Patrol No.4. It is mounted on a Caterpillar "2-ton". In 1927 Russel sold about 265 units of this type of crawler motor grader. This reflects the great demand and the popularity of these early graders. One year later Russel offered the No.6 grader, which was mounted on a Cat Twenty. Caterpillar recognized the signs of the time and acquired the Russel Company in 1928. Then they sold their own Motor Patrols No.10, No.15 and No.20 for the Caterpillar models Ten, Fifteen and Twenty. In 1931 Caterpillar introduced its own independent tired two axle grader, the Auto Patrol. It was not built on a crawler tractor as usual – it was a separate new development. The first rather modern looking motor grader was introduced in 1939, the model No.12, rated at 66 hp. This was such a popular model, that the No.12 is still available. It is listed as the model 12H, after there had been a lot of improvements and revised versions. A further milestone was the coming out of the No.16 motor grader in 1963. It was the biggest Cat grader in those times, even the world's largest. With the introduction of the full hydraulic G-series in 1973, Caterpillar was successful in consolidating its reputation as a pioneer in the grader market. The world's biggest current motor grader is the 24H. The 500 hp grader was introduced in 1996, equipped with a moldboard up to 24'.

Mit dem Aufkommen der Automobile und des Straßennetzes beginnt auch die Geschichte des Graders. 1903 wurde in Stephen/Minnesota die Firma Russel gegründet. Man begann mit dem Bau von verschiedenen Gradern, die von Pferden gezogen wurden. Der weltweit erste Motorgrader war der Motor Hi-Way Patrol No.1, den Russel 1920 vorstellte. 1926 baute Russel den Motor Patrol No.4, der an einen Caterpillar "2-Ton" angebaut wurde. 1927 wurden schon 265 Einheiten dieses Raupenmotorgraders verkauft. Dies spiegelt den Bedarf und die Popularität dieser frühen Grader wider. Ein Jahr später wird der Russel No.6 vorgestellt, der an eine Cat Twenty angebaut wurde. Caterpillar erkannte die Zeichen der Zeit, übernahm 1928 die Firma Russel und vertrieb dann seine eigenen Motor Patrols No.10, No.15 und No.20 für die Caterpillar Modelle Ten, Fifteen und Twenty. 1931 stellte Caterpillar seinen ersten eigenständigen luftbereiften 2-Achs-Grader vor, den Auto Patrol, der nicht an einen Traktor angebaut wurde, sondern eine komplette Neuentwicklung war. Der erste moderne Motorgrader wurde 1939 vorgestellt: Der No.12 mit 66 PS. Dieser Grader war so beliebt, daß er bis heute nach mehreren überarbeiteten Versionen als 12H in der Verkaufsliste steht. Ein weiterer Meilenstein war die Einführung des No. 16 Motorgraders 1963. Dies war der größte Caterpillar Grader und zugleich der weltgrößte Motorgrader seiner Zeit. Mit der vollhydraulischen G-Serie 1973 gelang es Caterpillar, seinen guten Ruf als Pionier im Graderbau zu festigen. Der weltgrößte aktuelle Motorgrader ist der 24H von Caterpillar. Der 500 PS starke und mit einer 7.300 mm breiten Schar ausgerüstete Grader wurde 1996 präsentiert.

The smallest Caterpillar motor grader from the fifties was the No.212 (79C) with 50 hp and an operating weight of 13,290 lb. I found the next bigger motor grader the Cat No.112 (3U1903) in a backyard in 1991.

Der kleinste Caterpillar Motorgrader aus den 50ern war der No.212 (79C) mit 50 PS und einem Dienstgewicht von 6.030 kg. Den nächstgrößeren, den Cat No.112 (3U1903) habe ich 1991 in einem Hinterhof gefunden.

This Caterpillar No.112 (3U) was built from 1947 to 1959 with a weight of 19,330 lb. It is powered by a Cat 4-cylinder diesel engine rated at 70 hp. When I returned later, in 1991, to take another look at this old motor grader, I couldn't believe my eyes. The 38 year-old motor grader passed under its own steam. Until 1968 the E-series with 85 hp was built. It was replaced by the F-series with 100 hp which stood in the sales lists until 1984.

Dieser Caterpillar No.112 (3U) wurde von 1947 bis 1959 gebaut mit einem Gewicht von 8.770 kg. Er wird von einem Cat 4-Zyl-Diesel-Motor mit 70 PS angetrieben. Als ich 1991 nochmals vorbeiging, um nach diesem alten Caterpillar Grader zu schauen, traute ich meinen Augen nicht. Der Grader fuhr mit eigener Kraft an mir vorbei, und das nach ca. 38 Jahren. Bis 1968 wurde die E-Serie mit 85 PS gebaut, danach kam die F-Serie mit 100 PS. Sie blieb bis 1984 im Verkaufsprogramm.

The first Cat No.120 (89G) motor grader with 115 hp and an operating weight of 23,100 lb was introduced in 1964. The picture shows a Cat No.120 (13U) with 125 hp and an operating weight of 24,300 lb. It works for the US army. This type was built until 1974. At the same time Caterpillar built the Cat 120B (64U) (Braz) in Brazil from 1972 to 1989.

Der erste Caterpillar No.120 (89G) Motorgrader wurde 1964 vorgestellt mit 115 PS und einem Gewicht von 10.480 kg. Das Bild zeigt einen Cat No.120 (13U) mit 125 PS und einem Gewicht von 11.000 kg, eingesetzt bei der US-Armee. Dieser Typ wurde bis 1974 gebaut. Zeitgleich wurde der Cat 120B (64U) (Braz) von 1972 bis 1989 in Brasilien gebaut.

In 1973 Caterpillar presented the new, fully hydraulic controlled G-series. In Europe Cat motor graders are often equipped with a front mounted blade, such as this Cat 120G in France. One of the most noticeable news is the Cat G-series cab and the frame articulation. The G-series was replaced by the current H-series in 1995.

1973 stellte Caterpillar die neue, voll hydraulisch gesteuerte G-Serie vor. Oft werden die Cat-Grader in Europa mit einem Frontschild ausgerüstet, so wie dieser 120G, der in Frankreich arbeitet. Eine der auffälligsten Neuerungen der Cat G-Serie sind das neue Fahrerhaus und die Rahmen-Knicklenkung. Die G-Serie wurde 1995 abgelöst durch die aktuelle H-Serie.

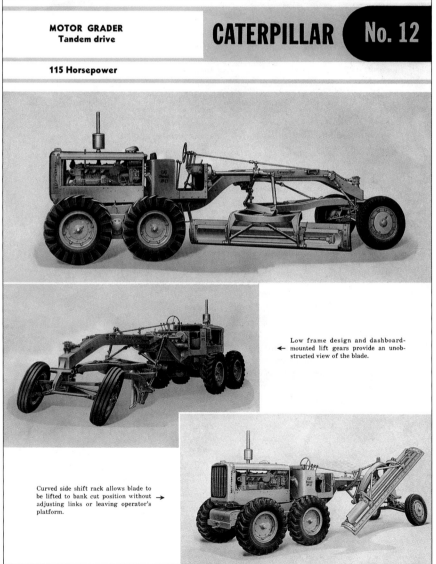

MOTOR GRADER
Tandem drive

CATERPILLAR No. 12

115 Horsepower

← Low frame design and dashboard-mounted lift gears provide an unobstructed view of the blade.

Curved side shift rack allows blade to be lifted to bank cut position without adjusting links or leaving operator's platform. →

This is a sales brochure from April 1957 and shows the Caterpillar No.12 motor grader.

Ein Verkaufsprospekt des Caterpillar No.12 Motorgraders von 1957.

The Caterpillar No.12 (6M) motor grader was built between 1939 and 1942 and became the most popular Cat motor grader model. This new painted Cat No.12 (7T) motor grader has been working for the road maintenance in the Yukon Territory.

Der Caterpillar No.12 (6M) Motorgrader wurde von 1939 bis 1942 gebaut und wurde der populärste Cat-Grader. Dieser neu lackierte Cat No.12 (7T) Motorgrader wird noch 1992 für den Unterhalt der Wege im Yukon Territory eingesetzt.

With an 100 hp Caterpillar engine and an operating weight of 22,375 lb this Cat No.12 (8T21640) was built between 1947 and 1955. The turning circle amounts only 35'65".

Mit einem 100 PS starken Cat-Motor, einem Einsatzgewicht von 10.100 kg und mit einer Schar von 3.660 mm Länge wird dieser Cat No.12 (8T21640) von 1947 bis 1955 gebaut. Der Wendekreis beträgt nur 10.870 mm.

In 1965 Caterpillar introduced the improved Cat No.12F (73G) motor grader. The most obvious difference are the two planetary blade lift gears. They are mounted on the front of the main frame. The 28,600 lb heavy and 115 hp strong Cat grader No. 12F works on a construction site in Anchorage/Alaska.

1965 stellte Caterpillar die Weiterentwicklung des Cat No.12E Motorgrader vor, den neuen No.12F (73G). Auffälligstes Merkmal sind die beiden Scharhubantriebe, die jetzt vorne auf dem Hauptrahmen montiert sind. Der 115 PS starke und 12.973 kg schwere Cat Grader No. 12F arbeitet auf einer Baustelle in Anchorage/Alaska.

The F-series was built until 1973. The picture shows another Caterpillar No.12F grader on a road construction site in Alaska. On this picture you can see the hydraulic front wheel lean. The models after 1967 were powered by Cat D333 6-cylinder diesel engine, rated at 125 hp by 2000 r.p.m.

Die F-Serie wurde bis 1973 gebaut. Das Bild zeigt einen anderen Cat No.12F Grader auf einer Straßenbaustelle in Alaska. Auf dem Bild kann man gut die Radsturzverstellung der Vorderräder sehen. Die letzten Modelle ab 1967 wurden von einem Cat D333 6-Zyl.-Diesel-Motor mit 125 PS bei 2.000 U/min. angetrieben.

The successor was the Caterpillar 12G (61M) motor grader with 135 hp and a weight of 29,860 lb. This Caterpillar 12G (61M) is equipped with a front blade and works on a highway project in Germany.

Nachfolger wird der Caterpillar 12G (61M) Motorgrader mit 135 PS und einem Gewicht von 13.554 kg. Das Bild zeigt einen mit Frontschild ausgerüsteten Caterpillar 12G (61M) auf einer Autobahnbaustelle in Deutschland.

A brand-new Caterpillar 12H with a 34,839 lb weight and a 12'13" long moldboard was built in 1998. The Cat 3306 6-cylinder turbo engine rates at 145 hp. With the Caterpillar power shift transmission the motorgrader reaches 26 mph in the eighth gear. This gives the grader a high mobility. In the same size class Cat built the 130G grader with 28,770 lb weight and 135 hp. It was in the sales lists from 1973 to 1995. Then it was replaced by the current Cat 135H.

Ein brandneuer Caterpillar 12H, Baujahr 1998, mit 15.800 kg Einsatzgewicht und einer 3.700 mm langen Schar. Der Cat 3306 6-Zyl.-Turbo-Motor leistet 145 PS. Mit dem Caterpillar 8-Gang-Getriebe kann eine Geschwindigkeit von 41,8 km/h erreicht werden. Dies verleiht dem Grader eine hohe Mobilität. In der gleichen Größenklasse wurde der Cat 130G mit 135 PS und 13.050 kg gebaut. Er stand von 1973 bis 1995 in der Verkaufsliste. Ersetzt wurde er durch den aktuellen Cat 135H.

The next size up Caterpillar motor grader was the No.140 (14U). It was built from 1971 to 1974. In British Columbia I found this Cat 140G (72V) at the Canadian Cat dealer Finning. The weight of the 150 hp Cat grader amounts 31,090 lb. An all-wheel drive version is also available.

Der nächstgrößere Motorgrader war der No.140 (14U), er wurde von 1971 bis 1974 gebaut. In British Columbia fand ich diesen Cat 140G (72V), der auf dem Vorplatz des kanadischen Cat-Händlers Finning stand. Das Gewicht des 150 PS starken Caterpillar Graders beträgt 14.102 kg. Eine Allradversion dieses Typs ist auch erhältlich.

Many motor graders in Alaska and in Northern America are used for road maintenance during the winter months. They are equipped with a second moldboard for the snow removal. The picture shows a Cat 140G (72V) with the second moldboard in transport position.

Viele Motorgrader werden in Alaska und Nordamerika für den Wegeunterhalt im Winter mit einer zweiten Schar ausgerüstet, um die großen Schneemassen zu räumen. Das Bild zeigt einen Cat 140G (72V) mit zweiter Schar in Transportstellung.

This Caterpillar 140G (72V) is equipped with a rear mounted ripper. It works on a road project in Portugal. In 1995 the current Cat 140H with 165 hp was offered. An all-wheel drive version, called 143H, is built, too.

Der Caterpillar 140G (72V), ausgerüstet mit einem Heckaufreisser, arbeitet auf einer Straßenbaustelle in Portugal. 1995 wurde der Cat 140H mit 165 PS vorgestellt, eine Allradversion ist ebenfalls

erhältlich unter der Bezeichnung 143H.

The Caterpillar 160H is 28' long. Because of the frame articulation with an angle of 20° and the steering range of 50° left and right, it has the tightest turning circle, 24'3". The 34,360 lb heavy Cat 160H is powered by a 180 hp Cat engine. The all-wheel drive version is called 163H.

Der Caterpillar 160H ist 8.533 mm lang. Dank seiner Rahmen-Knicklenkung mit je 20° und dem Lenkeinschlagwinkel der Vorderräder von je 50° zu jeder Seite, erreicht er mit 7.400 mm seinen kleinsten Wenderadius. Der 15.586 kg schwere Cat 160H wird von einem 180 PS starken Cat-Motor angetrieben. Die Allradversion wird mit 163H bezeichnet.

This is a sales brochure from 1961.

MOTOR GRADER
Tandem Drive

CATERPILLAR No. 14

Series D

150 Horsepower

30,300 Lb.

- Dependable, long-life OIL CLUTCH
- Accurate, positive MECHANICAL CONTROLS
- Economical, hard-lugging DIESEL ENGINE
- Wide-range BLADE POSITIONING
- Slope stability with low CENTER OF GRAVITY
- "Sit-down" operating VISIBILITY
- Broad selection of ATTACHMENTS

Ein Verkaufsprospekt aus dem Jahr 1961. The first Caterpillar No.14B (78E) was only built in 1959. The picture shows a Cat No.14C (35F). It was built at the same time as the B-series, which was produced from 1959 on. Powered is the 28,600 lb heavy motor grader by a Cat 6-cylinder turbo engine with a displacement of 524 in^3 and 150 hp. It was replaced by the D-series in 1961.

Der erste Caterpillar No.14B (78E) wurde nur 1959 gebaut. Das Bild zeigt einen Cat No.14C (35F), der zeitgleich zur B-Serie ab 1959 gebaut wurde. Angetrieben wird der 12.973 kg schwere Motorgrader von einem Cat 6-Zyl.-Turbo-Motor mit 8,6 l Hubraum und 150 PS. Er wird 1961 abgelöst durch die D-Serie.

In 1965 Caterpillar showed the new No.14E (99G) motor grader. The planetary blade lift gears are now mounted on the front of the main frame. This Cat No.14E (99G) works on the legendary Dempster Highway in Canada near Arctic Red River.

1965 wird der neue Caterpillar No.14E (99G) Motorgrader vorgestellt. Der Scharhubantrieb ist jetzt vorne auf dem Hauptrahmen montiert. Dieser Cat No.14E (99G) arbeitet in der Nähe von Arctic Red River auf dem legendären Dempster Highway in Kanada.

In 1991 I had the chance to take photos of this new painted Caterpillar No.14E (12K2292) out of the last E-series, built in 1974. This 31,600 lb heavy motor grader is powered by a Cat engine with 150 hp. A top speed of 24.3 mph is reached in the sixth gear.

1991 konnte ich diesen neu lackierten Caterpillar No.14E (12K2292), Baujahr 1974, aus der letzten E-Serie fotografieren. Der 14.300 kg schwere Motorgrader wird von einem Cat-Motor mit 150 PS angetrieben und erreicht im sechsten Gang 39,1 km/h.

The last E-serie was built from 1967 to 1973. This Caterpillar No.14E (12K) is equipped with a hydraulic moldboard control and a front mounted blade.

Die letzte E-Serie wurde von 1967 bis 1973 gebaut. Dieser Caterpillar No.14E (12K) ist schon mit der hydraulischen Scharverstellung und einem Frontschild ausgerüstet.

When buying a Caterpillar No.14E (12K) you could order two different transmissions: power shift transmission or sliding gear transmission. The moldboard length at all Cats No.14 up to the E-series amounts to 13'. This new painted Cat No. 14E works in Whitehorse/Canada.

Den Caterpillar No.14E (12K) konnte man wahlweise mit zwei Getriebevarianten bestellen: Planeten-Lastschaltgetriebe oder Wechselgetriebe. Die Scharlänge beträgt bei allen Cat No.14 bis zur E-Serie 3.960 mm. Dieser neu lackierte Cat No.14E arbeitet in Whitehorse/Kanada.

Caterpillar motor graders are often used for the maintenance of the haul roads. A very popular model is the Cat 14G (96U).

Oft werden Motorgrader für den Unterhalt der Transportwege eingesetzt. Ein beliebtes Modell ist der Cat 14G (96U).

In 1973 Caterpillar introduced the new Cat 14G-series (96U) motor grader with 180 hp and an operating weight up to 38,587 lb. This Cat 14G grades gravel on a road construction site near Fairbanks/Alaska.

Vorgestellt wurde die neue Caterpillar 14G-Serie (96U) 1973 mit 180 PS und einem Gewicht von 17.500 kg. Dieser Cat 14G planiert Kies auf einer Straßenbaustelle in der Nähe von Fairbanks/Alaska.

This Caterpillar 14G (96U) is equipped with a front blade and works on a highway project in Southern Germany.

Auf einer Autobahnbaustelle in Süddeutschland arbeitet dieser Caterpillar 14G (96U), ausgerüstet mit einem Frontschild.

The engine power and the operating weight increased when introducing the new Caterpillar model 14G (96U) with now 200 hp and a weight of 45,610 lb. The picture was taken on the TGV railroad project in Belgium.

Die Motorleistung und das Einsatzgewicht stiegen mit der Einführung des Cat 14G (96U) auf 200 PS, bzw. 20.688 kg. Das Bild entstand in Belgien auf einer Eisenbahnbaustelle des TGV Hochgeschwindigkeitszuges.

This is the best painted motor grader I`ve ever seen before: a Caterpillar 14G (96U). It is painted in the French national colours: blue, red, white and the colour of Caterpillar as well.

Dies ist wohl der am schönsten lackierte Motorgrader, den ich je gesehen habe: Ein Caterpillar 14G (96U). Er trägt die französischen Nationalfarben: Blau, rot, weiß und auch die Caterpillar-Farbe.

225 Flywheel H.P. Cat diesel engine with trouble-free fuel system.

48,000 lb. (21800 kg) shipping weight.

Positive mechanical controls, hydraulically actuated, provide blading accuracy with operating ease.

Nine-speed power shift transmission with Torque Divider.

Power steering, four wheel oil-disc brakes, and hydraulically leaned front wheels.

Hydraulic sideshift and moldboard tip.

Triple-box-sectioned main frame provides high strength rigidity for blade stability.

This is a sales brochure of the biggest Caterpillar grader from 1968.

Ein Verkaufsprospekt des größten Caterpillar Graders von 1968.

This picture shows Caterpillar's largest motor grader, the No.16 (49G). Powered is this 49,600 lb heavy grader by a Cat D348 6-cylinder turbo engine with a displacement of 890 in³ and a power output of 225 hp. It can reach a top travel speed of 30.8 mph. The Cat No.16 (49G) was built between 1963 and 1973.

Dieses Bild zeigt Caterpillars größten Motorgrader, den No.16 (49G). Angetrieben wird dieser 22.499 kg schwere Grader von einem Cat D348 6-Zyl.-Turbo-Motor mit 14,6 l Hubraum und 225 PS. Man erreicht eine max. Fahrtgeschwindigkeit von 49,7 km/h. Der No.16 (49G) wurde von 1963 bis 1973 gebaut.

In 1973 Caterpillar introduced the new 16G (93U) with now 275 hp and a weight of 60.150 lb. This Cat 16G (93U) is equipped with a ripper.

1973 stellte Caterpillar den neuen 16G (93U) mit 275 PS und einem Gewicht von 27.284 kg vor. Dieser 16G ist mit einem Heckaufreisser ausgerüstet.

A new Caterpillar 16G (93U) grades the old Alaska Highway.

Ein neuer Caterpillar 16G (93U) begradigt den alten Alaska Highway.

It seems as if this Caterpillar 16G (93U) was working on the moon, but in reality it works in a uranium mine.

Vor einer fast mondähnlichen Landschaft arbeitet dieser Caterpillar 16G (93U) in einer Uranmine.

A current Caterpillar 16H helps to maintain the haulroads in a big copper mine.

Ein aktueller Caterpillar 16H unterhält die Fahrtwege in einer großen Kupfermine.

Currently world`s largest motor grader is the Caterpillar 24H. It was introduced in 1996. The operation weight goes up to 136,610 lb. The "super" grader is powered by a Cat 3412E V12 turbo engine with a displacement of 1647 in³ and is rated at 500 hp.

Der weltgrößte aktuelle Caterpillar Motorgrader ist der 24H. Er wurde 1996 vorgestellt. Das Einsatzgewicht beträgt 61.955 kg. Angetrieben wird dieser "Super"-Grader von einem Cat 3412E V12-Turbo-Motor mit 27 l Hubraum und 500 PS.

The maximum travel speed of the Caterpillar 24H motor grader amounts 22.3 mph. in the sixth gear. The machine width amounts 13'85", the length 51'83" and the height 14'25". Noticeable is the 24' moldboard. Two of these "super" motor graders work in a uranium mine in Eastern Germany.

Max. Fahrtgeschwindigkeit des 24H Motorgraders: 36 km/h im sechsten Gan,. Breite 4.225 mm, Länge 15.802 mm und Höhe 4.346 mm. Die Schar mißt 7.300 mm. Eingesetzt werden zwei dieser "Super"-Grader in einer Uranmine in Ostdeutschland.

Scrapers

Caterpillar built the first cable operated pull scrapers in 1946. The model No.70 carried 11.0 yd³ (heaped) pulled by the Cat D7, and the model No. 80 carried 18.0 yd³ (heaped) pulled by the Cat D8. Further models followed in 1947: No. 60 for the D6, in 1949 the No. 40 for the D4 and in 1951 the No. 90 for the Caterpillar tractor D8. In 1955 three further models were built, the No. 435C, the No. 463 and the biggest, the No. 491 with a load capacity of 34 yd³ (heaped). They replaced the former models. The last pulled scraper, the No. 435G, was delivered in 1973. In 1941 Caterpillar introduced the forerunner for all the following scrapers: the wheel tractor DW10, carrying the No. 10 scraper with a load capacity of 11 yd³ (heaped). It was followed by the Cat DW15, attached with the No. 10 scraper, and the biggest, the Cat DW20 with No. 20 scraper, rated at 225 hp, introduced in 1951. The Cat DW20 was a very popular 3-axle scraper of the fifties. It was rugged, powerful and with a haul travel speed of up to 32 mph very fast. The first articulated scraper was built by Caterpillar in 1951, the DW21, rated at 225 hp and carrying 20 yd³ (heaped). In the sixties Caterpillar introduced a series of the new 2-axle and 3-axle scrapers. You could choose from five 3-axles scrapers, four 2-axle standard scrapers with one engine, three twin-engine scrapers and four elevator scrapers. With those Caterpillar offered the widest range of scrapers

for the contractors. Scrapers, working on good soils with a max. (one way) haul distance of 4,920 ft, are very efficiently and no other earth moving machine in the same class can comped with them. In average it needs less than one minute to fill the scraper bowl with 30 yd³ (heaped) of a Caterpillar 637 scraper push loaded by a Cat D9. When ejecting consistently with the bulldozer ejector you can fill the material in gaps or you can level it in constant high layers for good dozing and compacting by a soil compactor. Today Caterpillar is the world's biggest scraper manufacturer.

Schürfzüge

Die ersten gezogenen und seilgesteuerten Scraper baute Caterpillar 1946, das Modell No. 70 mit 8,4 m³ (gehäuft) für die Cat D7 und das Modell No. 80 mit 13,8 m³ (gehäuft) für die Cat D8. Weitere Modelle folgten 1947: No. 60 für die D6, 1949 der No. 40 für die D4 und 1951 der No. 90 für den Caterpillar Traktor D8. Weitere drei Modelle wurden ab 1955 angeboten: No. 435C, No. 463 und der größte mit einem Fassungsvermögen von 26,8 m³ (gehäuft), der No. 491. Sie lösten Ihre Vorgänger ab. Der letzte gezogene Scraper No. 435G wurde 1973 ausgeliefert. 1941 stellte Caterpillar den Urahn aller folgenden Scraper vor: Den Zugtraktor

DW10 mit No. 10 Scraper mit 8,4 m³ (gehäuft). Ihm folgte der Cat DW15 mit No. 10 Scraper und der große, 1951 vorgestellte Cat DW20 mit No. 20 Scraper. Mit 225 PS war der DW20 ein sehr beliebter 3-Achs-Scraper der 50er Jahre. Er war robust, leistungsstark und mit einer Transportgeschwindigkeit von 51,7 km/h sehr schnell. Den ersten knickgelenkten Scraper baute Caterpillar 1951, den DW21 mit 225 PS und 15 m³ (gehäuft) Kübelinhalt. In den 60ern stellte Caterpillar gleich eine ganze Reihe der neuen 2-Achs- und 3-Achs-Scraper vor. Man konnte zwischen fünf 3-Achs-Scrapern, vier 2-Achs-Standard-Scrapern mit einem Motor, drei Doppelmotor-Scrapern und vier Elevator-Scrapern wählen. Caterpillar bietet so die größte Palette an Scrapern an. Bei guten Böden sind Scraper bei einer Transportentfernung bis zu 1.500 m sehr wirtschaftlich einzusetzen und durch keine andere Baumaschine in der gleichen Größenklasse zu übertreffen. Wenn ein Caterpillar 637 Scraper von einer Cat D9 schubbeladen wird, beträgt die Ladezeit im Durchschnitt weniger als eine Minute, um den Kübel mit 23 m³ (gehäuft), das sind ungefähr 39.000 kg, zu beladen. Durch ein gleichmäßiges Ausstoßen durch den Auswerfer kann man gezielt Material in Senken einfüllen oder gleichmäßig hohe Schichten schütten, die durch einen Verdichter sehr gut zu planieren und zu verdichten sind. Caterpillar ist heute der größte Scraperhersteller der Welt.

A Caterpillar D9G (66A) dozer with 385 hp is equipped with a rear mounted power control unit No. 129 double drum winch to pull a Cat No. 463C (62C) towed scraper with a capacity of 28 yd³ (heaped). It was built between 1959 and 1960.

Ein Caterpillar D9G (66A) Kettendozer mit 385 PS ist ausgerüstet mit einer heckmontierten No. 129 Doppelseilwinde zum Ziehen eines Cat No. 463C (62C) Scraper mit 21,4 m³ (gehäuft). Gebaut wurde dieser von 1959 bis 1960.

A sales brochure from 1957 shows Caterpillar's DW20E (57C) tractor with 300 hp and the scraper No. 456 (67C) with a capacity of 24,8 yd³ (heaped). This scraper unit was built from 1955 to 1957. The last series were the Cat DW20F and No. 456 scraper, and the DW20G with No. 456/482 scraper built from 1958 to 1960. Its smaller brother was the Cat DW10 (1V) with 115 hp and No.10 (3C) scraper with 11yd³ capacity (heaped). It was replaced by the Cat DW15 (45C) rated at 150 hp and No.10 (19C) scraper with 9 yd³ capacity (heaped) in 1954.

Ein Verkaufsprospekt von 1957 zeigt den Caterpillar DW20E (57C) Traktor mit 300 PS und den Scraper No. 456 (67C) mit einem Fassungsvömgen von 19 m³ (gehäuft). Gebaut wurde diese Cat-Scrapereinheit von 1955 bis 1957. Die letzte Serie war der Cat DW20F mit No. 456 Scraper und der Cat DW20G mit No. 456/482 Scraper von 1958 bis 1960. Sein kleiner Bruder war der Cat DW10 (1V) mit 115 PS mit No. 10 (3C) Scraper mit 8,4 m³ (gehäuft). Er wurde 1954 durch den Cat DW15 (45C) mit 150 PS und No. 10 (19C) Scraper mit 6,9 m³ (gehäuft) abgelöst.

FOUR-WHEEL TRACTOR
(Series E) AND SCRAPER

CATERPILLAR DW20 No. 456

The DW20 (Series E) Tractor is powered by a six cylinder, Turbocharged Caterpillar Engine and is available with direct electric diesel starting system or gasoline starting engine. Large 29.5—29 wide-section tubeless tires provide maximum flotation and traction with less rolling resistance.

CATERPILLAR **DW·21**
No. 470

300 HP – 25 CU. YD. HEAPED CAPACITY

The DW21 Series C Tractor is powered by a six cylinder, Turbocharged Caterpillar Engine and is available with direct electric diesel starting system or gasoline starting engine. Large 29.5-29 wide-section tubeless tires provide maximum flotation and traction with less rolling resistance.

The No. 470 Scraper is cable operated and features the exclusive LOWBOWL design for bigger, faster loads. High apron lift and dozer-type ejector provide quick, positive ejection of any type of material. An automatic cable saver unit prevents breakage of both the bowl lift and ejector cables.

The first articulated Caterpillar scraper DW21 (58C) is shown on this sales brochure from 1957. The first Cat DW21 (8W) was rated at 225 hp, and the No. 21 (8) scraper carried up to 20 yd^3 (heaped). It was introduced in 1951 and was in the sales lists until 1955. The last series were the Cat DW21G (85E) rated at 345 hp, and the No.470 (86E) scraper with 27 yd^3 capacity (heaped). They were in the lists until 1960. Successor was the Caterpillar 619B (89E/90E).

Ein Verkaufsprospekt des ersten knickgelenkten Caterpillar Scraper DW21 (58C) von 1957. Der erste Cat DW21 (8W) mit 225 PS und No. 21 (8) Scraper mit 15 m^3 (gehäuft) wurde 1951 vorgestellt und blieb bis 1955 im Verkaufsprogramm. Die letzte Serie war der Cat DW21G (85E) mit 345 PS und der No. 470 (86E) Scraper mit dem 20,6 m^3 (gehäuft). Dieser blieb bis 1960 im Verkaufsprogramm. Nachfolger wurde der Caterpillar 619B (89E/90E).

The smallest single engine scraper is the brand-new 1999 Caterpillar 611, rated at 265 hp with a capacity of 14,3 yd^3 (heaped). The picture shows a Caterpillar 621 (43H) rated at 300 hp and load 20 yd^3 (heaped) on a job site in Alaska.

Der kleinste Standard-Scraper ist der brandneue Caterpillar 611 von 1999 mit 265 PS und einem Fassungsvermögen von 11 m^3 (gehäuft). Das Bild zeigt einen Caterpillar 621 (43H) mit 300 PS und einem Fassungsvermögen von 15,3 m^3 (gehäuft) auf einer Baustelle in Alaska.

A perfect team: the 621 (23H) is push loaded by a Cat D8H (46A) rated at 270 hp. That saves time, reduces tire wear and tear of the scraper.

Ein perfektes Team: Ein etwas neuerer Caterpillar 621 (23H) wird von einer Cat D8H (46A) mit 270 PS Schub beladen. Das spart Zeit und vermindert den Reifenverschleiß des Scrapers.

With a gross vehicle weight of 104,296 lb the Caterpillar scraper 621 (23H) reached a maximum travel speed of up to 31 mph. This requires good maintained haul roads. Powered is the Cat 621 by a Cat D336 V8 turbo engine.

Mit einem Gesamtgewicht von 47.300 kg erreicht der Caterpillar Scraper 621 (23H) eine max. Transportgeschwindigkeit von über 50 km/h. Dies erfordert einen guten Unterhalt der Fahrtwege durch den Einsatz von Motorgradern. Angetrieben wird der Cat 621 durch einen Cat D336 V8-Turbo-Motor.

The push loading of a scraper requires a lot of sensitivity by the dozer operator to avoid the damage of the rear scraper tires. This Caterpillar 621 (23H) was used on a scraper job site in Portugal in 1997. It was built from 1965 to 1974. The successors wese the Cat 621B (45P) until 1986 and the Cat 621E (6AB/2PD) until 1993. The current model is the Cat 621F with 330 hp and the same loading capacity as the former models.

Das Push-Laden der Scraper erfordert viel Fingerspitzengefühl des Dozerfahrers, um ein Beschädigen der hinteren Scraperreifen auszuschließen. Dieser Caterpillar 621 (23H) wurde noch 1997 auf einer Scraperbaustelle in Portugal eingesetzt. Er wurde von 1965 bis 1974 gebaut. Nachfolger waren der Cat 621B (45P) bis 1986, der Cat 621E (6AB/2PD) bis 1993. Das aktuelle Modell ist der Cat 621F mit 330 PS und gleicher Ladekapazität wie seine Vorgänger.

Schnellbetrieb im Erdbau Durch Caterpillar's neue Schürfzüge

A Caterpillar sales brochure from 1961 shows two scraper models: scraper 631A and tractor 630A with 630A scraper. Both are powered by a Cat D343 6-cylinder turbo engine, with a displacement of 890 in³ and a power output of 420 hp. Both have a load capacity of 28 yd³ (heaped). The fully loaded Cat 630A reached a travel speed of 40.9 mph with a weight of 132,322 lb. The Cat 631A with a gross weight of 129,698 lb reached a speed of 31 mph.

Ein Caterpillar Verkaufsprospekt von 1961 zeigt die Modelle Scraper 631A und Tractor 630A mit Scraper 630A. Beide werden von einem Cat D343 6-Zyl.-Turbo-Motor mit 14,6 l Hubraum und 420 PS angetrieben. Beide haben ein Fassungsvermögen von 21,4 m³ (gehäuft). Der beladene Cat 630A erreicht 66 km/h mit einem Gewicht von 60.010 kg, der Cat 631A mit 58.820 kg eine max. Fahrtgeschwindigkeit von 50 km/h.

Between 1960 and 1962 the Caterpillar 630A (52F) with 420 hp was built. The picture shows a Cat 630A (52F). It is equipped with Hyster compactor wheels and an Hyster compacting trailer. The new B-series came in 1962 and was in the sales lists until 1969.

Von 1960 bis 1962 wird der Caterpillar 630A (52F) mit 420 PS gebaut. Das Bild zeigt einen mit Hyster Compactor-Rädern und Hyster-Hänger ausgestatteten Cat 630A (52F). Die folgende B-Serie wird von 1962-1969 gebaut.

This Caterpillar 630B (14G/10G) is equipped with an Athey PW630 bottom dump trailer with a load capacity of 38 yd³ (heaped). An Athey coal bottom dump trailer PH630 with 54 metric/tons capacity and a rear dump PR630 with 29 yd³ capacity (heaped) are also available.

Dieser Cat 630B (14G/10G) ist mit einem PW630 Athey Bodenentleerwagen mit einem Fassungsvermögen von 29,1 m³ (gehäuft) ausgerüstet. Des weiteren steht ein Athey Kohlehänger PH630 mit 54,4 t Nutzlast und ein Hinterkipper PR630 mit 22,2 m³ (gehäuft) zur Auswahl.

This Caterpillar 631A (51F) is at work for more than 33 years. It was rebuild as a water wagon and worked on a big construction site in France in 1995. The Cat 631A was built between 1960 and 1962.

Seit mehr als 33 Jahren ist dieser Cat 631A (51F) im Einsatz. Er wurde als Wasserwagen umgebaut und arbeitet 1995 auf einer Großbaustelle in Frankreich. Der Cat 631A wurde von 1960 bis 1962 gebaut.

The Caterpillar 631B (13G) has an operating weight of 69,700 lb and reaches a travel speed of 32 mph. It is powered by a Cat 6-cylinder turbo engine rated at 420 hp.

Der Caterpillar 631B (13G) hat ein Einsatzgewicht von 31.620 kg und erreicht eine Höchstgeschwindigkeit von 52 km/h. Angetrieben wird er von einem Cat 6-Zyl.-Turbo-Motor mit 420 PS.

The load capacity of the Caterpillar 631B (13G) amounts 30 yd³ (heaped). The scraper 631B measures 43'57" and is 12'49" wide. Because of the articulation of 90° left/right, the turning circle gauge is only 37'42".

Das Fassungsvermögen des Caterpillar 631B (13G) beträgt 23 m³ (gehäuft). Der Scraper 631B ist 13.284 mm lang und 3.810 mm breit, dank eines Lenkeinschlags von je 90° mißt der Wendekreisdurchmesser nur 11.410 mm.

Successor of the B-series was the Caterpillar 631C (67M) with a weight of 80,150 lb. It was introduced in 1969.

Nachfolger der B-Serie wurde 1969 der Caterpillar 631C (67M) mit einem Gewicht von nun 36.350 kg.

This early Caterpillar 631D (24W) from 1975 has a weight of 93,410 lb and is powered by a Cat 3408 V8 turbo engine rated at 450 hp. It is works on a job site in France.

Dieser frühe Caterpillar 631D (24W) von 1975 mit einem Gewicht von 42.370 kg wird von einem Cat 3408 V8-Turbo-Motor mit 450 PS angetrieben und arbeitet auf einer Großbaustelle in Frankreich.

This is a new version of the Caterpillar 631D (24W). The front lights are now integrated in the radiator grill. It was used near Koblenz/Germany in 1995.

Dies ist die neuere Version des Caterpillar 631D (24W), die Frontscheinwerfer sind jetzt im Kühlergrill integriert. Er wird noch 1995 in der Nähe von Koblenz eingesetzt.

An overhauled Cat 631D (24W) with Caterpillar's ROPS cab is seen on a construction site in Whitehorse/Canada. When the models changed from the C- to the D-series, the operator station was renewed.

Ein überholter Cat 631D (24W) mit Caterpillar ROPS-Fahrerhaus steht auf einer Baustelle in Whitehorse/Kanada. Mit dem Modellwechsel von der C- zur D-Serie wurde auch die Inneneinrichtung des Fahrerhauses neu gestaltet.

A Caterpillar dozer D8L (7JC) pushes a Cat 631D (24W). With a good team, the loading cycle takes less than one minute. The production end for the 631D came in 1985.

Ein Caterpillar Dozer D8L (7JC) unterstützt einen Cat 631D (24W). Bei einem eingespielten Team dauert der reine Ladevorgang unter einer Minute. Das Produktionsende für den 631D kam 1985.

Caterpillar introduced the new 631E (1AB) in 1985, the cab was improved for a second time. Now there is a much better overview for the operator. This team, a Cat D9L (14Y) and a Cat 631E (1AB), works on the Alaska Highway.

1985 wurde der Caterpillar 631E (1AB) vorgestellt, das Fahrerhaus ist nochmals übersichtlicher gestaltet worden. Die größeren Glasflächen lassen eine bessere Rundumsicht zu. Dieses Team aus einer Cat D9L (14Y) und einem Cat 631E (1AB) arbeitet auf dem Alaska Highway.

The Caterpillar 631E (1AB) reaches a maximum travel speed of up to 30 mph when driving in the seventh gear.

Im siebten Gang erreicht der Caterpillar 631E (1AB) eine max. Fahrtgeschwindigkeit von 48,3 km/h.

This Caterpillar D10N (2YD) with 520 hp is equipped with a Balderson BDI 10-11'6C push blade. It was developed especially to push scrapers. The picture shows the moment when both machines, the D10N and the 631E (1AB), start the loading cycle.

Eine Caterpillar D10N (2YD) mit 520 PS ist ausgerüstet mit einem Balderson BDI 10-11'6C Schubschild, das eigens für das Schieben von Scrapern entwickelt wurde. Das Bild zeigt den Moment, in dem beide Maschinen D10N und 631E (1AB) mit dem Ladevorgang beginnen.

This specially built water wagon with a capacity of 10568 US gallons is towed by a Caterpillar 631E (1AB) tractor unit.

Dieser eigens gebaute Wassertanker mit 40.000 l Inhalt wird von einem Caterpillar 631E (1AB) Triebkopf gezogen.

If possible, a scraper should always load downhill. That reduces the cycle time and improves the fill factor of the bowl. The picture shows a new Cat D10R built in 1999, and a Cat 631E (1AB) scraper on a construction site in Germany.

Wenn es möglich ist, setzt man einen Scraper immer hangabwärts zum Laden ein. Das verkürzt die Arbeitstaktzeit und verbessert den Füllungsgrad des Kübels. Das Bild zeigt eine neue Cat D10R, Baujahr 1999, und einen Cat 631E (1AB) Scraper in Deutschland.

Scraper sites are very rare in Germany, but in France many of the big contractors still use a real fleet of scrapers, as this Caterpillar 631E (1AB) shows. The production end for the E-series came in 1991.

Scraperbaustellen werden in Deutschland immer seltener, in Frankreich dagegen gehören Scraper bei vielen großen Bauunternehmen zur Grundausstattung, so wie dieser Caterpillar 631E (1AB). Die Produktion der E-Serie wurde 1991 eingestellt.

Successor of the popular 631 Caterpillar scraper was the Cat 631E II in 1992, with an operating weight of 97,483 lb and a load capacity of 31 yd³ (heaped). Powered is the new series II by a Cat 3408E V8 turbo engine with a displacement of 1098 in³ and an output of 490 hp. Further improvements of the new model: it is equipped with an 8-gear transmission which allows a top speed of up to 33 mph. In 1996 I saw this brand-new Cat 631E II on a scraper job site in France.

Nachfolger des beliebten Caterpillar Scraper 631 wurde der neue, 1992 vorgestellte, Cat 631E II mit einem Einsatzgewicht von 44.210 kg und einem Fassungsvermögen von 23,7 m³ (gehäuft). Angetrieben wird die neue Serie II von einem Cat 3408E V8-Turbo-Motor mit 18 l Hubraum und 490 PS. Des weiteren besitzt das neue Modell nun ein 8-Gang-Getriebe. Damit wird eine Höchstgeschwindigkeit von 53,5 km/h erreicht. 1996 konnte ich diesen Cat 631E II auf einer Scraperbaustelle in Frankreich bewundern.

A picture out of a sales brochure from 1991 shows a Caterpillar 651E scraper. In the same class as the Cat 650, the Caterpillar 651 (33G) and the 651B (67K) with a capacity of 44 yd³ (heaped) were offered. The later ones were built between 1962 and 1968, respectively 1969 and 1984. With the introduction of the new E-series a new Cat 3412 V12 turbo engine rated now at 550 hp and a new cab was introduced. These are only a few of the many improvements of the new series.

Ein Verkaufsprospekt des Caterpillar 651E Scraper von 1991. In der gleichen Klasse wie der Cat 650 wird der Caterpillar 651 (33G) und der 651B (67K) mit einem Fassungsvermögen von 33,6 m³ (gehäuft) angeboten. Sie wurden von 1962 bis 1968 bzw. von 1969 bis 1984 gebaut. Mit der neuen E-Serie wurde ein neuer Cat 3412 V12-Turbo-Motor mit 550 PS und einem neuen Fahrerhaus vorgestellt, um nur einige Verbesserungen aufzuzählen.

WHEEL TRACTOR-SCRAPER **CATERPILLAR** 632

38 CU. YD. HEAPED CAPACITY

The CAT 632 —

Four wheel tractor with scraper

- 420 HP (maximum) engine for efficient, hard lugging power.
- Cat power shift transmission with exclusive, automatic shifting in each of three ranges — plus loading range. Top speed is 43.5 MPH.
- Operating ease and safety that increase productivity.
- New 38 cu. yd. (heaped), 28 cu. yd. (struck) Positive Action Scraper for fast, easy loading.
- Service accessibility means more working time — less maintenance time.

WHEEL TRACTOR-SCRAPER **CATERPILLAR** 641

38 CU. YD. HEAPED CAPACITY

The CAT 641 —

Two wheel tractor with scraper

- 560 HP (maximum) V-8 engine for efficient, hard lugging power.
- Cat power shift transmission with exclusive, automatic shifting in each of three ranges — plus loading range. Top speed is 30 MPH.
- Operating ease and safety that increase productivity. Hydraulic retarder is standard.
- New 38 cu. yd. (heaped), 28 cu. yd. (struck) Positive Action Scraper for fast, easy loading.
- Service accessibility means more working time — less maintenance time.

A 1962 sales brochure shows the Caterpillar 632 (14G) scraper. The Cat 632 (14G) is a little bit heavier than the Cat 630B. Now it loads 38 yd³ (heaped). It was found in the sales lists until 1966.

Ein Verkaufsprospekt des Caterpillar 632 (14G) Scraper von 1962. Der Cat 632 (14G) ist ein wenig größer als der Cat 630B. Er fasst nun 29 m³ (gehäuft) und blieb bis 1966 im Verkaufsprogramm.

Caterpillar 641 (64F) scraper. This 2-axle scraper has the same loading capacity 38 yd³ (heaped) as the 3-axle scraper 632. The 95,256 lb heavy scraper is powered by a Cat V8 turbo engine with 560 hp. It was built between 1962 and 1965.

Caterpillar 641 (64F) Scraper. Der 2-Achs-Scraper hat das gleiche Fassungsvermögen mit 29 m³ (gehäuft) wie der 3-Achs-Scraper 632. Angetrieben wird der 43.200 kg Scraper von einem Cat V8-Turbo-Motor mit 560 PS. Er wurde von 1962 bis 1965 gebaut.

SCHÜRFZUG **CATERPILLAR** 650

ZWANGSSCHURFUNG
- Fassungsvermögen (gehäuft)   33,6 m³
- Fassungsvermögen (gestrichen)   24,5 m³
- Eindringen des Schneidmessers, Schließen der Schürze und Ausstoßung des Materials erfolgen zwangsläufig durch Hydraulikdruck

DIESELMOTOR
- CATERPILLAR-Dieselmotor mit 500 PS (Schwungscheibe)
- Optimale Motorleistung in jedem Drehzahlbereich durch automatische Spritzversteller

PLANETEN-LASTSCHALTGETRIEBE
- Schaltet in allen drei Vorwärtsgängen automatisch zwischen Wandlerstufe, Direktstufe und Schnellstufe
- Höchstgeschwindigkeit: 64,3 km/h

LEICHTE BEDIENUNG UND WARTUNG
- Hydraulisch unterstützte Lenkung, Druckluftbremsen, Einhebelschaltung, reaktionsschnelle Schürfkübelhydraulik
- Alle größeren Baugruppen sind leicht zugänglich und können einzeln ausgebaut werden

WHEEL TRACTOR-SCRAPER **CATERPILLAR** 660

POSITIVE ACTION SCRAPER —
- 54 Cu. Yd. (41,3 m³) heaped.
- 40 Cu. Yd. (30,6 m³) struck.
- Hydraulically controlled for positive cutting edge penetration, apron closure and material ejection.

DIESEL TRACTOR —
- 500 HP (flywheel) Caterpillar engine.
- Automatic, fuel-injection timing advance to give optimum performance at all RPM.

POWER SHIFT TRANSMISSION —
- Automatic shifting from torque divider drive to direct drive to overdrive in each of three forward speed ranges.
- Top speed 42 MPH (67,6 km/h).

OPERATING AND SERVICING EASE —
- Power steering, air brakes, single lever shift control, quick-response scraper controls.
- Major components accessible and independently removable.

This sales brochure shows the next sized up Caterpillar scraper of the 600-series. The 99,500 lb heavy scraper Cat 650 (63F) with a 500 hp Cat engine reaches a respectable travel speed of up to 39.7 mph. It was built between 1962 and 1964, while the B-series of the Cat 650 (22G) was built from 1962 to 1972.

Ein Verkaufsprospekt zeigt den nächstgrößeren Caterpillar-Scraper der 600-Serie. Der Cat 650 (63F) hat einen 500 PS starken Cat-Motor. So erreicht der 45.130 kg schwere Scraper eine Fahrtgeschwindigkeit von 64,3 km/h. Er wurde von 1962 bis 1964 gebaut, die B-Serie des Cat 650 (22G) von 1962 bis 1972.

A sales brochure from 1965 shows Caterpillar's biggest scraper, the 660 (90F). It is powered by a Cat V8 turbo engine with a displacement of 1189 in³ and an output of 500 hp. The 56'65" long scraper weighs fully loaded 243,760 lb and reaches a maximum travel speed up to 42.8 mph.

Ein Verkaufsprospekt von 1965 zeigt Caterpillars größten Scraper, den 660 (90F). Er wird angetrieben von einem V8-Turbo-Motor mit 19, 5 l Hubraum und 500 PS. Der 17.272 mm lange Scraperzug hat voll beladen ein Gewicht von 110.549 kg. Dennoch erreicht er eine max. Geschwindigkeit von 69 km/h.

The picture shows a Caterpillar 660 (90F) with an Athey PH660 hooked up coal dump bottom trailer with a load capacity of 131 yd³ (heaped) or 100 tons. The 59'63" long unit weighs fully loaded 315,658 lb. The Cat unloads by opening the bottom floor. The Cat 660 was built from 1962 to 1964, followed by the heavier Cat 660B (58K).

Ein Caterpillar 660 (90F) mit einem Athey PH 660 Kohleanhänger mit 100 m³ (gehäuft) und 90 t Nutzlast. Der 18.180 mm lange Zug wiegt voll beladen 143.156 kg, entladen wird der Hänger durch das Öffnen der Bodenklappen. Der Cat 660 wird von 1962 bis 1964 gebaut. Ihm folgt der schwerere Cat 660B (58K).

This Caterpillar 660 (90F) is hooked up with an Athey PW660 bottom dump trailer. The 41'06" long wagon has a capacity of 64 yd³ (heaped). The empty weight of the complete unit amounts 117,989 lb. The production of the biggest Caterpillar single engine scraper ended in 1978.

Mit einem Athey PW660 Hänger ist dieser Caterpillar 660 (90F) ausgerüstet. Der 12.520 mm lange Hänger hat ein Fassungsvermögen von 48,9 m³ (gehäuft). Das Leergewicht des Zuges beträgt 53.510 kg. 1978 wurde der Bau des größten Cat-Standard Scrapers eingestellt.

The 627, Caterpillar's smallest twin engine scraper, was introduced in 1968. The picture shows a Cat 627 (54K). It is powered by two Cat D333 6-cylinder turbo engines both rated at 225 hp. This scraper works in a clay pit in Germany.

Caterpillars kleinster Doppelmotor-Scraper, der 627, wurde 1968 vorgestellt. Das Bild zeigt einen Cat 627 (54K). Er wird angetrieben durch zwei Cat D333 6-Zyl.-Turbo-Motoren mit je 225 PS. Dieser Scraper wird für die Tongewinnung in Deutschland eingesetzt.

This Caterpillar 627 (54K) works on a highway project in Germany. It is pushed by a Cat D8 dozer.

Auf einer Autobahnbaustelle in Deutschland arbeitet dieser Caterpillar 627 (54K). Er wird durch einen Cat-Kettendozer D8 beim Laden unterstützt.

Two Caterpillar 627 (54K) work in push pull application, two scrapers support each other without requiring a push dozer. The first scraper begins to load while it is pushed by the second unit. The picture shows the beginning of the second loading cycle. The rear scraper loads and the one in front pulls it. After the loading cycle is finished the hydraulic activated bail is raised and both scrapers drive to the dump area separately.

Zwei Caterpillar 627 (54K) im Push-Pull-Betrieb. Es unterstützen sich zwei Scraper beim Beladen, ohne daß ein Schubdozer benötigt wird. Der vordere Scraper beginnt als erster mit dem Ladevorgang. Er wird durch den zweiten Scraper geschoben. Das Bild zeigt gerade den Beginn des zweiten Ladevorgangs. Der hintere Scraper schürft und der vordere Scraper zieht ihn dabei. Nach Beendigung des Ladevorgangs wird der hydraulisch betätigte Anhängebügel gelöst und beide Scraper fahren getrennt zur Entladestelle.

With a loading capacity of 20 yd³ (heaped) the Caterpillar 627 (54K) reached a travel speed in the eighth gear of up to 31.7 mph. In 1973 Cat introduced the new 627B (14S) with 11,025 lb more weight as the old 627 with 66,000 lb. The Cat 627B is already equipped with the new ROPS cab.

Mit einem Fassungsvermögen von 15,3 m³ (gehäuft) erreicht der Caterpillar 627 (54K) eine Transportgeschwindigkeit im 8. Gang von 51 km/h. 1973 wurde der neuere Cat 627B (14S) mit einem fast 5.000 kg höheren Einsatzgewicht als der alte 627 mit 29.900 kg vorgestellt. Der Cat 627B wird schon mit neuem ROPS-Fahrerhaus ausgeliefert.

A fleet of Caterpillar 627E (6EB) scrapers.   Eine 627E (6EB) Caterpillar Scraper-Flotte.

The Caterpillar 627E (6EB) scraper mines clay selectively in a clay pit in Switzerland. The picture shows a Cat 627E which is pushed by a Cat D8K (77V) with 300 hp. The operating weight of the new E-series goes up to 76,435 lb.

In einer Tongrube in der Schweiz wird mit 627E (6EB) Caterpillar Scrapern selektiv Ton abgebaut. Das Bild zeigt den Cat 627E, der durch eine Cat D8K (77V) mit 300 PS schubbeladen wird. Das Einsatzgewicht der neuen E-Serie liegt bei 34.670 kg.

In less than one and a half minute a Caterpillar 627E (6EB) with a pay load of 48,069 lb is push loaded by a Cat D9G (66A) with 385 hp.

In weniger als 1,5 Min. wird ein Caterpillar 627E (6EB) mit einer Nutzlast von 21.800 kg durch eine Caterpillar D9G (66A) mit 385 PS schubbeladen.

On this picture you can see the steep grade of the haul road. Here the twin engine concept of the 627E (6EB) is used to its full advantage.

Auf diesem Bild ist die enorme Neigung des Transportweges zu erkennen. Hier kommt das Antriebskonzept des Caterpillar 627E (6EB) mit zwei Motoren voll zum Tragen.

Two Caterpillar 627E PP (6GP) with an operating weight of 79,655 lb and an engine output rated at 450 hp. They were built until 1989. The successor was the new Cat 627E (7CG), powered by a Cat 3406B 6-cylinder turbo engine with 330 hp in the tractor unit, and with a Cat 3306 6-cylinder turbo engine with 225 hp in the scraper unit. The current Caterpillar scraper is the 627F.

Zwei Caterpillar 627E PP (6GP) mit einem Einsatzgewicht von 36.130 kg und 450 PS Motorleistung. Sie wurden bis 1989 gebaut, es folgte der 627E (7CG) mit einem Cat 3406B 6-Zyl.-Turbo-Motor mit 330 PS in der Zugeinheit und einem Cat 3306 6-Zyl.-Turbo-Motor mit 225 PS in der Kübeleinheit. Der aktuelle Caterpillar Scraper ist der 627F.

In 1970 Caterpillar offered the 30 yd³ (heaped) 637 (65M). It was powered by a Cat D343 6-cylinder turbo engine rated at 415 hp in the tractor unit, and a Cat D3306 6-cylinder turbo engine rated at 225 hp in the scraper unit. The picture shows a Cat 637 PP (79P) which was rebuilt in 1980 into a 55,125 lb capacity special spreader wagon for lime.

1970 wurde der 23 m³ (gehäuft) fassende Caterpillar 637 (65M) vorgestellt, angetrieben durch einen Cat D343 6-Zyl.-Turbo-Motor mit 415 PS in der Zugeinheit und einem Cat D3306 6-Zyl.-Turbo-Motor mit 225 PS in der Kübeleinheit. Das Bild zeigt einen Cat 637 PP (79P), der 1980 zu einem 25.000 kg fassenden Spezial-Streuwagen für Kalk umgebaut wurde.

This Caterpillar 637 PP (79P) is equipped with a rear mounted hydraulic activated disc harrow. The special scraper measures 65'6" in length. For more than 24 years this Caterpillar has been working on innumerable construction sites.

Dieser Caterpillar 637 PP (79P) ist ausgerüstet mit einer hydraulisch anhebbaren Scheibenegge. Der Spezial-Scraper hat eine Länge von ca. 20.000 mm. Dieser Cat arbeitet seit mehr als 24 Jahren.

Two Caterpillar 637D PP (27W) scrapers with a total length of 97'28".

Zwei Caterpillar 637D PP (27W) Scraper mit einer Gesamtlänge von 29.660 mm.

This Caterpillar 637D PP (27W) is push loaded by a Cat D9N (1JD). The picture shows an early version of the Cat 637D with the front lights mounted inside the radiator grill. The later models had the lights mounted outside the radiator grill. This version was built between 1975 and 1985 and is powered by a Cat 3408 V8 turbo engine in the tractor unit rated at 450 hp and by a Cat 3306 6-cylinder turbo engine in the scraper unit rated at 255 hp.

Ein Caterpillar 637D PP (27W) wird von einer Cat D9N (1JD) schubbeladen. Das Bild zeigt eine frühe Version des Cat 637D. Man kann dies an den Scheinwerfern, die im Kühlergrill integriert sind, erkennen. Bei späteren Modellen wurden die Scheinwerfer außen am Kühler installiert. Diese Version wurde von 1975 bis 1985 gebaut mit einem Cat 3408 V8-Turbo-Motor mit 450 PS in der Zugeinheit und einem Cat 3306 6-Zyl.-Turbo-Motor mit 255 PS in der Kübeleinheit.

Caterpillar introduced the new 637E (1FB) in 1985 with a redesigned scraper bowl and a new ROPS cab. The picture shows a Cat 637E PP (1FB). By the way, all twin engine scrapers are equipped with two separate accelerator pedals, one for each engine. It depends on the current job conditions, which of the accelerators the operator applies. The current model is the Cat 637E II. It was introduced in 1991.

1985 wird der neue Caterpillar 637E (1FB) vorgestellt mit überarbeitetem Schürfkübel und neuem ROPS-Fahrerhaus. Das Bild zeigt einen Cat 637E PP (1FB), der durch eine Cat D9H (90V) schubbeladen wird. Übrigens haben alle Doppel-Motor-Scraper zwei Gaspedale, die der Fahrer unterschiedlich, je nach Einsatzbedingung, betätigen kann. Das aktuelle Modell ist der Cat 637E II, der 1991 vorgestellt wurde.

The picture shows a Cat 657 (46M90), built in 1969. This one is push loaded by two Cat D9G (66A). The tractor unit is powered by a Cat D346 V8 turbo engine rated at 500 hp, and the scraper unit is powered by a Cat D343A 6-cylinder turbo engine with 360 hp. The load capacity of the 50'6" long Cat 657 (46M) scraper amounts 44 yd³ (heaped). It was produced between 1968 and 1969.

Das Bild zeigt einen Cat 657 (46M90), Baujahr 1969, der durch zwei D9G (66A) schubbeladen wird. Die Zugeinheit wird von einem Cat D346 V8-Turbo-Motor mit 500 PS und die Kübeleinheit von einem Cat D343A 6-Zyl.-Turbo-Motor mit 360 PS angetrieben. Das Fassungsvermögen des 15.392 mm langen Cat 657 (46M) Scrapers beträgt 33,6 m³ (gehäuft). Er wurde von 1968 bis 1969 gebaut.

The first version of the Caterpillar 657 (31G) was presented in 1962 and was in the sales program until 1968. The picture shows a Cat 657 (31G395) and a Cat 657 (31G396), both built in 1968 as push pull versions. The empty scraper weight goes up to 124,700 lb and fully loaded up to 229,209 lb.

Die erste Version des Caterpillar 657 (31G) Scraper wurde 1962 vorgestellt und blieb bis 1968 im Programm. Das Bild zeigt einen Cat 657 (31G395) und einen Cat 657 (31G396), Baujahr 1968, beide ausgerüstet als Push-Pull-Version. Das Gewicht des Scrapers beträgt leer 56.550 kg und beladen 103.950 kg.

The picture shows the Caterpillar 657 (31G) train, with a length of 100'97". It is just finishing the second load cycle. In a few seconds the both scraper units will be separated. The maximum travel speed of the Cat 657 amounts 32 mph. The redesigned B-series, the 657B (68K), rated at 950 hp, was presented in 1969. It was found in the program until 1984. The current version is the further improved Cat 657E. The biggest of all Cat scrapers ever built was a "train" of three coupled 657 (31G) scrapers. They became one unit with a length of 200'15" and a load capacity of 149.98 yd³ (heaped). The 2850 hp Cat scraper was operated by one person, who was sitting in a top mounted cab on the first scraper bowl unit. This "super" scraper was developed and built by the Cat dealer Peterson Tractor and Equipment Co. in San Leandro/California. This one of a piece unit ran the first time in 1965.

Das Bild zeigt den 30.784 mm langen Caterpillar 657 (31G) Zug kurz vor dem Beenden des zweiten Ladevorgangs und dem Aus-einanderkuppeln der beiden Scraper. Die Höchstgeschwindigkeit des Cat 657 beträgt 51,5 km/h. 1969 wird die überarbeitete B-Version, der 657B (68K) mit 950 PS vorgestellt. Er blieb bis 1984 im Programm. Die aktuelle Version ist der Cat 657E, der nochmals weiterentwickelt wurde. Der größte Caterpillar Scraper, der je gebaut wurde, war ein Zug von drei Cat 657 (31G), zusammengekup-pelt zu einer Einheit mit einer Länge von 61.023 mm und einem Fassungsvermögen von 114,7 m³ (gehäuft). Der 2.850 PS starke Scraper wird von einem Fahrer bedient, der erhöht in einem Fahrerhaus auf der Kübeleinheit des ersten Scrapers arbeitet. Der "Super"-Scraper wurde vom Cat-Händler Peterson Tractor and Equipment Co. in San Leandro/Kalifornien entwickelt und gebaut. Dieses Einzelstück wurde 1965 zum ersten Mal in Betrieb genommen.

Caterpillar's biggest 3-axle scraper, the 666 (77F), was introduced in 1963. It was founded on the tractor unit of the Cat 660 (90F) with a second engine on the scraper unit. The load capacity of this 785 hp 666 (77F) is identical with the Cat 660 scraper unit. The operating weight goes up to 125,000 lb. This sales brochure from 1970 shows the Cat 666B (66K) with 950 hp and a weight of 149,500 lb, introduced in 1969. The production ended in 1978.

1963 wurde Caterpillars größter 3-Achs-Scraper, der 666 (77F), vorgestellt. Er basiert auf der Zugeinheit des Cat 660 (90F) und hat zusätzlich noch einen Motor auf der Kübeleinheit. Das Fassungsvermögen des 785 PS starken Cat 666 (77F) ist identisch mit dem des Cat 660 Scraper. Das Einsatzgewicht beträgt 56.700 kg. Das Verkaufsprospekt von 1970 zeigt den 1969 vorgestellten Cat 666B (66K) mit einer Motorleistung von 950 PS und einem Einsatzgewicht von 67.630 kg. Die Produktion wird 1978 eingestellt.

CATERPILLAR 666B

30,6/41,3 m³ **Fassungsvermögen.** Besonders breiter Kübel ermöglicht rasches, leichtes Laden.

550 PS Caterpillar-Dieselmotor.

Acht Vorwärtsgänge, Höchstgeschwindigkeit 69,2 km/h mit halbautomatischem Caterpillar-Plane-ten-Lastschaltgetriebe.

Starke Hydraulik für optimales Eindringen des Schneidmessers, hohe Schließkraft der Schürze und einwandfreies Ausstoßen.

Differentialsperre sichert maximale Zugkraft.

Einfache Wartung durch unabhängigen Ausbau aller Hauptaggregate.

The smallest Caterpillar elevator scraper was the 613A (71M) rated at 150 hp. It was built between 1969 and 1976 with a load capacity of 11 yd³ (heaped). The B-series was built from 1976 to 1984. It was followed by the C-series with now 175 hp. It was in the sales lists until 1993. The current model is the Cat 613C II. The picture shows Caterpillar's first elevator scraper, the J619C (43F), rated at 250 hp with a load capacity of 20 yd³ (heaped). This scraper unit was produced by the Johnson Manufacturing Company from 1964 to 1965.

Der kleinste Caterpillar Elevator Scraper war der 613A (71M) mit 150 PS. Er wurde mit einem Fassungsvermögen von 8,4 m³ (gehäuft) von 1969 bis 1976 gebaut. Nach der B-Serie von 1976 bis 1984 kam die C-Serie mit nun 175 PS, die bis 1993 im Verkaufsprogramm blieb. Das aktuelle Modell ist der Cat 613C II. Das Bild zeigt Caterpillars ersten Elevator Scraper, den J619C (43F) mit 250 PS und einem Fassungsvermögen von 15,3 m³ (gehäuft). Die Scrapereinheit wurde von der Firma Johnson Manufacturing Company von 1964 bis 1965 gebaut.

In 1981 Caterpillar introduced the 615 (46Z) elevator scraper rated at 250 hp and load capacity of 16 yd³ (heaped). The successor was the Cat 615C rated at 265 hp in 1987. It was replaced by the current series II in 1993. The picture shows a Cat J621 elevator scraper rated 300 hp and load capacity of 21.6 yd³ (heaped). This scraper was developed by Caterpillar and Johnson. It was built from 1965 to 1972.

1981 wird Caterpillars 615 (46Z) Elevator Scraper mit 250 PS und 12,2 m³ (gehäuft) Fassungsvermögen vorgestellt. Nachfolger wurde 1987 der Cat 615C mit 265 PS. Er wird 1993 durch die aktuelle Serie II abgelöst. Das Bild zeigt einen Cat J621 Elevator Scraper mit 300 PS und einem Fassungsvermögen von 16,5 m³ (gehäuft). Dieser Scraper wurde von Caterpillar und der Firma Johnson entwickelt, er wurde von 1965 bis 1972 gebaut.

I saw my first Caterpillar 623B (46P) elevator scraper working in France. With 330 hp and a load capacity of 22 yd³ (heaped) it's a real Cat-machine. Caterpillar's first elevator scraper 623 (52U) with 300 hp was introduced in 1972.

Dies ist mein erster Caterpillar Elevator-Scraper, den ich im Einsatz sah. Dieser Cat 623B (46P) ist durch und durch eine Cat-Maschine. Mit 330 PS und einem Fassungsvermögen von 16,8 m³ (gehäuft) arbeitet er auf einer Straßenbaustelle in Frankreich. Erstmals wurde der Cat 623 (52U) mit 300 PS 1972 vorgestellt.

From 1973 to 1986 the Caterpillar 623B (46P) elevator scraper was built. The elevator scraper type is the only self loading scraper, which doesn't need any pusher to work efficiently.

Von 1973 bis 1986 wird dieser Caterpillar 623B (46P) Elevator Scraper gebaut. Der Elevator Scraper ist der einzige Selbst-lade-Schürfzug, der ohne Schubunter-stützung wirtschaftlich arbeitet.

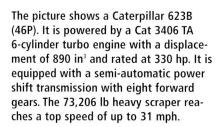

The picture shows a Caterpillar 623B (46P). It is powered by a Cat 3406 TA 6-cylinder turbo engine with a displacement of 890 in³ and rated at 330 hp. It is equipped with a semi-automatic power shift transmission with eight forward gears. The 73,206 lb heavy scraper reaches a top speed of up to 31 mph.

Das Bild zeigt einen Caterpillar 623B (46P). Er wird angetrieben durch einen Cat 3406 TA 6-Zyl.-Turbo-Motor mit 14,6 l Hubraum und 330 PS. Mit einem Planeten-Lastschalt-Getriebe mit acht Vorwärtsgängen erreicht der 33.200 kg schwere Scraper eine Geschwindigkeit von 50 km/h.

A newer version of the Caterpillar 623B (46P) works on a vineyard recultivation job site in Germany. The successor is the Cat 623E (6CB), built from 1986 to 1989. This one again is followed from 1989 to 1993 by the improved Cat 623E (6YF), rated at 365 hp and with a bowl capacity of 23 yd³ (heaped). The current model is the Cat 623F with an operating weight of 55,210 lb.

Eine etwas neuere Version des Caterpillar 623B (46P) arbeitet bei der Rekultivierung eines Weinbergs in Deutschland. Nachfolger wird der Cat 623E (6CB) von 1986 bis 1989 und ab 1989 bis 1993 der überarbeitete Cat 623E (6YF) mit 365 PS und einem Fassungsvermögen von 17,6 m³ (gehäuft). Das aktuelle Caterpillar-Modell ist der Cat 623F mit 25.039 kg Einsatzgewicht.

The first Caterpillar 633 (44J) elevator scraper was introduced in 1967 with 400 hp and a 32 yd³ (heaped) scraper bowl. This Caterpillar 633D (25W) was built from 1975 to 1985. This model is equipped with the new ROPS cab and the new Cat 3408 V8 turbo engine rated at 450 hp. The operating weight increased to 104,870 lb.

Der erste Caterpillar 633 (44J) Elevator Scraper wurde 1967 mit einem Fassungsvermögen von 24,5 m³ (gehäuft), und 400 PS vorgestellt. Von 1975 bis 1985 wird dieser Caterpillar 633D (25W) gebaut. Dieses Modell ist mit dem neuen ROPS-Fahrerhaus ausgestattet, der neue Cat 3408 V8-Turbo-Motor leistet nun 450 PS und das Einsatzgewicht stieg auf 47.570 kg.

CATERPILLAR 639D
Wheel Tractor-Scraper

Summary of features

- **34 cu. yd. (26 m³)** heaped capacity . . . excellent loadability . . . high productivity.
- **700 flywheel horsepower (522 kW)** with two Cat diesel Engines.
- **Cushion hitch** absorbs haul road shocks, stabilizes machine travel, substantially increases usable working speeds.
- **Eight forward speeds** up to 30 MPH (48.3 km/h) with Cat semiautomatic power shift transmission.
- **Variable capacity torque converter** with four load ranges to suit different job conditions.
- **Two-speed elevator** to match material loading requirements.
- **90° steering** both right and left, even with ROPS . . . for excellent maneuverability.
- **Differential lock** . . . operator controlled, rigidly connects both tractor drive wheels for positive traction.
- **Servicing ease** . . . easy access . . . localized service area . . . independent removal of major components.
- **CAT PLUS** . . . from your Caterpillar Dealer . . . the most comprehensive, total customer support system in the industry.

Shown with optional ROPS cab.

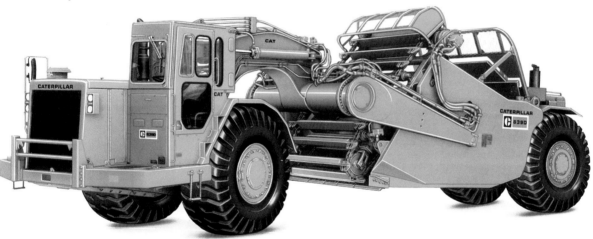

Caterpillar Engines

	Tractor	Scraper
Horsepower	450	250
Kilowatts	335	187
Rated engine RPM	2000	2200

The net power at the flywheel of the vehicle engines operating under SAE standard ambient temperature and barometric conditions, 85° F (29° C) and 29.38" Hg (995 mbar), using 35 API gravity fuel oil at 60° F (15.6° C). Vehicle engine equipment includes fan, air cleaner, water pump, lubricating oil pump, fuel pump, air compressor, muffler and alternator. Engines will maintain specified power up to 5,000 ft. (1500 m) altitude.

Tractor engine:
Caterpillar four-stroke-cycle 3408 diesel Engine, 65° V-8 with 5.4" (137 mm) bore, 6.0" (152 mm) stroke and 1,099 cu. in. (18.0 liters) displacement.

Turbocharged and jacket water aftercooled. Precombustion chamber fuel injection system. Valves are actuated by a pushrod mechanism. Single camshaft is mounted into "V" of engine.

Scraper engine:
Caterpillar four-stroke-cycle 3306 diesel Engine with six cylinders, 4.75" (121 mm) bore, 6.0" (152 mm) stroke and 638 cu. in. (10.5 liters) displacement.

Turbocharged and jacket water aftercooled. Precombustion chamber fuel injection system.

Self contained starting system including batteries and alternator.

A sales brochure from 1979 shows the biggest Caterpillar elevator scraper, the 639D (99X) with an operating weight of 121,318 lb. It was built between 1979 and 1984.

Ein Verkaufsprospekt von 1979 zeigt den größten Caterpillar Elevator Scraper, den 639D (99X). Der 55.030 kg schwere Scraper wurde von 1979 bis 1984 gebaut.

Caterpillar 830 M

This brochure shows the original version of the 830M Caterpillar wheel dozer, equipped with a Curtiss-Wright type 18M scraper with a capacity of 23.6 yd³ (heaped). This wheel dozer was specially developed and built for the US army. The first series was delivered to the US army in 1962.

Der Prospekt zeigt die Original-Version des Caterpillar Raddozers 830M mit einem Curtiss-Wright Typ 18M Scraper mit einem Fassungsvermögen von 18 m³ (gehäuft). Es handelt sich hierbei um einen speziell für die US-Streitkräfte entwickelten und gebauten Raddozer. Die erste Serie wurde 1962 an das Militär ausgeliefert.

A fleet of four ex Army Caterpillar 830M 400 hp wheel dozers are waiting for the next construction job. The width of the blade measures 11'31" and the height 4'26". A height-adjustable mechanical ripper is mounted on the left and on the right side at the rear of the blade. So, if necessary, the Cat 830M can ripp the soil by travelling in reverse gear.

Eine Flotte von vier Ex-Militär-Caterpillar 830M Raddozern mit 400 PS wartet auf den Baustelleneinsatz. Die Schildbreite beträgt 3.450 mm und die Höhe 1.300 mm. An der Schildrückseite sind links und rechts je ein Aufreißzahn angebracht, der mechanisch in der Tiefe verstellt werden kann. So kann der Cat 830M bei der Rück-wärtsfahrt den Boden aufreißen.

CATERPILLAR-BULLDOZER 830 M

A Caterpillar 830MB (41E626), built in 1967. It is equipped with an hydraulic controlled Wabco CT4 scraper, built in 1969, with a capacity of 18 yd^3 (struck). With the power shift transmission the Caterpillar 830MB reached a maximum travel speed of 25 mph. The engine power of the B-version increased to 448 hp.

Der Caterpillar 830MB (41E626), Baujahr 1967, ist ausgerüstet mit einem hydraulisch betätigten Wabco-CT4 Scraper, Baujahr 1969, mit einem Fassungsvermögen von 13,7 m^3 (gestrichen). Mit dem Power-Shift-Getriebe erreicht der Caterpillar 830MB eine Höchstgeschwindigkeit von 40,2 km/h. Die Motorleistung stieg mit der B-Version auf 448 PS.

This is the dashboard of the Caterpillar 830MB. You can see the shift lever for the power shift transmission and the three levers for controlling the scraper.

So sieht das Armaturenbrett des 830MB aus. Man kann gut den Schalthebel für das Power-Shift-Getriebe und die drei Hebel für die Bedienung erkennen.

This Caterpillar 830MB is equipped with an Athey PR621 (6100043) rear dump unit with a capacity of 30 tons.

Dieser Caterpillar 830MB ist speziell mit einem Athey PR621 (6100043) Hinterkipper mit 30 t Nutzlast ausgerüstet.

Because of the all-wheel drive, frame articulation and the powerful Caterpillar 6-cylinder turbo engine with 448 hp, this Cat rear dump 830MB controls every situation.

Dank Allradantrieb, Rahmen-Knicklenkung und eines leistungsstarken Caterpillar 6-Zyl.-Turbo-Motors mit 448 PS wird dieser Cat 830MB Hinterkipper mit jeder Situation fertig.

This is another Caterpillar 830MB scraper. It is equipped with a bail to be used as a push pull scraper. All Caterpillar 830 have an articulation of 45° to each side. This results in a really good manoeuvrability of the scraper.

Ein anderer Caterpillar 830MB Scraper, ausgerüstet mit einem Zugbügel für den Einsatz als Push-Pull-Scraper. Alle Caterpillar 830 haben eine Rahmen-Knicklenkung mit 45° zu jeder Seite hin, dadurch ergibt sich eine gute Manövrierfähigkeit des Scrapers.

A Caterpillar 830MB painted in the original camouflage colours of the US Army. A civil contractor rebuilt it to use it on the construction sites. With a weight ofat 52,897 lb and a length of 24' the turning circle is only 22'30".

Ein Caterpillar 830MB, noch in den Original-Tarnfarben, wird umgerüstet für den Baustelleneinsatz. Mit einem Gewicht von 23.990 kg und einer Länge von 7.315 mm beträgt der Wendekreis nur 6.800 mm.

Back to the roots
Zurück zu den Wurzeln

Job report 1997 to 1998

Contractor:
Amann GmbH
Location:
motor highway construction site A98
Weil at the Rhine-Waldshut
Road section:
Waidhof - Dultenaugraben
Milage:
9+200-12+300
Distance:
3 km (1.86 miles)
Earth movement for the
Hyw. approx:
1451880 yd³· 739020 yd³
refilled on site
Material:
clay-loam mixture

Einsatzbericht 1997 bis 1998

Ausführendes Bauunternehmen:
Amann GmbH
Autobahnbaustelle:
A98 Weil am Rhein-Waldshut
Streckenabschnitt:
Waidhof-Dultenaugraben
Bau-km:
9+200-12+300
Streckenlänge:
3 km
Erdbewegungen für BAB:
**ca. 1.110.000 m³,
davon 565.000 m³ Einbau in
Seitenablagerungen**
Material:
Ton-Lehmgemisch

A Caterpillar 834 (43E) wheel dozer rated at 400 hp. is equipped with a cushione push blade with a width of 13'23" and a height of 4'62" and a rear mounted push block.

Caterpillar 834 (43E) Raddozer mit 400 PS, ausgerüstet mit gefedertem Schubschild mit 4.035 mm Breite und 1.410 mm Höhe und einem heckmontierten Schubblock.

The picture shows Caterpillar's first elevator scraper, the Cat J619C (61F2686), with a Johnson elevator (5J3674), built in 1966.

Das Bild zeigt Caterpillars ersten Elevator Scraper, den Cat J619C (61F2686) mit dem Johnson Elevator (5J3674), Baujahr 1966.

A Caterpillar 637 PP (79P) with total of 640 hp is push loaded by a Cat D9G (66A) rated at 385 hp. After less than one minute loading time the Caterpillar 637 scraper with a capacity of 30 yd³ (heaped) is loaded with an average of 85,995 lb .

Ein Caterpillar 637 PP (79P) mit insgesamt 640 PS wird von einer Cat D9G (66A) mit 385 PS schubbeladen. Nach weniger als einer Minute Ladezeit ist der Caterpillar 637 Scraper mit einem Fassungsvermögen von 23 m³ (gehäuft) im Durchschnitt mit 39.000 kg beladen.

This Caterpillar 637 PP (79P) was attached with an additional safety roll over bar for the cab. On the haul road the scraper reached a maximum travel speed of 29.8 mph. It was built between 1970 and 1975.

Dieser Caterpillar 637 PP (79P) Scraper wurde nachträglich mit einem Überrollbügel für das Fahrerhaus ausgestattet. Auf der Transporttrasse erreicht er eine max. Geschwindigkeit von 48 km/h. Er wurde von 1970 bis 1975 gebaut.

The picture shows the loading area with two Caterpillar 631B (13G3011) scrapers rated at 400 hp with a load capacity of 30 yd³ (heaped). The Cat D9G works as a push dozer.

Das Bild zeigt die Entnahmestelle mit zwei Caterpillar 631B (13G3011) Scrapern mit 400 PS und einem Fassungsvermögen von 23 m³ (gehäuft) sowie die Cat D9G, die als Schubdozer arbeitet.

The Caterpillar 631B (13G) scraper starts loading. The Cat 631B was built between 1962 and 1966. It was a modern looking and reliable scraper.

Ladebeginn des Caterpillar 631B (13G) Scraper. Der Cat 631B wurde von 1962 bis 1966 gebaut und galt als einer der modernsten Scraper seiner Zeit.

Because of the good haul roads maintained by a Caterpillar No. 16 motor grader, the Caterpillar scraper fleet could reach a high transport travel speed.

Dank des guten Fahrbahnzustandes, der durch einen Caterpillar No. 16 Grader hergestellt wurde, kann die Caterpillar Scraper-Flotte eine hohe Transportgeschwindigkeit erreichen.

This was Caterpillar's biggest motor grader, No. 16 (49G) rated at 225 hp. It is equipped with a 14' long moldboard and is used to maintain the haul road. It was built between 1963 and 1973.

Caterpillars größter Motorgrader No. 16 (49G) mit 225 PS und einer 4.270 mm langen Schar unterhält die Transportwege. Er wurde von 1963 bis 1973 gebaut.

The two steering cylinders allow an articulation of the tractor unit of 90° to each side. The Caterpillar 631B (13G) requires only the half width of the haul road for a full turn on the dump site.

Durch die beiden Lenkzylinder, die ein Einknicken der Zugeinheit von je 90° ermöglichen, benötigt der Caterpillar 631B (13G) nur die Hälfte der Fahrbahn, um auf der Entladestelle zu wenden.

This picture shows one of the first Cat 769B (99F) trucks rated at 415 hp and with a load capacity of 35 tons.

Das Bild zeigt einen der ersten Caterpillar 769B (99F) Muldenkipper mit 415 PS und einer Nutzlast von 32 t.

A Caterpillar 825B (43N) compactor rated at 300 hp and with a weight of 66,300 lb. It is used as a high speed compactor on the dump area with a travel speed of up to 12.4 mph.

High Speed Compacting auf der Einbaustelle durch einen Cat 825B (43N) mit 300 PS und 30.075 kg Einsatzgewicht. Er verdichtet das geschüttete Material mit einer Geschwindigkeit bis zu 20 km/h.

A newer Caterpillar 631B (13G) scraper is on its way back to the load area.

Ein etwas neuerer Caterpillar 631B (13G) Scraper ist auf dem Weg zurück zur Ladestelle.

This is Caterpillar's biggest hydraulic excavator from the seventies: the 245 (82X) rated at 325 hp and with a weight of 144,967 lb.

Dies ist Caterpillars größter Hydraulikbagger aus den 70er Jahren, der 245 (82X) mit 325 PS und 65.745 kg Einsatzgewicht.

The Amann Company offered the best example for the durability of a Caterpillar fleet. Each machine is in average older than 30 years. In spite of the bad weather and soil conditions the contractor could finish this job site with approx. 1451,880 yd³ on time. Thanks to the high reliability and durability of the Caterpillar machines he could always work efficiently. When I visited this job site, it was a tremendous experience looking back to the sixties and seventies, - the time of the big construction sites and the time, when Caterpillar scrapers on German job sites were common.

Das beste Beispiel für die Langlebigkeit eines Caterpillar-Fuhrparks bietet die Firma Amann. Im Durchschnitt sind die Maschinen über 30 Jahre alt. Trotz schlechten Wetters und schlechter Bodenverhältnisse konnte das Bauvorhaben mit 1.110.000 m³ termingerecht fertiggestellt werden. Dank der Zuverlässigkeit und Langlebigkeit der Maschinen konnte trotz des hohen Alters wirtschaftlich gearbeitet werden. Es war ein Erlebnis, auf dieser Baustelle in die 60er-/70er-Jahre zurückzuschauen, in eine Zeit, in der Caterpillar-Scraper auf deutschen Erdbaustellen zur Tagesordnung gehörten.

During the construction time between 1998 and 1999 the contractor Amann used the following Caterpillar machines:

Während der Bauzeit von 1998 bis 1999 wurden folgende Caterpillar Maschinen der Firma Amann eingesetzt:
3 x Caterpillar scrapers 631B
2 x Caterpillar scrapers 637
2 x Caterpillar track type tractors D9G
1 x Caterpillar track type tractor D9H
2 x Caterpillar trucks 769B
1 x Caterpillar excavator 245
1 x Caterpillar motor grader No. 16
1 x Caterpillar compactor 825B

The complete engine output rated at 5740 hp.

Die Gesamtmotorleistung beträgt stolze 5.740 PS.

Pipelayers

Rohrverleger

With growing mechanization and industrialization we needed more and more raw materials such as oil and gas or water. That' s why a lot of pipeline projects were carried out. The first pipelayer built by Caterpillar came in 1951, the model MD7 rated at 140 hp and with a lifting capacity of 54,200 lb. This was followed by the smaller Cat MD6, only one year later. Already in the fifties three further models were introduced, the 561B, 572C and the 583C. Then, in 1974, Caterpillar presented the 594, based on the Cat D9, with a lift capacity of 200,000 lb. Today Caterpillar pipelayers are as progressive as the track type tractors. The only difference is the reinforced non oscillated undercarriage. That guarantees a very good stability. Today you can choose from four Caterpillar models with a lift capacity between 40,000 lb and 230,000 lb. These models are the most advanced pipelayers on the market.

Mit der zunehmenden Industrialisierung benötigte man auch mehr Rohstoffe wie Öl, Gas und Wasser, was den Bau vieler Pipelines zur Folge hatte. Der erste Rohrverleger, den Caterpillar 1951 baute, war der MD7 mit 140 PS und einer Hubkapazität von 24.585 kg. Ihm folgte der kleinere Cat MD6 ein Jahr später. Noch drei weitere Modelle wurden in den 50ern vorgestellt: Der 561B, der 572C, und der 583C. 1974 erschien der 594, der auf der Basis der D9 gebaut wurde, mit einer Hubkapazität von 90.700 kg. Caterpillar-Rohrverleger haben heute die gleichen fortschrittlichen Merkmale wie ihre Verwandten, die Kettendozer. Der verstärkte Laufwerksträger, der nicht pendelt, um eine bessere Standfestigkeit zu gewährleisten, ist der einzige Unterschied. Es stehen heute vier Modelle zur Auswahl mit einer Hubkapazität von 18.145 kg bis 104.330 kg. Sie sind die modernsten Rohrverleger auf dem Markt.

The picture shows a fleet of three Caterpillar 561D (54X) pipelayers with a lift capacity of up to 40,000 lb. The 35,000 lb heavy pipelayer is pow-ered by a 105 hp Cat engine and was built between 1978 and 1989. The former models were the Cat 561B (62A), built from 1959 to 1967, and the Cat 561C (85H/92J), built from 1966 to 1977.

Eine Flotte von drei Caterpillar 561D (54X) Rohrverlegern des kleinsten Typs mit einer Hubkapazität von 18.100 kg. Der 15.800 kg schwere Rohrverleger mit 105 PS wird von 1978 bis 1989 gebaut. Seine Vorgänger waren der Cat 561B (62A) von 1959 bis 1967 und der Cat 561C (85H/92J) von 1966 bis 1977.

The production of the Cat 561D (54X) pipelayers was stopped in 1989. It started again with the introduction of the new Caterpillar 561H with high drive sprocket in 1993. In the meantime Caterpillar D6E tractors were specially rebuilt and equipped as pipelayers.

Die Produktion des Cat 561D (54X) Rohrverlegers wurde 1989 eingestellt und erst wieder mit der Einführung des neuen Caterpillar 561H mit Delta-Laufwerk im Jahr 1993 begonnen. Bis dahin wurden Cat Kettendozer D6E für den Pipeline-Bau umgerüstet.

The picture shows a nearly brand-new Caterpillar D6E pipelayer. The Cat 561H was improved in 1997. The current model is called 561M with a lift capacity of 40,000 lb. The 35,809 lb heavy pipelayer is powered by a Cat 3116 6-cylinder turbo engine rated at 121 hp.

Das Bild zeigt einen fast neuen Caterpillar D6E Rohrverleger. Der Cat 561H wurde 1997 überarbeitet. Das aktuelle Modell heißt nun 561M mit einer Hubkapazität von 18.145 kg. Der 16.240 kg schwere Rohrverleger wird von einem Cat 3116 6-Zyl.-Turbo-Motor mit 121 PS angetrieben.

This Caterpillar pipelayer MD7 (17A) with a lift capacity up to 54,200 lb is equipped with a No. 7A blade and a No. 46 hydraulic-control system. You can choose three different lengths of the boom: 15', 18' and 20'. The Cat MD7 (17A) pipelayer with 140 hp was built from 1951 to 1957. It was replaced by the Cat 572C (21A).

Ein Caterpillar Rohrverleger MD7 (17A) mit einer Hubkapazität von 24.585 kg ist mit einem No. 7A Bulldozer und No. 46 Hydrauliksystem ausgerüstet. Es wurden drei verschiedene Längen des Auslegers angeboten: 4.921 mm, 5.905 mm und 6.561 mm. Der Cat Rohrverleger MD7 (17A) mit 140 PS wurde von 1951 bis 1957 gebaut. Nachfolger wird der Cat 572C (21A).

The next size up pipelayer is the Cat 571E (64A) with 160 hp and a lift capacity of 60,600 lb. It was built between 1961 and 1967. Successor was the Cat 571F (95N) with 180 hp. This Caterpillar 571G (916W) with a lift capacity of 60,600 lb works on a pipeline construction site in Switzerland . It was built between 1975 and 1981.

Der nächstgrößere Rohrverleger ist der Cat 571E (64A) mit 160 PS und einem Hubvermögen von 27.500 kg. Er wurde von 1961 bis 1967 gebaut. Nachfolger wird der Cat 571F (95N) mit 180 PS. Auf einer Pipeline-Baustelle in der Schweiz arbeitet dieser Caterpillar 571G (916W) mit einer Hubkapazität von 27.500 kg. Er wurde von 1975 bis 1981 gebaut.

The picture shows two Caterpillars 571G (52D JPN) built in Japan with an operating weight of 50,800 lb. It is powered by a Cat 3306 6-cylinder turbo engine rated at 200 hp. The production end for this pipelayer came in 1996.

Das Bild zeigt zwei Caterpillar 571G (52D JPN), die in Japan gebaut wurden, mit einem Einsatzgewicht von 23.040 kg. Sie werden von einem Cat 3306 6-Zyl.-Turbo-Motor mit 200 PS angetrieben. Das Produktionsende für diesen Rohrverleger war 1996.

Successor of the first pipelayer MD7 was the 572-series, introduced in 1957 with the Caterpillar 572C (21A) with 128 hp and a lift capacity of 86,000 lb. The Cat 572D (21A) with 140 hp was only built in 1959. The picture shows a Caterpillar 572E (65A) on a pipeline job site in 1994. Powered is the 62,000 lb heavy Caterpillar 572E (65A) pipelayer by a Cat 6-cylinder turbo engine rated at 180 hp. The lift capacity amounts 90,000 lb.

Nachfolger des "Ur"-Rohrverleger MD7 wird die 572-Serie, die 1957 mit dem Caterpillar 572C (21A) mit 128 PS und einer Hubkapazität von 39.000 kg vorgestellt wurde. Der Cat 572D (21A) mit 140 PS wurde nur 1959 gebaut. Das Bild zeigt den Caterpillar 572E (65A) auf einer Pipeline-Baustelle 1994.
Angetrieben wird der 28.000 kg schwere Caterpillar 572E (65A) Rohrverleger von einem Cat 6-Zyl.-Turbo-Motor mit 180 PS. Die Hubkapazität beträgt 40.800 kg.

The pipeline tubes are prebended by a track mounted pipe bender. Then a Caterpillar 572E (65A) lays the pipeline tubes to the side. The Cat pipelayer runs on special wooden pontoons to reduce ground pressure.

Nach dem Vorbiegen in einem auf Ketten montierten Rohrbieger werden die Pipelinerohre mit einem Caterpillar 572E (65A) zur Seite hin abgelegt. Der Cat-Rohrverleger fährt auf extra ausgelegten Pontons, um den Boden zu schonen.

A Caterpillar 572G rated at 200 hp and with a weight of 60,417 lb. With the maximum overhang of 19'36" the Cat 572G lifts a little bit more than 13,230 lb. It was built from 1975 to 1997.

Ein Caterpillar 572G mit 200 PS und einem Einsatzgewicht von 27.400 kg. Bei einer max. Ausladung von 5.905 mm hebt der Cat 572G noch etwas über 6.000 kg. Er wurde von 1975 bis 1997 gebaut.

In 1970 Cat introduced the 572F (96N). It was in the sales lists until 1974. Equipped with a 3-speed planetary power shift transmission the 61,000 lb heavy pipelayer reached a travel speed of 6 mph.

1970 wird der Caterpillar 572F (96N) vorgestellt, der bis 1974 im Programm bleibt. Ausgerüstet mit einem 3-Gang-Power-Shift-Getriebe erreicht der 27.600 kg schwere Rohrverleger 9,7 km/h.

Caterpillar 572R pipelayer. (Caterpillar Inc.)

Caterpillar 572R Rohrverleger. (Caterpillar Inc.)

The Caterpillar 583C (16A) with 190 hp and a lift capacity of 130,000 lb was introduced in 1955. Since 1960 Cat 583H (61A) models were equipped with a power shift transmission. Powered is the 85,720 lb heavy pipelayer by a Cat 6-cylinder turbo engine rated at 270 hp. The Cat 583H is equipped with a 20' long boom with a reach of 12' the lift capacity is still 44,100 lb.

Der Caterpillar 583C (16A) mit 190 PS und einer Hubkapazität von 58.970 kg wurde 1955 vorgestellt. Angetrieben wird dieser 38.900 kg schwere 583H von einem Cat 6-Zyl.-Turbo-Motor mit 270 PS. Bei einer Ausladung von 3.500 mm hebt der mit einem 6.100 mm langen Ausleger versehene Cat 583H noch über 20.000 kg.

This Caterpillar 578 (8HB00458) was built in 1992. It is the successor of the Cat 583K, and it is equipped with the high drive sprocket, an hydraulic controlled boom and a totally closed cab. The Cat 3406B 6-cylinder turbo engine rated at 300 hp powers the 101,893 lb heavy pipelayer.

Das Bild zeigt einen Caterpillar 578 (8HB00458), Baujahr 1992. Er ist der Nachfolger des Cat 583K, ausgestattet mit Caterpillars Delta-Laufwerk, einem Ausleger mit Hubzylinder und einem Fahrerhaus. Der Cat 3406B 6-Zyl.-Turbo-Motor mit 300 PS treibt den 46.210 kg schweren Rohrverleger an.

In this picture you can see the different dimensions of the Caterpillar 578 (8HB) with its 20' long boom and a lift capacity of 155,026 lb compared with the Cat 572G pipelayer. The Cat 578 was built between 1989 and 1997. Successor is the current Caterpillar pipelayer 583R with 328 hp and a lift capacity of 140,026 lb.

Man kann hier gut den Größenunterschied des Caterpillar 578 (8HB) mit dem 6.100 mm langen Ausleger mit einer Hubkapazität von 70.307 kg gegenüber einem Cat 572G Rohrverleger erkennen. Der Cat 578 wird von 1989 bis 1997 gebaut. Nachfolger wird der aktuelle Caterpillar Rohrverleger 583R mit 328 PS und einem Hubvermögen von 63.504 kg.

CATERPILLAR 594H
Pipelayer

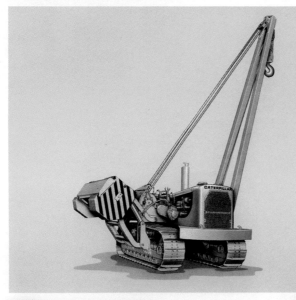

- **410 flywheel horsepower**

- **200,000 lb. (90 700 kg) lift capacity**

- **Planetary power shift transmission**

- **Bolt-on sprocket rim segments**

- **Sealed Track**

power shift transmission

Single-lever control for three speeds forward and three reverse.

Torque divider: Single-stage torque converter with planetary gear set provides high-torque, anti-stall characteristics with direct drive response and efficiency.

Range transmission: Planetary gear sets controlled by large, oil-cooled, hydraulically actuated clutches. Special valve system permits smooth, instant shifting under full load without braking or decelerating engine.

Gear	Forward Speed MPH	(km/h)	Reverse Speed MPH	(km/h)
1	0-2.5	(4.0)	0-3.1	(5.0)
2	0-4.3	(6.9)	0-5.4	(8.7)
3	0-6.7	(10.8)	0-8.2	(13.2)

steering

Hydraulically actuated, multiple-disc oil clutches with 30 friction surfaces in each clutch. Hydraulically boosted, oil-cooled contracting band brakes. Combined steering clutch and brake controls.

undercarriage

Sealed Track extends pin and bushing life and reduces wear on links and rollers. Track rollers, carrier rollers and idlers are Lifetime-Lubricated. Sprockets have bolt-on replaceable rim segments.

Number of track rollers (each side)	8
Track gauge	100" (2540 mm)
Track shoe width (standard)	34" (860 mm)
Optional width	40" (1020 mm)
Track length on ground	147.75" (3750 mm)
Ground contact area (standard shoes)	10,050 sq. in. (6.48 m²)
Ground clearance, from ground face of track shoe	25" (630 mm)
Grouser height from ground face of shoe	3.44" (87 mm)

counterweights

Full hydraulic control. High mounting of counterweight pivot point gives excellent side and bottom clearance. Over-center design prevents creep-out when retracted. Minimum overall width for easier maneuvering and shipping.

boom control

Safety pawl holds boom drum. Interlock prevents accidental reversal with pawl engaged. Safety kick out prevents boom bending.

Caterpillar engine

Flywheel horsepower @ 1375 RPM 410

The net power at the flywheel of the vehicle engine operating under SAE standard ambient temperature and barometric conditions, 85° F. (29° C) and 29.38" (995 mbar) Hg, using 35 API gravity fuel oil at 60° F. (15.6° C). Vehicle engine equipment includes fan, air cleaner, water pump, lubricating oil pump, fuel pump and alternator. Engine will maintain full power up to 7,500 ft. (2300 m) altitude.

Caterpillar four-stroke-cycle diesel Model D353 with 6 cylinders, 6.25" (159 mm) bore, 8" (203 mm) stroke and 1,473 cu. in. (24.2 litres) piston displacement.

Turbocharged and aftercooled. Individual adjustment-free fuel injection pumps and non-fouling precombustion chambers. Stellite-faced valves, valve rotators and hard alloy steel seats. Spray-cooled, cam-shaped and tapered aluminum alloy pistons with three-ring design. Both compression rings carried in cast-iron bands. Full-flow filtered lubrication. Dry-type air cleaner. 24-volt direct electric starting.

This sales brochure from 1975 shows the biggest Caterpillar pipelayer, the 594H. The first Cat 594 (62H) rated at 385 hp, was introduced in 1974. The H-series was built until 1982. Successor is the current Cat 589 pipelayer rated at 420 hp with an operating weight of 150,945 lb and a lift capacity of 230,047 lb.

Ein Verkaufsprospekt von 1975 zeigt den damals größten Caterpillar Rohrverleger, den 594H. Der erste Cat 594 (62H) mit 385 PS wurde 1974 vorgestellt, die H-Serie wurde bis 1982 gebaut. Nachfolger wird der aktuelle Cat 589 Rohrverleger mit 420 PS, einem Einsatzgewicht von 68.456 kg und einem Hubvermögen von 104.330 kg.

Welders

Schweißtraktoren

"From forest to woodshed to kitchen stove. That was the way to get fuel for cooking in my boyhood. What progress we've made when a housewife in Detroit can have fuel at her fingertips from a Texas gas field to use in preparing food for her family!"

A Caterpillar D4D is equipped with a welder platform and a 500 amp.-welding unit and two bottles of propane for preheating the pipe joints.

Ein Caterpillar D4D Schweißtraktor ist mit einem 500 Ampere Schweißaggregat und zwei Propanflaschen für das Vorwärmen der Rohre ausgerüstet.

This Caterpillar D4E tractor is used as a towing tractor on a pipeline job in Switzerland. It is equipped with an electric power unit.

Ein Caterpillar D4E Traktor, ausgerüstet mit einem Stromaggregat, wird als Zugfahrzeug auf einer Pipelinebaustelle in der Schweiz eingesetzt.

A Caterpillar D6 welder is equipped with an hydraulic crane and two welding units.

Dieser Caterpillar D6 Schweißtraktor ist mit einem hydraulischen Hebekran und einem Schweißaggregat ausgerüstet.

Usually the welders are equipped with a longer undercarriage with wider track shoes than the standard tractors, because cranes or aggregates for the power are installed in front and at the back. On this Caterpillar D6 welder you can see the cable boom with the electric cables.

Die Schweißtraktoren haben meistens ein längeres Laufwerk mit breiteren Kettenplatten als der Standardtraktor, weil vorne und hinten Kran oder Aggregate für die Stromerzeugung angebracht sind. An diesem Caterpillar D6 Schweißtraktor kann man gut den Kabelbaum mit den Stromkabeln erkennen.

As I teach welding it was really interesting to watch the colleagues at work.

Für mich als Lehrschweißer war es natürlich sehr interessant, den Kollegen bei der Arbeit über die Schulter zu schauen.

Two welders begin with the welding process simultaneously, it is welded from the top to the down position.

Zwei Schweißer beginnen gleichzeitig mit dem Schweißprozeß, es wird fallend von oben nach unten geschweißt.

The picture shows two Caterpillar D6 welders one behind the other.

Das Bild zeigt zwei Caterpillar D6 Schweißtraktoren hintereinander.

This Caterpillar D6 welder is equipped with a special 7-roller-undercarriage.

Ein Caterpillar D6 Schweißtraktor ist ausgerüstet mit einem speziellen 7-Rollen-Laufwerk.

This Caterpillar D6 welder is attached with an air compressor and with an air pressure tank. The plant on tracks supplies the welders with everything they need on that pipeline project site: direct current D.C. or alternating current A.C. welding power and air pressure.

Dieser Caterpillar D6 Schweißtraktor ist mit Druckluftkompressor und großem Drucklufttank ausgestattet. Die Fabrik auf Ketten liefert Gleich-, Wechsel-, Schweißstrom und Druckluft, alles, was die Arbeiter und Schweißer auf einer Pipelinebaustelle benötigen.

Epilog

We are looking back at 75 years earthmoving history of the Caterpillar Inc. 75 years full of new ideas and technologies in the construction of earthmoving machinery. What would we have done without those yellow machines from the United States of America? How would our life have developed? What would be about our streets, our supplies, water and electricity? I'm proud of being able to publish my book: "Caterpillar - 75 Years" just as an anniversary edition.

Epilog

Wir blicken mittlerweile auf 75 Jahre Erdbewegungsgeschichte mit der Firma Caterpillar Inc. zurück. 75 Jahre voller neuer Ideen und Technologien im Baumaschinenbau. Was hätten wir ohne diese gelben Maschinen aus Amerika gemacht? Wie hätte sich unser Leben weiterentwickelt und auf welchen Wegen müßten wir heute gehen? Wie hätten wir unsere Versorgung mit Grundnahrungsmitteln, mit Wasser und Elektrizität weitgehend sicherstellen können? Ich bin stolz darauf, gerade im Jubiläumsjahr des Hauses Caterpillar mein Buch "Caterpillar Seventy five Years" herausbringen zu dürfen.

This picture shows a Caterpillar D6H made out of concrete in 1997. It is called: 'De Dijker'. It reminds us of the terrible flood disaster in the Netherlands. Simultaneously it represents Caterpillar's most modern track type tractor with top mounted elevated drive train. We all will follow with keen interest, what Caterpillar Inc. and their products will be about in the next years.

Das Bild zeigt eine Caterpillar D6H aus Beton von 1997 mit dem Namen "De Dijker". Sie steht auf einem Deich als Monument für die große Flutkatastrophe in den Niederlanden. Gleichzeitig repräsentiert sie auch Caterpillars modernsten Kettendozer mit Delta-Laufwerk und oben liegendem Antrieb. Man darf gespannt in die Zukunft blicken, wie sich die Produkte der Firma Caterpillar Inc. in den nächsten Jahren weiterentwickeln.

Weitere Literatur unseres Verlages

Fordern Sie kostenlos und völlig unverbindlich unseren neuesten Prospekt an mit Büchern über:

- ■ Traktoren
- ■ Baumaschinen
- ■ Lastwagen
- ■ Omnibusse
- ■ Feuerwehren
- ■ Autos
- ■ Motorräder

Podszun-Verlag GmbH
Postfach 1525
D-59918 Brilon
Telefon 02961 / 53213
Fax 02961 / 2508

144 Seiten, fester Einband
ISBN 3-923448-89-9
DM 39,80 SFr 39,80 ÖS 309,00

144 Seiten, fester Einband
ISBN 3-86133-222-1
DM 39,80 SFr 39,80 ÖS 309,00

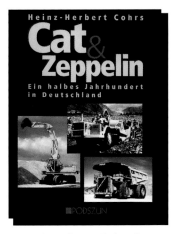

208 Seiten, fester Einband
ISBN 3-86133-242-6
DM 68,00 SFr 65,00 ÖS 529,00

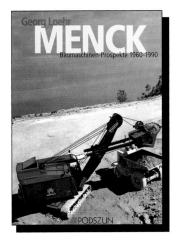

144 Seiten, fester Einband
ISBN 3-86133-238-8
DM 39,80 SFr 39,80 ÖS 309,00

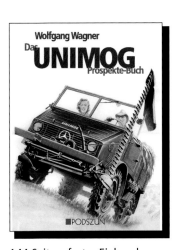

144 Seiten, fester Einband
ISBN 3-86133-239-6
DM 39,80 SFr 39,80 ÖS 309,00

165 Seiten, fester Einband
ISBN 3-86133-115-2
DM 48,00 SFr 46,00 ÖS 380,00

erscheint jährlich im Oktober neu

144 Seiten, Leinenbroschur
ISBN 3-86133-227-254-x
DM 29,80 SFr 29,80 ÖS 232,00

180 Seiten, fester Einband
ISBN 3-86133-207-8
DM 68,00 SFr 65,00 ÖS 529,00

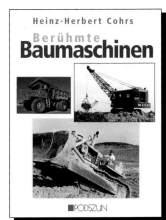

144 Seiten, fester Einband
ISBN 3-86133-221-3
DM 39,80 SFr 39,80 ÖS 309,00